The geology of the Hebrides and West Shetland shelves, and adjacent deep-water areas

BRITISH GEOLOGICAL SURVEY

United Kingdom Offshore Regional Report

The geology of the Hebrides and West Shetland shelves, and adjacent deep-water areas

M S Stoker, K Hitchen and C C Graham

with contributions by
D A Abraham and J D Ritchie

LONDON HMSO 1993

Production of this report was funded by the Department of
Energy (now incorporated into the Department of Trade and
Industry) and the Natural Environment Research Council

The coastline used on many maps and diagrams in this book is
based on Ordnance Survey mapping

Bibliographic reference

STOKER, M S, HITCHEN, K, and GRAHAM, C C. 1993.
*United Kingdom offshore regional report: the geology of the Hebrides
and West Shetland shelves, and adjacent deep-water areas.*
(London: HMSO for the British Geological Survey.)

Printed in the United Kingdom for HMSO
Dd 0292042 C20 1/94 3396/2 20249

ISBN 0 11 884499 7

Contents

FIGURES

Foreword

The area to the north and west of Scotland is a relatively unexplored frontier region where possibly significant hydrocarbon reserves remain undiscovered. A rift system or chain of basins may have existed in the area since Late Carboniferous or Early Permian times, although the current configuration of the continental margin is a legacy of late Mesozoic to early Cenozoic, Atlantic sea-floor spreading. In Early Cretaceous times, the region was the focus of extreme crustal attenuation associated with abortive continental breakup along the axis of the Rockall Trough, Faeroe–Shetland Basin and Møre Basin. When the axis of spreading shifted westwards, the area was affected by extensive volcanism concomitant with the split between Rockall Plateau and Greenland, forming the northeast Atlantic Ocean. Since then, sedimentation has been outstripped by subsidence in the Rockall Trough and Faeroe–Shetland Channel, resulting in starved deep-water basins, although a wedge of sediment has built up on the outer shelf and slope.

Since 1966, the British Geological Survey (BGS) has been studying the area in order to produce geological and geophysical maps on a scale of 1:250 000 as part of a survey of the United Kingdom (UK) Continental Shelf (see inside back cover). Following the production of these maps, this report has been produced as one of a series of UK Offshore Regional Reports; these integrate BGS data and interpretations with commercial data and published information. Most of the commercial data is restricted to the area to the west and north of Shetland; the northern Rockall Trough and its margins have only recently begun to attract the interest of the oil industry. University groups have been active in the area for over twenty years, including BIRPS (British Institutions Reflection Profiling Syndicate) since the early eighties. BGS data acquisition, mapping and report production have been largely funded by the Department of Energy (now incorporated into the Department of Trade and Industry).

Peter J Cook DSc
Director
British Geological Survey

April 1993

ACKNOWLEDGEMENTS

Responsibilities of individual authors during the production of this report have been as follows:

M S Stoker — Basement (incorporating a contribution by J D Ritchie), structure, Devonian to Lower Carboniferous (Old Red Sandstone), Carboniferous, Permo-Triassic, Jurassic, Neogene, and Quaternary.

K Hitchen — Introduction (with a contribution by D A Abraham), Cretaceous, Paleogene, and economic geology.

C C Graham — Physiography, Sea-bed sediments, and economic geology.

The Offshore Regional Report Series is co-ordinated by the Marine Geology Group, and edited by D Evans and A G Stevenson.

In addition to the work of the authors, the report has drawn extensively upon the knowledge and expertise of other BGS staff, not only within the marine sphere, but also from the Land Survey and specialists within the fields of sedimentology, biostratigraphy, cartography and publication. In particular, much use has been made in this report of palaeontological analyses carried out on borehole material by BGS biostratigraphers. The authors and editors are grateful to the following for constructive comment: I B Cameron, C D R Evans, R W Gallois, R Holmes, D I J Mallick, J R Mendum, S K Monro, A C Morton, T C Pharaoh, J B Riding and G Warrington.

BP Exploration is gratefully thanked for permission to use unreleased analytical data from BGS borehole 72/37 in the West Orkney Basin, as is Shell UK for allowing the use of the seismic section reproduced in Figure 33. The Institute of Oceanographic Sciences is thanked for permission to illustrate their sea-bed photographs in Figure 85.

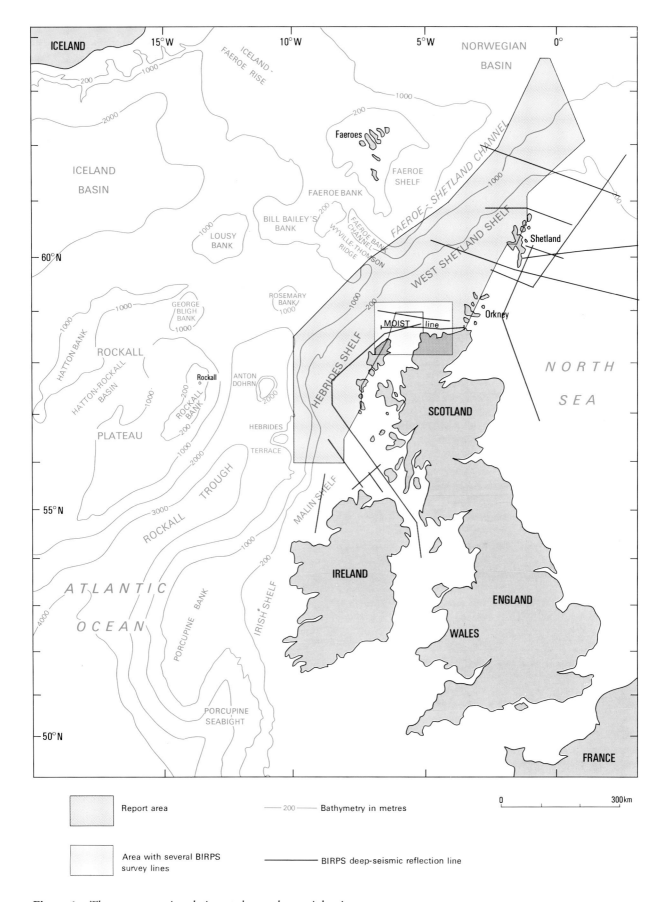

Figure 1   The report area in relation to the north-east Atlantic.

1   Introduction

This report describes the offshore geology of the area to the north and west of Scotland; its limits are 56°N in the south and 63°30'N in the north, and from 10°W in the south-west to just beyond 1°E in the north-east, a south-west to north-east distance of approximately 1000 km (Figures 1 and 2). To the north of Shetland, the area borders on the United Kingdom (UK)–Norway Median Line, whereas the southern limit is close to the UK–Republic of Ireland boundary. The eastern and western limits have been selected so that the report includes the whole of the West Shetland and Hebrides shelves. The western limit also corresponds approximately to the limit of surveys by the British Geological Survey (BGS) in their offshore mapping programme (Fannin, 1989). However, some features from outside the area are also described where appropriate.

Throughout the report, a clear distinction is attempted between geographical (including bathymetric) and geological terms. Hence the Faeroe–Shetland Channel is the approximate present-day bathymetric expression of the underlying Faeroe–Shetland Basin, and the Outer Hebrides Platform, Flannan Trough, Flannan Ridge and North Lewis Basin all occur beneath the Hebrides Shelf. However, in some cases, common usage has led to the same term being used in either context, as for the Rockall Trough and the Wyville–Thomson Ridge.

There is a wide range of water depths within the report area (Figure 1 and see Figure 5). Most of the shelf is covered by less than 200 m of water, with the shelfbreak usually between 130 m and 240 m depth, although it may be deeper on the Wyville–Thomson Ridge. The deeper-water areas of the northern Rockall Trough and Faeroe–Shetland Channel, which exceed 1000 m in depth, are separated by the Wyville–Thomson Ridge, which rises to less than 400 m below the sea surface. Slopes descending into the deeper-water areas typically have angles ranging from 1° to 4°.

Continental crust, consisting mainly of Lewisian metamorphic rocks, probably underlies most of the report area, although it is thinned beneath the northern Rockall Trough and the Faeroe–Shetland Basin. Precambrian Moine rocks overlie the Lewisian on parts of the Orkney–Shetland Platform (Figure 3), but Torridonian and Lower Palaeozoic rocks are almost entirely absent. Following the Caledonian orogeny, Devono-Carboniferous nonmarine sediments were deposited in the Orcadian and Clair basins (see Chapter 5), after which, during an extensional regime, several basins developed beneath the West Shetland and Hebrides shelf areas, with infill ranging in age from Permian to Cretaceous. During the early Tertiary, the area was dominated by uplift and massive volcanism caused by the onset of sea-floor spreading to the west of Rockall Plateau. From the Eocene onwards, Tertiary sediments were deposited as a wedge on the outer shelf as the depocentres of the Faeroe–Shetland Basin and Rockall Trough to the west subsided passively. Modern water-circulation patterns developed in the Neogene, and glaciations affected the shelf during the latter part of the Pleistocene.

The pattern of Bouguer gravity anomalies (Figure 4) illustrates the principal structural features of the report area; gravity highs occur over the platforms and ridges, and lows are found over the basins (compare Figure 17). The pattern is however complicated by the highs associated with Tertiary igneous centres, which are clearly identified from their closely spaced, circular, contour patterns.

Compared to some other parts of the UK Continental Shelf, and especially the North Sea, the area to the north and west of Scotland is relatively unexplored. In particular, hydrocarbon exploration has been very limited west of the Hebrides. As a result, no formal lithostratigraphies have been established, although some oil companies are using their own informal nomenclature, or extrapolating terms into the area from the North Sea. The literature also reveals examples of different names being used for the same structural feature (see Figure 20).

Geological information from the report area has come from two main sources. Firstly, exploration for hydrocarbons has produced thousands of kilometres of seismic-reflection data, and although this remains confidential, much of it has been interpreted by BGS on behalf of the Department of Energy, and some of the results have been incorporated into this report. Furthermore, more than 80 commercial wells have been drilled (Figure 2), of which over 50 have now been released (Fannin, 1989). Secondly, BGS has undertaken a systematic offshore regional mapping programme of the UK Continental Shelf. Within this report area, shallow-seismic, gravity and magnetic data have been supplemented by sea-bed sampling and coring, and the drilling of over 70 shallow boreholes (Figure 2), to produce a comprehensive suite of geological and geophysical maps (see inside back cover). This work has been largely funded by the Department of Energy. Other sources of data include conference proceedings and papers in technical journals, many of which relate to commercial exploration.

Most hydrocarbon exploration has been concentrated to the north and west of Shetland, hence the deeper geology is better known here than elsewhere within the report area. Nevertheless, exploration here started much later than in the North Sea; the first systematic seismic surveys were undertaken in the late 1960s, but the first well was not drilled until 1972. Only a single oilfield, Clair (Figure 2), has been discovered, although other significant oil and gas discoveries have been reported. Much of the report area, notably in the deeper water, has never been licensed for hydrocarbon exploration, and remains an area of great potential awaiting further exploration. In recent licence rounds, the Department of Energy has offered larger-than-normal licence areas, with advantageous conditions, in order to encourage oil-company interest, but the area is still regarded as frontier, high-risk acreage.

PREVIOUS RESEARCH

The area to the north and west of Scotland has been researched only since the mid-1960s, before which its geology was almost totally unknown. However, some of the adjacent land areas had previously been the subject of detailed surveys, such as those for the Outer Hebrides (Jehu and Craig, 1934) and St Kilda (Cockburn, 1935). Several landings have also been made on Rockall, to the west of the area (Figure 1), with the earliest possibly being in 1810 (Sabine, 1960; Harrison, 1975). More recently, the marine geology of the

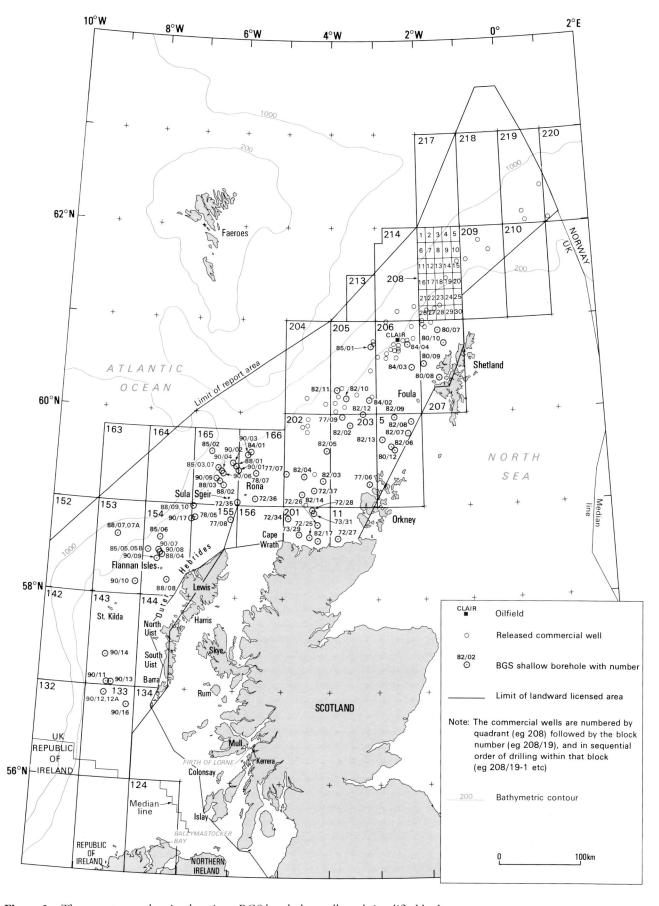

Figure 2   The report area, showing locations, BGS boreholes, wells and simplified bathymetry.

Rockall Plateau has been described (e.g. Roberts, 1969, 1975a and b; Jones et al., 1972, Scrutton, 1972).

The earliest seismic-reflection data were recorded in 1965, and published as a series of down-slope profiles by Stride et al. (1969). Early university geophysical surveys, mainly from Durham, located several sedimentary basins on the shelf (e.g. Bott and Watts, 1970; Watts, 1971; Jones, 1978). Thousands of kilometres of seismic-reflection data have now been collected in connection with hydrocarbon exploration, predominantly over the shelf and slope to the north and west of Shetland, with relatively little being shot on the shelf west of Orkney or in the northern Rockall Trough.

Several Tertiary igneous centres were located and modelled in the 1970s by Himsworth (1973), since when detailed accounts of submarine centres within the report area, including Brendan, Erlend, West Erlend and Geikie, have been given by Smythe et al. (1983), Gatliff et al. (1984) and Evans et al. (1989). The St Kilda intrusive centre is partially emergent, and Harding et al. (1984) described the petrology and structural relationships of the component igneous bodies. The relative sizes of the igneous centres to the north and west of Scotland are compared by Abraham and Ritchie (1991), and many studies of early Tertiary volcanism in the area are to be found in a volume edited by Morton and Parson (1988).

The crust under the Hebrides has been investigated by Bott et al. (1979) and Jones (1981). The debate about the nature (continental or oceanic) and age (Late Palaeozoic or Cretaceous) of the crust beneath the Rockall Plateau and Trough started in the 1970s (e.g. Roberts, 1975a; Russell and Smythe, 1978), and continues (e.g. Smythe, 1989; Morton and Taylor, 1991).

The crustal structure under the north Scottish shelf and Faeroe–Shetland Channel was first investigated by seismic-refraction experiments in 1972 (Smith, 1974; Smith and Bott, 1975; Bott and Smith, 1984). In 1981, the British Institutions Reflection Profiling Syndicate (BIRPS) shot their first deep seismic-reflection line, the Moine and Outer Isles Seismic Traverse (MOIST), parallel to the north coast of Scotland (Figure 1; Smythe et al., 1982; Brewer and Smythe, 1984). This was recorded to 15 seconds two-way travel time in order to investigate the structure of the continental crust. Several more BIRPS lines have subsequently been shot in the area (Figure 1).

Accounts of the subsurface offshore geology could not be produced until sufficient data had been collected by the oil industry. The first account based on hydrocarbon exploration data was by Cashion (1975) on the West Shetland Basin, followed in the 1980s by several structural or review papers. In the West Shetland area, the geology was appraised by Ridd (1981; 1983), and the structure to the north of the Scottish mainland described by Kirton and Hitchen (1987), Enfield and Coward (1987), Coward and Enfield (1987), and Coward et al. (1989). Wood et al. (1987; 1988) discussed the north-eastern part of the Rockall Trough with special reference to the early Tertiary lavas and later subsidence history. The structural and stratigraphical evolution of the whole shelf area from 58°N to 61°N is given by Earle et al. (1989), and numerous papers relevant to the report area are included in conference proceedings edited by Bott et al. (1983) and Brooks and Glennie (1987).

Publications concerning the morphology of the sea floor have been less frequent. Limited details of the Hebrides Shelf and Slope were given by Stride et al. (1969) and Jones et al. (1986b), whereas Roberts (1972; 1975a and b) concentrated on the Rockall Plateau and Trough. An account of the continental slope of north-west Europe was published by Kenyon (1987). Numerous high-resolution, shallow-seismic profiles

have been obtained by the BGS, and interpretations of these data are incorporated into published BGS maps. The BGS maps, at a scale of 1:250 000 (see inside back cover), encapsulate the results of BGS surveys run mainly during the late 1970s and early 1980s, and which cover the whole report area south of 62°N.

Although some rock samples have been obtained by dredging the sea bed (e.g. Jones et al., 1986a), nearly all samples have been retrieved in situ from commercial wells or BGS shallow boreholes. Both types of drilling started within the report area in 1972. Very few rock samples have been obtained west of the Outer Hebrides, and most commercial drilling has taken place west of Shetland.

GEOLOGICAL SUMMARY

Continental crust probably underlies the whole of the report area, but beneath the major rift axis of the Rockall Trough and Faeroe–Shetland Basin it is stretched, and thinner than beneath the adjacent shelf areas. Indeed, it is so attenuated and intruded beneath the Rockall Trough that it may be considered transitional between continental and oceanic in character. The crust probably comprises mostly basement Lewisian gneiss which formed the foreland for the Caledonian orogeny. However, other crustal terranes are presumed to be juxtaposed against the Lewisian, including those recognised on Rockall Bank and in western Islay and Colonsay (Figures 1, 2 and 3). These, and possibly other terranes, may underlie parts of the report area.

East of the line which marks the offshore continuation of the Moine Thrust (see Figure 17), basement rocks form the allochthonous (mobile) belt of the Caledonian orogeny; these yield younger isotopic ages than rocks of the foreland area to the west. Between Orkney and Shetland, the Lewisian is overlain by Moine and Devonian rocks and, adjacent to the north-west corner of the Scottish mainland, by Torridonian and Cambro-Ordovician sediments.

Since the Caledonian orogeny, the area has undergone episodic extension, resulting in the formation of many half-graben-style basins, some of which owe their origin to the relaxation of Caledonian thrusts. A number of basins may have originated in the Late Carboniferous or Early Permian, to be reactivated during the Mesozoic and early Tertiary. The polarity of these basins changes across the area; those to the south of the North Orkney/Wyville–Thomson transfer zone (see Figure 19) generally have eastward-dipping basin-bounding faults on the western sides of the basins, whereas north of the transfer zone, basin-bounding faults on the eastern sides of the basins dip westwards.

Devono-Carboniferous rocks consist of postorogenic, lacustrine, aeolian and fluvial sediments, and occur in two main areas. Those cropping out on the Orkney–Shetland Platform (Figure 3) were deposited on the western margin of the Orcadian Basin, mainly during the Mid-Devonian. Sediments of the Clair Group, situated at depth on the Rona Ridge west of Shetland (see Figure 17), range in age from Late Devonian to Early Carboniferous. Devonian rocks may also occur in the deeper parts of some basins, such as the West Orkney Basin. Carboniferous sediments crop out in Northern Ireland, and have also been proved in wells drilled on the Malin and Irish shelves (Figures 1 and 2).

A rifting phase during the Early Permian allowed widespread and thick sequences to accumulate in syntectonic half-grabens. On seismic sections, such deposits may appear as wedges up to 8000 m thick against basin-bounding faults. Permo-Triassic sediments were deposited during a major re-

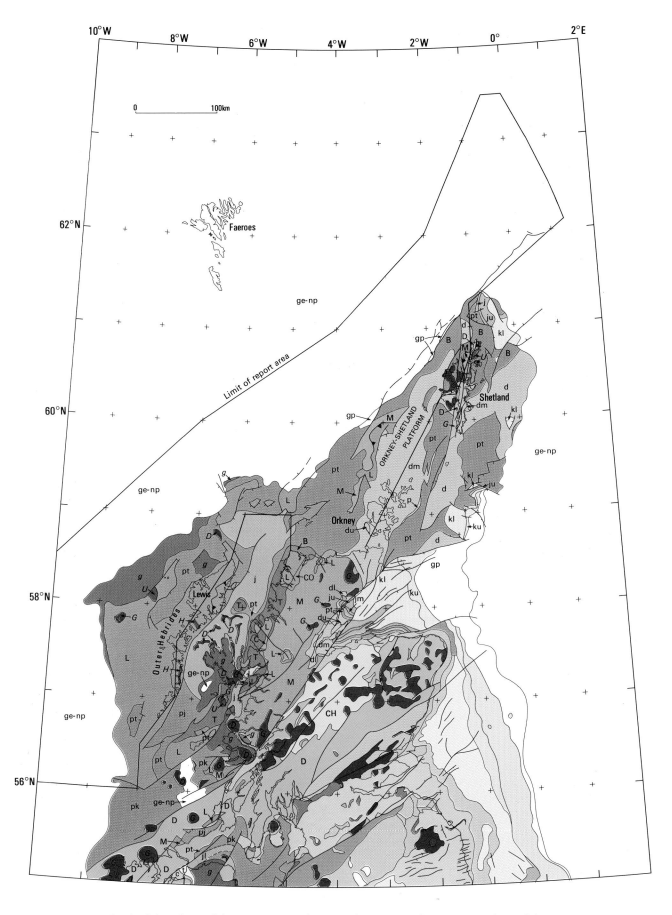

Figure 3 Generalised solid geology of the report area and surrounding areas. After: BGS Geology of the United Kingdom, Ireland and the adjacent Continental Shelf (North Sheet). In places this map differs from diagrams illustrated in this report.

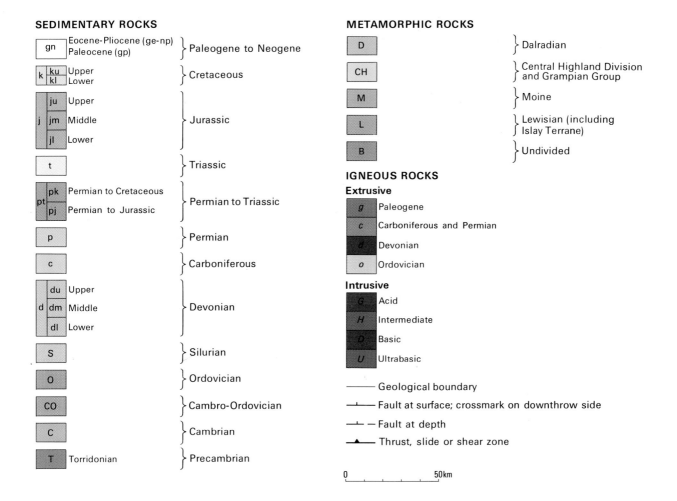

SEDIMENTARY ROCKS

| gn | Eocene-Pliocene (ge-np) Paleocene (gp) | } Paleogene to Neogene |

| k | ku Upper / kl Lower | } Cretaceous |

| j | ju Upper / jm Middle / jl Lower | } Jurassic |

| t | | } Triassic |

| pt | pk Permian to Cretaceous / pj Permian to Jurassic | } Permian to Triassic |

| p | | } Permian |

| c | | } Carboniferous |

| d | du Upper / dm Middle / dl Lower | } Devonian |

| S | | } Silurian |

| O | | } Ordovician |

| CO | | } Cambro-Ordovician |

| C | | } Cambrian |

| T | Torridonian | } Precambrian |

METAMORPHIC ROCKS

D	} Dalradian
CH	} Central Highland Division and Grampian Group
M	} Moine
L	} Lewisian (including Islay Terrane)
B	} Undivided

IGNEOUS ROCKS

Extrusive

g	Paleogene
c	Carboniferous and Permian
d	Devonian
o	Ordovician

Intrusive

G	Acid
H	Intermediate
D	Basic
U	Ultrabasic

——— Geological boundary

—⊢— Fault at surface; crossmark on downthrow side

—⊦ — Fault at depth

—▲— Thrust, slide or shear zone

0   50km

gression, and are represented almost entirely by biostratigraphically barren, continental, clastic redbeds, although evaporites have been reported.

Neither Jurassic nor Cretaceous rocks crop out extensively on the shelf (Figure 3), but have been recovered in most commercial wells drilled in the area. Proven Jurassic rocks in the area are largely marine. West of Shetland, circumstantial evidence suggests that a thin Lower Jurassic sequence may have been deposited and removed prior to the Mid-Jurassic. The Middle Jurassic generally consists of a thin, sandstone-dominated succession, with local highs acting as the source areas. The overlying Upper Jurassic, shale-dominated sequences are more typical of deeper-water environments. Farther south, Lower Jurassic marine shales occur in The Minch, but Middle and Upper Jurassic sediments have been proved only in shallow boreholes on the Hebrides Shelf. Jurassic rocks may be present in the deeper parts of the Faeroe–Shetland Basin and northern Rockall Trough.

A further extensional tectonic phase during the Early Cretaceous caused renewed movement on existing faults, and rejuvenation of local highs. Clastic sediments were shed into adjacent basins as shallow-water fans, whereas in deeper water, marine shales continued to accumulate. In mid-Cretaceous times, the tectonic regime changed to one of passive subsidence, and sea levels were high during the Late

Cretaceous. Thick Upper Cretaceous successions are seen in the Møre and Faeroe–Shetland basins, where the sediments typically consist of dark grey, marine shales which blanket all pre-existing structures. A minor tectonic pulse associated with igneous activity occurred during the Campanian.

The early Tertiary was dominated by the opening of the adjacent north-east Atlantic Ocean, and sea-floor spreading to the west of Rockall Plateau in the Iceland Basin (Figure 1). This was accompanied by widespread and voluminous outpouring of basaltic lavas, the intrusion of many sills, and the formation, or continued development, of several major igneous centres. Igneous activity waned after the early Eocene, since when up to 3 km of passive thermal subsidence has occurred in the Rockall Trough, Faeroe–Shetland Basin and Møre Basin. Paleogene and Neogene sediments were therefore deposited as a seaward-thickening wedge on the outer shelf. The mid-Tertiary saw the onset of abyssal water circulation which caused erosion of older Tertiary sediments. Since that time, the present-day bathymetry and modern water-circulation patterns have developed, and there was an important period of sediment-drift accumulation in the northern Rockall Trough during the Miocene. At about 2.5 Ma ago there was a marked cooling of the climate, and from about 0.44 Ma the shelf was subjected to widespread glacial activity on at least three occasions.

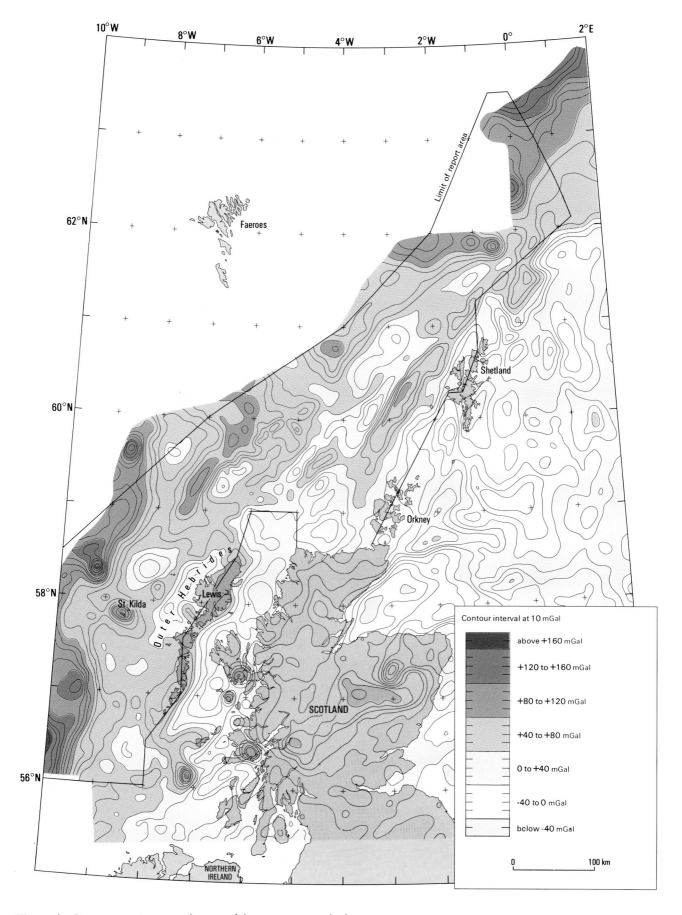

Figure 4 Bouguer gravity anomaly map of the report area and adjacent areas.

2　Physiography

The report area can be divided into the following major physiographic zones (Figure 5):
1. The relatively shallow, pericontinental Hebrides and West Shetland shelves that extend from the coast to the shelfbreak.
2. The shelfbreak.
3. The Hebrides and West Shetland slopes, which lie beyond the shelfbreak.
4. The Rockall Trough and Faeroe–Shetland Channel basin plains, and the intervening Wyville–Thomson Ridge.

The geographical names used are those of Roberts et al. (1979), except that the Hebrides Shelf is extended southwards to include part of their Malin Shelf. The boundary between the Hebrides and West Shetland shelves is defined arbitrarily at a line extending north-westwards from Cape Wrath to the crest of the Wyville–Thomson Ridge. Many of the features or processes referred to briefly below are considered further in later chapters.

THE HEBRIDES AND WEST SHETLAND SHELVES

Coastal areas

The coastlines bordering the report area are generally rugged, for they are formed from a variety of Precambrian and Palaeozoic rocks. The coasts of the Outer Hebrides, Orkney and Shetland have a submerged appearance as a result of eustatic and isostatic rises in sea level following deglaciation.

Although there is a great deal of variation, the western coastline of the Outer Hebrides is mostly low and flat in the south, where there are wide beaches with extensive machair. Cliffs are more common in the north, notably around headlands (Steers, 1973). On the Scottish mainland, the Lewisian gneiss typically forms rounded and hummocky slopes, although in the vicinity of Cape Wrath it forms steep cliffs, as do Torridonian rocks (Steers, 1973). In Caithness, the Old Red Sandstone forms high cliffs with stacks and geos, whereas the more intricate and indented coastline between Strathy Point and Loch Eriboll is largely formed of Moine rocks.

On Orkney, as in Caithness, Old Red Sandstone forms many stretches of cliffs; these are up to 335 m high on the west side of Hoy, where the Old Man of Hoy stack rises to a height of 137 m. The coastline of Shetland is formed by a variety of metamorphic, igneous and sedimentary rock types, and has a very complex shape. There are extensive stretches of exposed cliffs and rocky shorelines (see Front Cover), with long, narrow inlets, known locally as voes, which extend for several kilometres inland. Sand spits, tombolos and other types of bars are well displayed on both Orkney and Shetland (Flinn, 1964; Steers, 1973).

Below sea level, there is a general northward increase in the gradient of the coastal slope. Off the Outer Hebrides, the sea bed slopes gently seawards with no well-defined coastal break of slope. West of South Uist and North Uist, the 20 m isobath is typically about 7 to 10 km offshore. The various channels and sounds running between the islands are generally shallower than 20 m, and depths off the Butt of Lewis in the north are about 30 m.

In contrast, the sea bed off Shetland dips steeply from the coast at an angle of between about 6° and 9° to a break of slope where the sea bed flattens out at about 82 m (Flinn, 1964; 1969). This slope is interrupted locally by terraces at depths of about 24 m and 45 m. The distinctive break of slope can be traced around most of Shetland, and occurs within about 1.6 km of the coast off headlands. Water depths exceed 100 m in nearshore deeps such as Yell Sound and St Magnus Bay.

In between these two extremes, slope angles off the Scottish mainland range from about 1° to 4°, although in the vicinity of headlands the slope can be as steep as 7°. Along the western side of Orkney, slopes range from about 3° to 6°; the major break of slope occurs at about 65 m below sea level, although it is poorly developed along some stretches (Flinn, 1969), and erosion surfaces are developed at depths of about 19 m and 37 m (Flett, 1920).

Inner shelf and offshore islands

The inner shelf comprises both upstanding, basement highs, and lower-lying tracts of sea bed above sedimentary basins. The basement is glacially eroded and marine-planated, and is generally covered by only a thin, patchy Quaternary sediment cover. Rock outcrop is common, especially where bottom currents are strong, or where there is significant positive relief. The softer sedimentary basins have been preferentially eroded, and then partially infilled by rather thick glacial deposits which form a relatively flat sea bed. The resulting topography has a general north to north-easterly Caledonian trend, reflecting inherited influences.

Extensive basement platforms occur on the inner parts of both the Hebrides and West Shetland shelves. The morphology west and south-west of the Outer Hebrides is dominated by a gently sloping Lewisian platform. This has a similar morphology to the knob-and-lochan scenery developed onshore (Pantin, 1991), with a local relief of up to 40 m above, and 20 m below, the general level of the sea bed. The relief is greater on the Stanton Banks in the south. The highs form rock outcrop, whereas the lows are partially infilled with glacial and postglacial sediments (BGS Tiree Sea Bed Sediments sheet). The northernmost portion of the Lewisian platform (Figure 3) is the Flannan Ridge, which shallows northwards and rises above sea level to form the Flannan Isles. The Flannan Trough between these islands and Lewis may have formed part of a late-glacial drainage system (Perry, 1987). The prominent St Kilda massif, which lies at the south-western end of the Flannan Ridge, is a Tertiary igneous centre some 25 km in diameter that rises from a depth of about 130 m below sea level to over 400 m above sea level. Cliffs on the north coast of Soay rise to 305 m above sea level, and Stac an Arnim rises to 191 m, the highest stack around the UK (Steers, 1973).

On the West Shetland Shelf, the sea bed from Caithness northwards to Shetland is formed by a broad, relatively flat, Old Red Sandstone platform where water depths range from about 70 to 100 m. Carbonate-rich sea-bed sediments overlying the platform are commonly formed into sand waves and sandbanks by strong bottom currents; these bedforms range up to more than 20 m in height. The platform is flanked to the north-west of Orkney by rugged metamorphic basement ridges. West of Shetland, the Foula Ridge rises above the general level of the surrounding platform; at its southern end,

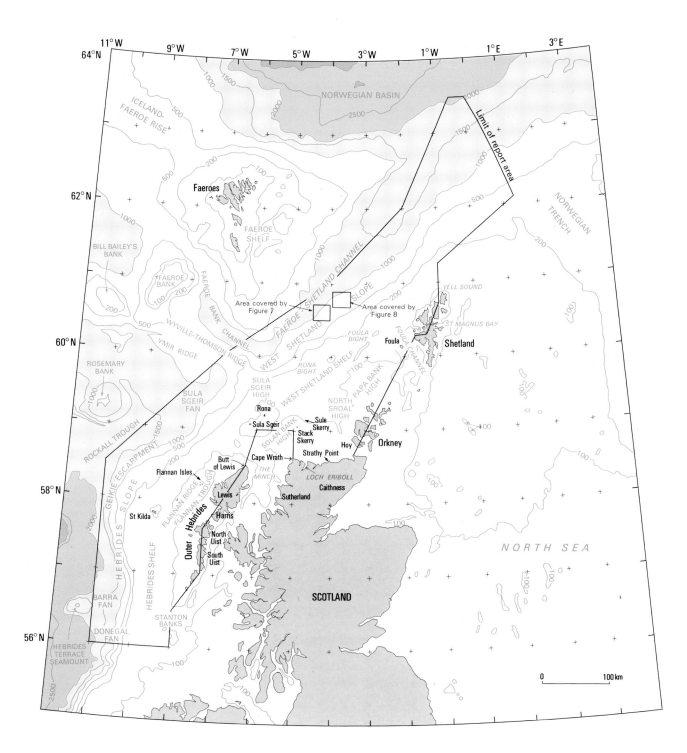

Figure 5 Bathymetry of the report area and surrounding regions. After Roberts et al. (1977).

Devonian rocks on the island of Foula form cliffs which rise to 372 m above sea level (Mykura, 1976), and extend to about 80 m below sea level (Flinn, 1969).

Elsewhere on the inner shelves, Lewisian basement occurs as isolated basement highs with rugged topography, separated by the smoother sea bed overlying sedimentary basins. To the north of Lewis and the Scottish mainland, ridges rise above sea level to form small islands and stacks, such as at Sula Sgeir and Rona (Figure 5).

Outer shelf

The outer shelf generally shows low relief compared with the inner shelf, as it is largely underlain by soft Tertiary sediments that form a seaward-thickening wedge. The sea bed is

formed by sequences of sheet-like, mounded or ridged, glacigenic deposits, and the detailed topography mainly reflects their geometry.

Most of the sea bed consists of broad, low-amplitude rises and depressions, with a width ranging from several hundred metres to upwards of 20 km, generally with a relief of between 20 and 50 m. In detail, large areas, have a very irregular surface due to the presence of iceberg ploughmarks, especially in the vicinity of the shelfbreak. Submarine end-moraine complexes on the outer edge of the West Shetland Shelf form distinctive ridges running parallel to the shelfbreak (Stoker and Holmes, 1991).

A number of basinal areas and overdeepened channels have been identified as possible remnants of major, across-shelf, late Tertiary to Quaternary sediment pathways (Ting, 1937;

Perry, 1987; BGS Foula Quaternary Geology sheet). For example, to the north-west of Sula Sgeir, a re-entrant at the shelfbreak in water depths of between 180 and 200 m is the remnant of a partially infilled canyon cut into the outer shelf and upper slope (BGS Sula Sgeir Quaternary Geology sheet). This may be the culmination of a series of bathymetric deeps that can be traced north-westwards from The Minch. Similarly, the Foula Bight, some 40 km north-west of Foula, is linked to a system of partially infilled depressions and glacially over-deepened channels which extends northwards from west of Orkney and Foula (BGS Foula Quaternary Geology sheet).

THE SHELFBREAK

The shelf slopes gently seawards at average angles ranging from about 0.07° to 0.2°, whereas the adjoining slope is relatively steep, with average slope angles ranging from about 0.9° to 4°. The shelfbreak, which delineates the major physiographic boundary between shelf and slope, is defined as marking the first major change in gradient of the sea bed (Vanney and Stanley, 1983).

In the report area, the shelfbreak occurs at varying distances from the shore, ranging from 200 km west of the south-west Scottish mainland to less than 50 km west of Shetland (Figure 6). Its depth is also highly variable, generally ranging from 120 to 250 m, although it is as deep as 500 m on the Wyville–Thomson Ridge (BGS Sula Sgeir Sea Bed Sediments sheet). Surface trend studies by Flinn (1969; 1973) indicated that it has an overall tilt towards the north-east on the West Shetland Shelf. In profile, the shelfbreak varies from a sharp, easily located boundary (Figure 6G), to a smooth, ill-defined increase in inclination (Figure 6A). It does not necessarily represent the maximum change in seabed gradient; west of the Outer Hebrides, the shelfbreak occurs at about 200 m, although the maximum change in slope angle occurs at about 600 m, at the Geikie Escarpment (Figure 6E and F).

In plan, the shelfbreak is sinuous, with re-entrants such as the Foula Bight incised into the outer shelf. To the south of about 58°N, the orientation of the shelfbreak is north–south, but farther north it runs in a north-easterly direction, a change accompanied by a similar swing in the trend of the Outer Hebrides. This change in orientation may be linked to zones of structural weakness in the Precambrian basement (Jones et al., 1986b). On the Wyville–Thomson Ridge, the shelfbreak is poorly defined (Figure 6C), for the shelf–slope transition is marked by a series of terraces (BGS Sula Sgeir Sea Bed Sediments sheet).

Reconstruction of the Pliocene or early Pleistocene palaeo-shelfbreak shows that the shelf has prograded to the north-west by up to 50 km since that time (Figure 6). The bulk of this change occurred prior to the mid-Pleistocene (Anglian) glacial interval. Shelf progradation continued during the mid- to late Pleistocene glacial phases, although the location of the modern shelfbreak indicates two main areas of post-Anglian shelfbreak retreat. These are west of the Outer Hebrides and north of Shetland; they may partly be attributable to erosion and degradation of the outer shelf through iceberg scouring, although the influence of current activity also needs to be considered.

THE HEBRIDES AND WEST SHETLAND SLOPES

The slopes are relatively narrow compared to the shelves, and their overall morphology and detailed topography can be attributed to factors that include the volume of sediment transported from the shelves, the angularity of underlying Tertiary erosion surfaces, slope instability, deposition and erosion by along-slope currents, and iceberg scouring (Perry, 1987; Kenyon, 1987; Omran, 1990; BGS map sheets).

The upper slopes, to a maximum depth of over 500 m, generally show small-scale irregularity due to iceberg scouring, whereas the middle and lower slopes range from smooth to undulating and hummocky, as they are formed by mass-flow deposits and contourite drifts. Scarps related to both erosion and slope failure are common, as are gullies and channels. Mounds and ridges can either be contourite deposits or the products of slumping and downslope creep. Diapirism, perhaps related to shallow gas, may occur locally.

The southern part of the Hebrides Slope is formed by the Barra and Donegal fans (Figure 5), which are major sediment accumulations up to 1000 m thick that cover an area of almost 8400 km^2 (Roberts et al., 1979; Omran, 1990). Their development is the result of a rich supply of sediment from the Hebrides Shelf in mid- to late Tertiary and Pleistocene times, combined with the blocking effect of the Hebrides Terrace Seamount, which has hindered downslope movement on to the floor of the Rockall Trough. Figure 6G shows a profile across the Barra Fan, where slope angles range from about 5° to 7° on the upper slope, 1.5° to 3° on the middle slope, and less than 1° on the lower slope. The surfaces of the fans are smooth to hummocky, with debris flows developed locally. The slope to the north of the Barra Fan is characterised by channels and gullies (Kenyon, 1987; Omran, 1990; BGS Peach Sea Bed Sediments sheet). Immediately to the south of the report area lies a small canyon (Figure 5) through which sediment has been discharged directly into the Rockall Trough (Omran, 1990).

West of the Outer Hebrides, the upper slope consists of a very gently sloping terrace, with a slope angle of only about 0.6° (Jones et al., 1986b), which descends to a maximum depth of between 600 and 700 m (Figure 6E). Beyond lies the steep Geikie Escarpment (Jones et al., 1986b). The escarpment is thought to be an Oligocene erosion surface (Evans et al., 1989; Strachan and Evans, 1992) rather than a rotational fault scarp (Kenyon, 1987). It extends along slope for 215 km, and is best developed north-west of St Kilda where it is up to 230 m in height, and has its base at depths of between 860 and 910 m. It generally has a slope angle of about 7°, but this increases locally, and can be over 26°. Its sea-bed expression diminishes both to the north and south, and the base shallows to depths of less than 700 m. There is additionally a generally less-steep scarp farther downslope (Figure 6F), which was termed the lower St Kilda scarp by Kenyon (1987). It continues on a northerly trend to the north of 58°N, whereas the Geikie Escarpment curves in a north-easterly direction (Figure 5; Evans et al., 1989). Both scarps have contourite mounds and moats developed at their bases.

Slope angles towards the northern end of the Hebrides Slope range between about 2° and 4° on the upper slope, and decrease downwards (Figure 6D). A slight seaward bulge is formed by the Sula Sgeir Fan (Figure 5), a late Tertiary to Quaternary feature consisting of mass-flow deposits developed below the mouth of an infilled canyon cut into the outer shelf and slope. This region also contains three gullies up to 10 km in length, described as bottle-neck slides by Kenyon (1987).

Slope angles on the upper West Shetland Slope are typically less than about 1°, increasing to between about 1.5° to

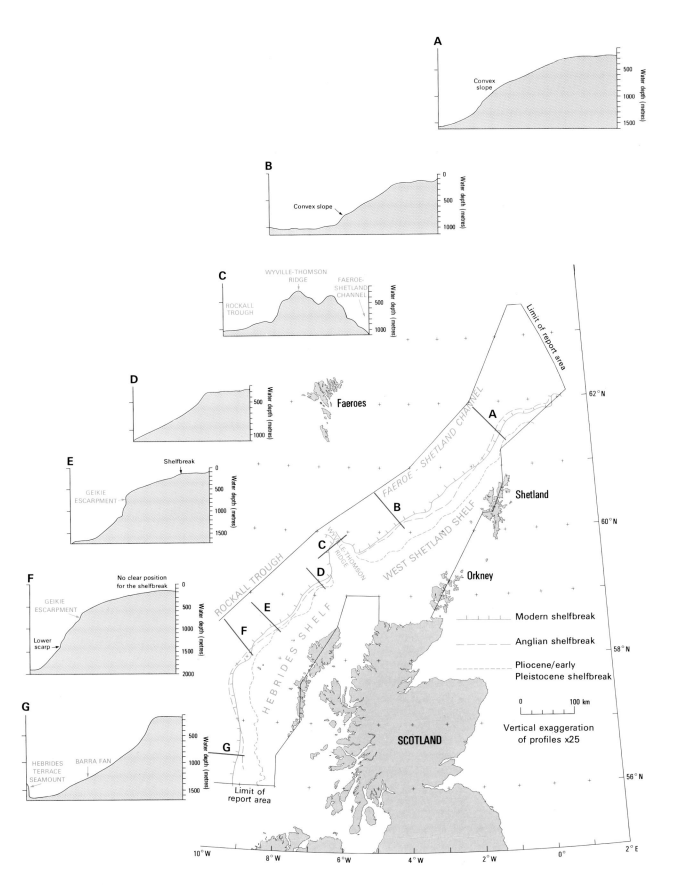

Figure 6 Profiles across the shelfbreak, and its location since Pliocene/early Pleistocene times.

2° in midslope, before decreasing towards the basin floor. The shape of the upper and middle slope is controlled mainly by prograding Plio-Pleistocene sediments, whereas the lower slope reflects the morphology of the underlying Tertiary erosion surface (BGS Quaternary Geology sheets). Small, scarp-like features and depressions related to slope failure are widespread, especially downslope from the Foula and Rona bights. The characteristic, convex profile towards the base of the slope (Figure 6A and B) may be partly the result of bottom-current erosion. In the south, linear deeps with graben-like morphologies occur at the base of the slope (Figure 7); it is possible that these are the surface ex-

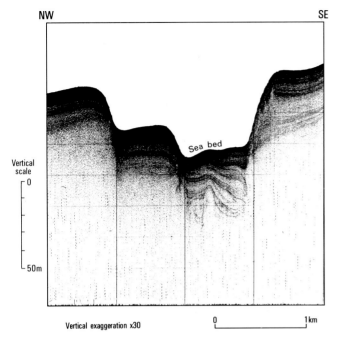

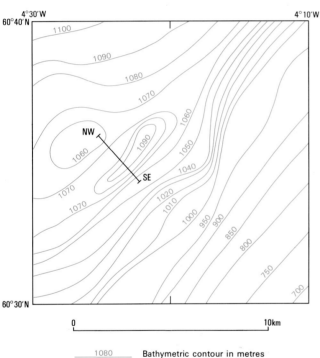

1080 ──── Bathymetric contour in metres

Figure 7 High-resolution seismic profile across an enclosed deep at the base of the West Shetland Slope, with detailed bathymetry in its vicinity. For area covered by diagram see Figure 5.

pression of a more extensive channel/base-of-slope erosional feature.

A number of unusual, subparallel, V-shaped channels (Figure 8), which start and end abruptly, extend downslope from seaward of the Foula Bight in water depths ranging from about 600 m to over 1000 m (Kenyon, 1987). They are 10 to 40 m deep, 200 to 500 m wide, and the steep side walls show evidence of slumping. Their location below the Foula Bight suggests that their formation may be linked to the dispersal and downslope transfer of sediment originating from the shelf during the late Pleistocene (BGS Foula Quaternary Geology sheet). They may represent a localised and specific type of slope failure, or are debris chutes.

ROCKALL TROUGH, FAEROE–SHETLAND CHANNEL, AND WYVILLE–THOMSON RIDGE

The Rockall Trough is a south-westerly trending basin which lies between the British Isles and the Rockall Plateau, and opens into the Porcupine Abyssal Plain to the south (Figure 1). The northern part of the basin contains three seamounts: Rosemary Bank, Anton Dohrn and Hebrides Terrace, all of which rise over 1000 m above the level of the surrounding sea bed. Within the report area, the basin floor slopes gently south-westwards in the north, in water depths ranging from about 1000 m to over 1500 m; farther south, the sea bed slopes westwards from about 1700 m to over 2100 m. The basin-floor topography ranges from smooth to gently undulating and hummocky. The greatest relief generally occurs near the base of the Hebrides Slope, where doming of the sea bed may represent either the surface expression of debris flows, sediment drifts, or gas at shallow depth. Neogene sediment waves result in a local area of undulating sea floor in the north of the trough (Richards et al., 1987).

The prominent, north-westerly trending Wyville–Thomson Ridge forms a major topographic barrier between the Rockall Trough and the Faeroe–Shetland and Faeroe Bank channels (Figure 5). The ridge, formed of Paleogene basalts and sediments, is over 200 km long, and its axis lies almost at right angles to the predominant physiographic trend. Prior to its formation in the early Tertiary, the Rockall Trough and Faeroe–Shetland Channel formed a continuous seaway. Its relatively narrow summit occurs mainly in water depths of less then 400 m, and the average slope angles on its flanks range between about 2° and 6° (Figure 6C); countourite mounds are formed on its lower slopes. The present-

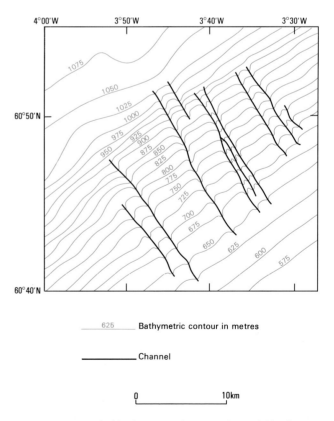

625 ──── Bathymetric contour in metres

──── Channel

0 ──────── 10km

Figure 8 Detailed bathymetry showing channel-like features on the West Shetland Slope. After Kenyon (1987). For area covered by diagram see Figure 5.

day topography is essentially that of a pre-Miocene erosion surface overlain by thin Pliocene to Pleistocene deposits that tend to reduce the angularity of the sea bed (BGS Sula Sgeir Quaternary Geology sheet).

To the north of the Wyville–Thomson Ridge, the Faeroe–Shetland Channel extends north-eastwards for over 400 km before opening into the Norwegian Basin (Figure 5). The southern end of the channel is deflected abruptly north-westwards by the Wyville–Thomson Ridge to form the Faeroe Bank Channel. The basin floor is generally smooth to undulating, and is formed of Neogene sediments draped over, and partially infilling, an irregular mid-Tertiary erosion surface. To the north of 60°30'N, the basin floor slopes gently northwards from about 1000 m to over 1700 m, and widens from about 30 km to over 65 km. Beyond, the sea bed slopes gently northwards to over 2000 m at the northern limit of the report area.

South of 60°30'N, the basin narrows to about 20 km, and although the topography is relatively complex in detail, there is an overall slope southwards (Figure 5), where water depths range from about 950 m to over 1200 m. There are several enclosed deeps; those in the north are steep sided, with slope angles of up to 6° (BGS Judd Sea Bed Sediments sheet), whereas in the south, the basin floor consists of a single deep which trends to the south-west as far as the Wyville–Thomson Ridge, before continuing to the north-west within the Faeroe Bank Channel. The existence of these deeps may be related to erosion by bottom currents which have been active since mid-Tertiary times, and which may be enhanced within this narrow part of the Faeroe–Shetland Channel.

3 Pre-Devonian

Basement rocks, embracing all pre-Devonian strata, crop out over much of the report area (Figure 3), and can be separated into two major provinces (Figure 9): the Foreland Province, and the Orthotectonic Caledonide Province (Kelling et al., 1985). The two display markedly different tectonostratigraphical histories (Figure 10). The Foreland Province constitutes the greater part of the basement in the area, and consists predominantly of Lewisian gneiss locally overlain by Torridonian and Cambro-Ordovician sediments. The Orthotectonic Caledonide Province includes Moine, Dalradian and Caledonised Lewisian, together with syn- and postorogenic granites. The two provinces are separated by the Moine thrust zone, which marks the western limit of the allochthonous Caledonian orogen (Watson, 1984). Their juxtaposition is a direct result of the late Caledonian collision of the Laurentian–Greenland and Fennoscandian–Russian continental plates (Figure 11). The present surface distribution of the basement rocks, including the structural elements to which they relate, is a consequence of the post-Caledonian structural development of the area (see Chapter 4).

The Foreland Province forms numerous platforms on the Hebrides and West Shetland shelves (Figure 12). These represent the offshore extension of the Lewisian Complex, which forms the north-western seaboard of Scotland. The Lewisian Complex is a residual fragment of the Archaean massif (Figure 11) which constituted part of the Laurentian–Greenland continental craton (Bridgewater et al., 1973; Anderton et al., 1979; Park, 1991). It generally consists of an assemblage of highly metamorphosed and migmatised, acidic to ultrabasic gneisses (Park, 1980). These rocks subsequently formed the basement on to which was deposited the predominantly continental, mid- to late Proterozoic Torridonian succession, which was in turn overlain unconformably by Cambro-Ordovician, marine, clastic and carbonate sediments (Johnstone and Mykura, 1989). As far as is known, these cover sequences are restricted to north-west Scotland and the nearby offshore area, where they remain virtually undeformed.

The Orthotectonic Caledonide Province is bounded to the north-west by the Moine thrust zone, and to the south-east by the Highland Boundary Fault (Figure 9). Offshore, rocks of this province are preserved in the Orkney–Shetland–West Shetland–North Shetland platform area. The Great Glen–Walls Boundary transcurrent-fault system broadly divides the province into two allochthonous, fault-bounded, crustal blocks: the Northern Highlands and western Shetland, and the Grampian Highlands and eastern Shetland. In the Northern Highlands, both the Lewisian and the unconformably overlying middle Proterozoic Moine metasediments have suffered the effects of extensive Precambrian and Caledonian (Ordovician to Silurian) orogenesis (Fettes et al., 1986).

In contrast, the Grampian Highlands portion consists largely of upper Proterozoic Dalradian metasediments which have undergone Grampian (late Precambrian) and Caledonian orogenesis (Lindsay et al., 1989; G Rogers et al., 1989), although some of these rocks may have gone through a pre-Dalradian orogenic cycle (Harris et al., 1978). The Dalradian may be underlain by lower Proterozoic crust that was accreted to the Archaean craton in mid-Proterozoic times (Dickin and Bowes, 1991).

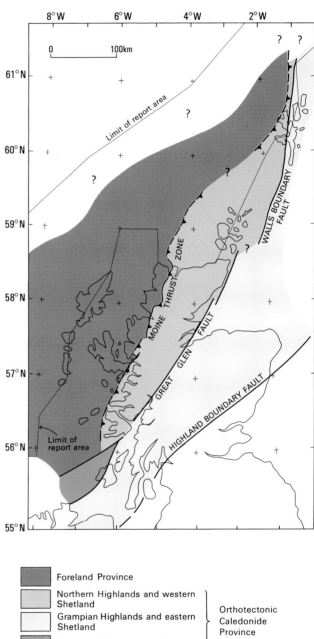

Foreland Province

Northern Highlands and western Shetland

Grampian Highlands and eastern Shetland

Colonsay-Western Islay Terrane

Orthotectonic Caledonide Province

Figure 9 Megatectonic framework of northern Scotland and the adjacent shelf. After Bridgewater et al. (1973) and Marcantonio et al. (1988).

The boundary between the two blocks in Shetland is greatly simplified in Figure 9, for here, Moine- and Dalradian-like lithologies are tectonically juxtaposed on either sides of the Walls Boundary Fault (Flinn, 1985; 1988). Syn- to postorogenic granitic bodies, belonging respectively to the 'Older' and 'Newer' granites, intrude the rocks of the Orthotectonic Caledonides.

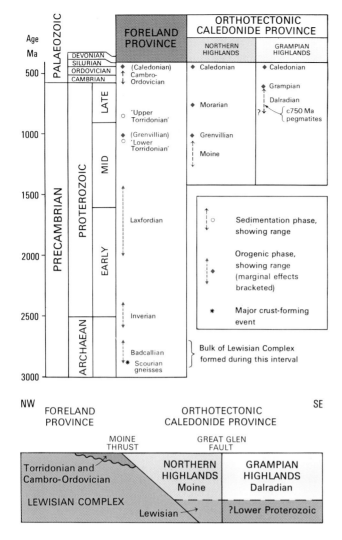

Figure 10 Late Archaean to Early Palaeozoic tectonostratigraphical evolution of the basement in northern Scotland. Stratigraphical information derived from a variety of sources quoted in the text. Timescale after Cowie and Johnston (1985) and Snelling (1985).

FORELAND PROVINCE

Lewisian Complex

In north-west Scotland and the Outer Hebrides, the Lewisian Complex consists of quartzofeldspathic gneisses, ultrabasic to acid intrusives, and metasediments which are largely semipelitic but include calc-silicates (Fettes and Mendum, 1987; Park and Tarney, 1987; Fettes et al., 1992). This assemblage resulted from a phase of extensive late Archaean crustal generation at about 2900 Ma, when large volumes of granodioritic and tonalitic magmas were intruded into a supracrustal sequence of metasediments, metavolcanics and associated layered basic and ultrabasic complexes. The rocks, traditionally known as Scourian gneisses, were subsequently modified during three orogenic cycles, the Badcallian, the Inverian, and the Laxfordian (Figure 10).

The late Archaean Badcallian event from about 2900 to 2700 Ma was the main gneiss-forming episode, and was accompanied by granulite-grade metamorphism; structural trends are predominantly north-easterly (Park, 1980). The high-grade gneisses subsequently suffered inhomogeneous tectonic and metamorphic modifications during the Inverian (c.2500 Ma) and Laxfordian (c.2000 to 1400 Ma) events.

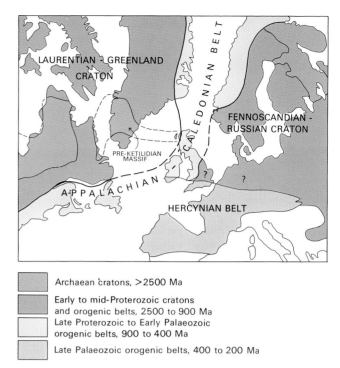

Figure 11 Permian predrift reconstruction of the North Atlantic region. After Anderton et al. (1979).

These led to widespread amphibolite-facies retrogression of the gneisses, and the development of north-westerly trending shear zones. However, whereas Inverian deformation was confined to shear zones, Laxfordian deformation was accompanied by the formation of north-westerly trending folds; the related foliation is locally very intense.

A suite of early Proterozoic basic and ultrabasic bodies, including the Scourie dykes and the South Harris Igneous Complex (see Figure 15), were intruded into the Lewisian Complex between 2400 and 2000 Ma (Fettes and Mendum, 1987; Park and Tarney, 1987). Laxfordian granites were emplaced at about 1700 Ma, and pegmatites were intruded between 1750 and 1500 Ma. Grenvillian (c.1000 Ma) and Caledonian (460 to 420 Ma) reworking in east-south-easterly dipping shear zones, mainly related to the Outer Isles thrust zone, may have locally modified the Lewisian in the Outer Hebrides (Cliff and Rex, 1989; Lailey et al., 1989).

Offshore, Lewisian basement crops out extensively across much of the shelf, where it forms a series of upstanding, partly fault-bounded platforms (Figure 12). The widespread extent of the Lewisian was initially established from gravity data (Figure 4), which revealed numerous large-amplitude, north-easterly trending highs (Watts, 1971; Brewer and Smythe, 1986; Jones et al., 1986b). The structural pattern was subsequently refined by systematic mapping which showed that the structurally high areas commonly consist of Lewisian rocks at or near the sea bed (BGS Solid Geology sheets). On shallow-seismic records (Figure 13), outcropping Lewisian platforms commonly exhibit a rugged bathymetric profile (Jones et al., 1986b). Towards the shelfbreak and on adjacent slope areas, the Lewisian is progressively buried beneath Quaternary and older sediments, and commercial drilling has confirmed its presence beneath a number of sedimentary basins (Figure 14).

The most extensive area of the Lewisian is found on the Outer Hebrides Platform (Figures 12 and 15), on which the Outer Hebrides form the partially exposed eastern margin. The Flannan Isles to the west are composed of hornblende

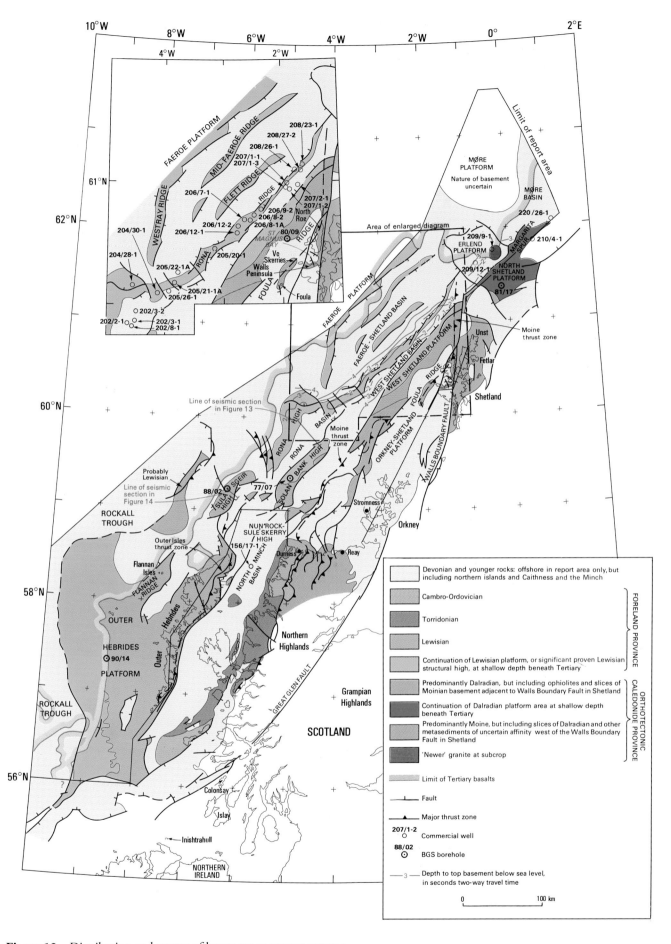

Figure 12 Distribution and nature of basement at or near outcrop.

15

NORTH
LEWIS
BASIN

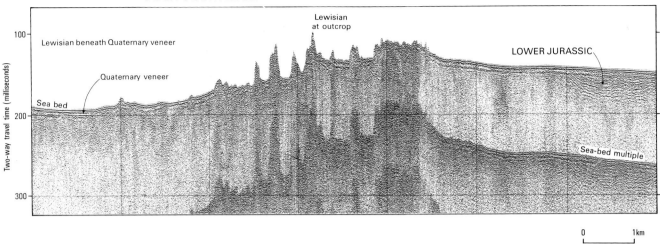

Figure 13 Annotated seismic section showing the typically rugged morphology of the Lewisian sea-bed outcrop. For location see Figure 12.

gneiss cut by pegmatites (Stewart, 1933), and are the subaerial expression of the Flannan Ridge. The ridge has been sampled by rock drill and gravity corer, which recovered banded quartz-feldspar-biotite-gneiss, garnetiferous acid-gneiss, and pink microgranite (BGS Lewis Solid Geology sheet). Additionally, on the central part of the Outer Hebrides Platform, BGS borehole 90/14 penetrated 19 m of weathered, kaolinised, Lewisian gneiss saprolite overlying grey, banded, quartz-feldspar-biotite-pyroxene-gneiss.

Seismic-refraction data suggest that the Lewisian forming the upper part of the platform is cracked and weathered to a depth of about 1000 m, below which 'intact' Lewisian extends to the Moho (Jones et al., 1984). Aeromagnetic and

gravity data indicate that the South Harris Igneous Complex and the late Laxfordian granites on North Harris extend offshore (Figure 15), with the former possibly continuing on to the Flannan Ridge (McQuillin and Watson, 1973; Brewer and Smythe, 1986; BGS Lewis Solid Geology sheet). The apparent south-westward displacement of the igneous complex across the Flannan Trough (Figure 15) may be a result of Precambrian shear movements along a fracture currently marked by the fault bounding the eastern margin of the Flannan Trough (Jones, 1981). Aeromagnetic data across the platform reveal a predominantly north-westerly orientated lineation which swings north-eastwards on the Flannan Ridge.

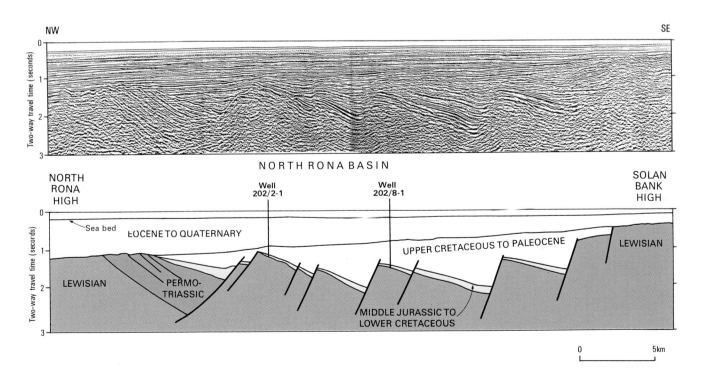

Figure 14 Annotated seismic section showing Lewisian basement flooring the North Rona Basin. For location see Figure 12.

The Outer Hebrides Platform may essentially mark the southern limit of foreland rocks on the shelf to the west of the British Isles. Previously inferred occurrences of Lewisian-type gneisses on Colonsay, Islay and Inishtrahull (Watson, 1983; Figures 9 and 12) are now thought to be part of an allochthonous, early Proterozoic, Colonsay–Western Islay Terrane (Bentley et al., 1988; Marcantonio et al., 1988; Dickin and Bowes, 1991).

To the north-east of the Outer Hebrides Platform, the Sula Sgeir High (Figures 12 and 13) includes the island of Sula Sgeir, which is composed of hornblende-gneiss with cross-cutting pegmatite veins (Stewart, 1933). On the Sula Sgeir High, BGS borehole 88/02 recovered a fractured, strongly banded, coarse-grained, quartzofeldspathic gneiss. Nearby, gravity cores have retrieved samples of quartz-feldspar-granulite-gneiss and heavily fractured, weakly foliated, quartz-feldspar-hornblende-gneiss (BGS Sula Sgeir and Rona Solid Geology sheets).

On the Rona High, to the east of the Sula Sgeir High and separated from it by Mesozoic sediments, the island of Rona consists of garnetiferous amphibolite and acid gneiss pervasively intruded by pegmatite veins (Stewart, 1932; Nisbet and Bowes, 1961). Although structural trends on Rona display a north-westerly Laxfordian orientation, a relict north-easterly trend, depicted by hornblende inclusions in garnets, suggests that the basic mass may be of Scourian origin (Nisbet and Bowes, 1961). A foliated granite-gneiss was recovered from the surrounding platform (BGS Rona Solid Geology sheet).

West of Orkney (Figures 5 and 12), the rocks forming the islands of Stack Skerry and Sule Skerry form part of the Nun Rock–Sule Skerry High, from which amphibolite and pink biotite-gneiss have been retrieved (BGS Sutherland and Rona Solid Geology sheets). On the adjacent Solan Bank High, BGS borehole 77/07 encountered very weathered and altered, dark green amphibolite-schist.

On the West Shetland Platform (Figure 12), BGS borehole 80/09 proved medium to dark grey and pink, basic and acid gneisses, with locally developed augen structures and cross-cutting granite veins. To the south, gravity cores from the Foula Ridge have recovered grey-green banded gneisses, hornblende-gneiss, and pale grey granulite (BGS Shetland Solid Geology sheet). The Ve Skerries, which form the subaerial expression of the Foula Ridge, consist largely of albite-gneiss with subordinate, lenticular masses of foliated granite and partially granitised hornblende- and mica-schist (Mykura, 1976). These are comparable to the Western Series orthogneisses of North Roe, Shetland, which also include sheets of basic and ultrabasic gneiss. Although these rocks have been assigned to the Lewisian, they may have been reworked during the Caledonian orogeny in the vicinity of the Moine thrust zone (Pringle, 1970; Andrews, 1985).

The Rona Ridge and North Rona High, as well as the adjacent West Shetland, North Rona and Faeroe–Shetland basins, have been extensively sampled by deep wells (Figures 12 and 16). These have proved a varied assemblage of foreland rocks, including grey, granitic and tonalitic gneisses, retrogressed pyroxene granulites, and minor occurrences of amphibolite, metagabbro and biotite-garnet-sillimanite-gneiss (Ritchie and Darbyshire, 1984; Hitchen and Ritchie, 1987). These rocks are generally heavily fractured and highly altered, with locally developed calcite and pyrite mineralisation, and veins of quartz and serpentine.

Rb-Sr whole-rock analysis of core (Figure 16) from wells 202/2-1, 205/20-1, 205/26-1 and 207/2-1, on and adjacent to the Rona Ridge, yielded a latest Archaean age of 2527 ± 73 Ma (Ritchie and Darbyshire, 1984). Unspecified

'Lewisian' ages have been obtained from wells 206/7-1, 206/8-2, 206/9-2, 207/1-3 and 208/26-1 on the ridge (Ritchie et al., 1987). Several wells have produced more anomalous age dates; well 205/22-1A gave a Caledonian age of some 400 Ma (Rb-Sr), whereas wells 202/8-1, 204/30-1 and 206/12-2 provided 'intermediate' ages of about 700 Ma (Rb-Sr), 858 ± 35 Ma (K-Ar), and 693 ± 10 Ma (K-Ar) respectively. Hitchen and Ritchie (1987) suggested that the basement in these wells has undergone alteration, thus yielding spuriously young ages. This is supported by a previous dating of well 205/26-1, which realised ages of 997 ± 50 Ma and 559 ± 30 Ma from samples taken within 1.5 m of each other (Ziegler, 1982).

The extent of the Lewisian beyond the shelf is uncertain. Although it has been inferred to continue beneath the Rockall Trough and Rockall Plateau (Roberts, 1975a; Roberts et al., 1988), recent isotopic and geochemical data suggest that the Rockall Bank is underlain by early Proterozoic crust (Morton and Taylor, 1991). To the north-east, a series of faulted basement ridges, interpreted to underlie the Faeroe–Shetland Basin and Faeroe Platform, have been assigned a Lewisian age on the basis of proven Lewisian rocks on the shallow, eastern margin of the basin and adjacent platforms (Mudge and Rashid, 1987). North of Shetland, the trace of the Moine Thrust is poorly defined in the region of the Møre Platform and Møre Basin, where the boundary between the Foreland and Orthotectonic Caledonide provinces is unknown.

Torridonian and Cambro-Ordovician

In north-west Scotland, the Lewisian is unconformably overlain by mid- to late Proterozoic Torridonian, and Cambro-Ordovician sediments (Figures 3 and 12). The latter locally overstep the Torridonian to rest directly on the Lewisian. These cover sequences have not been subjected to severe deformation or metamorphism, although all are folded and disrupted within the Moine thrust zone.

The Torridonian consists predominantly of fluvial sediments which are subdivided into the 'lower Torridonian' Stoer Group and the 'upper Torridonian' Sleat and Torridon groups (Figure 10). The Stoer and Torridon groups are separated by an angular unconformity; the Stoer Group was probably laid down in a rift-basin setting partly controlled by the Outer Isles Fault, although this fault is not considered to have been a controlling feature of Torridon Group deposition (Anderton et al., 1992). Although Torridonian sediments occur offshore adjacent to, and underlying the North Minch Basin (well 156/17-1) and farther south (Figure 12; Fyfe et al., 1993; BGS Solid Geology sheets), they have not been proved in the report area. Roberts et al. (1988) have nevertheless speculated on their presence in the Rockall Trough.

The Cambro-Ordovician succession consists predominantly of shallow-marine quartzites and carbonates which comprise respectively the Lower Cambrian Eriboll Sandstone and An t'Sron groups, and the Lower Cambrian to Lower Ordovician Durness Group (Johnstone and Mykura, 1989). Sedimentation probably occurred on a slowly subsiding shelf, but with a phase of uplift and erosion during the mid- to late Cambrian (Palmer et al., 1980).

Durness Group sediments are exposed on small islands immediately offshore from Durness (Figure 12), but the occurrence of Cambro-Ordovician rocks elsewhere in the area has not been established. However, Brewer and Smythe (1984) inferred their presence below sediments of the West Orkney Basin for up to 80 km north of the Scottish mainland, and extending some 60 to 70 km east of the Moine thrust zone.

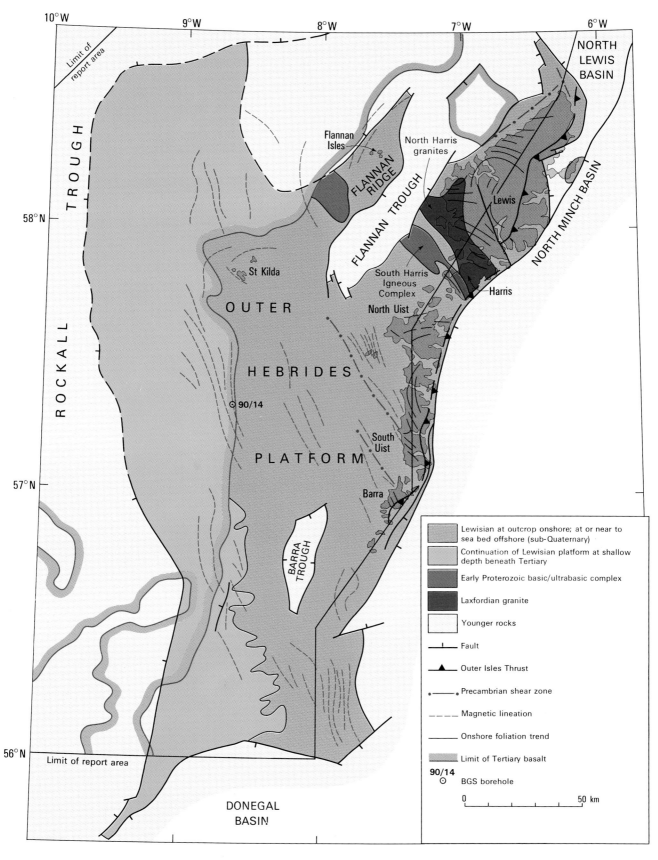

Figure 15 The Lewisian of the Outer Hebrides Platform. Compiled from BGS maps, Jones (1981), and Brewer and Smythe (1986).

Well	Lithology
202/2-1*	Biotite-garnet-sillimanite-gneiss
202/3-1	Granodiorite/granite-gneiss
202/3-2	Gneiss
202/8-1*	Hornblende-gneiss, hornblendite, granite-gneiss
204/28-1	Gneiss, amphibolites, metagabbros
204/30-1*	Gneiss, amphibolites, metagabbros
205/20-1*	Hypersthene-clinopyroxene-granulite
205/21-1A	Gneiss
205/22-1A*	Quartzofeldspathic gneiss
205/26-1*	Tonalitic gneiss
206/7-1*	Quartzofeldspathic gneiss
206/8-1A	Quartzofeldspathic gneiss
206/8-2*	Meta-granite
206/9-2*	Quartzofeldspathic gneiss
206/12-1	Quartzofeldspathic gneiss
206/12-2*	Granite-gneiss
207/1-1	Metagranodiorite/tonalite
207/1-2	Garnet-mica-gneiss
207/1-3*	Quartzofeldspathic gneiss
207/2-1*	Granite-gneiss
208/23-1	Acid gneiss
208/26-1*	Quartzofeldspathic gneiss
208/27-2	Gneiss

*Radiometrically dated: see text for details

Figure 16   Basement rock types recovered in wells west of Shetland.

ORTHOTECTONIC CALEDONIDE PROVINCE

Northern Highlands and western Shetland: Moine

The Moine is a middle Proterozoic metasedimentary succession consisting predominantly of psammites and pelitic schists. In northern Scotland they have been divided into the Morar (oldest), Glenfinnan and Loch Eil divisions (Johnstone et al., 1969). These strata were originally deposited in a dominantly shallow-marine setting between about 1250 and 1050 Ma (Brook et al., 1976; Winchester, 1988). This succession was subjected to Proterozoic tectonothermal events: the Morarian event at about 750 Ma, and possibly a Grenvillian event at about 1000 Ma (Brook et al., 1976), prior to its emplacement on to the foreland during Caledonian (460 to 420 Ma) thrust-related orogenesis (Barr et al., 1986; Roberts et al., 1987). The rocks were locally migmatised during the orogenic episodes, and numerous basic dykes and sheets and large granitic bodies reflect extensive magmatic activity (Brown, 1991). Infolded and interleaved thrust-wedges of Lewisian probably represent slices of basement on which the Moine was deposited.

Evidence for the continuation of Moine-like basement to the north of the Scottish mainland is restricted to isolated inliers on Orkney, Foula, Shetland, and a poorly defined area of the adjacent shelf (Figure 12). On Orkney, foliated granite and granite-gneiss, intimately mixed with psammites and amphibolite pods, form inliers near Stromness. These rocks have been compared both with Lewisian inliers (Wilson et al., 1935) and with the 'Older' granites which intrude the Moine rocks of the Northern Highlands (Mykura, 1976). On Foula, the metamorphic basement consists of a fault-bounded sequence of garnetiferous, granular psammites, and pelitic schists containing lenses of amphibolite (Mykura, 1976).

On Shetland, three separate occurrences of metasedimentary rocks occur west of the Walls Boundary Fault (Figure 12). Rocks of uncertain affinity, but having undergone

Precambrian (greater than 860 Ma) and Caledonian orogenesis, crop out on the Walls Peninsula and extend into St Magnus Bay; these include quartzo-feldspathic gneisses, hornblendites, limestones, calc-silicate rocks and semipelites (Flinn, 1985; BGS Shetland Solid Geology sheet). To the north, psammitic rocks tentatively correlated with the Morar Division of the Northern Highland Moine, occur interleaved with hornblendic gneisses of Lewisian-inlier type that form the Sand Voe schuppen zone (Flinn, 1988). These rocks are separated from the Walls Boundary Fault by the third unit, schists and metavolcanic greenstones of the Quey Firth Group, which probably represent a tectonised slice of Dalradian basement (Flinn, 1985) interleaved with Moinian rocks. Rocks correlated with the Moine and Dalradian also occur to the east of the Walls Boundary Fault. The continuation of these basement units to the north of Shetland is largely conjectural.

On the south-western margin of the Orkney–Shetland–West Shetland platform, rock samples, combined with marine-magnetic data, have been used to identify juxtaposed basement of Moinian and Lewisian aspect (Figure 12). The former is characterised mainly by psammitic lithologies with subordinate calc-silicate, amphibolite and pelite; the latter consists largely of variably foliated, mafic, hornblende-rich gneisses (BGS Orkney Solid Geology sheet). The boundary between the Lewisian and the northern area of Moine is marked by high-amplitude and high-frequency magnetic anomalies in the Moine to the west of the contact, decreasing markedly to the east. Interpretation of this boundary as a thrust is supported by a sample of mylonite collected adjacent to the boundary. The structural setting of the basement to the east of the Moine Thrust suggests that the Lewisian is an allochthonous inlier within the Moine.

Grampian Highlands and eastern Shetland: Dalradian

In the Grampian Highlands, the Dalradian Supergroup consists of late Proterozoic sandstones, quartzites, phyllites, slates and carbonates with subordinate volcanic rocks and glacial tillites (Harris et al., 1978; Anderton, 1985; Fettes et al., 1986). These were deposited between about 800 and 600 Ma (Winchester, 1988; D A Rogers et al., 1989) in a progressively deepening, ensialic basin, or on a shelf; they show a gradual change from a stable, estuarine or intertidal facies to an increasingly tectonically unstable, turbiditic environment. These rocks have been divided into the Grampian (oldest), Appin, Argyll and Southern Highland groups (Harris et al., 1978), that were considered by Lindsay et al. (1989) to form a continuous stratigraphical sequence (Figure 10). All the rocks bear the imprint of the Grampian (about 600 Ma) and late Caledonian (460 to 420 Ma) orogenesis (Fettes et al., 1986; D A Rogers et al., 1989). The pre-Appin Group rocks have also been intruded by pegmatites at about 750 Ma (Piasecki and van Breemen, 1983).

Lithologically similar rocks comprise the bulk of the East Mainland Succession of Shetland east of the Walls Boundary Fault (Figure 12). The Scatsta, Whiteness and Clift Hills divisions may be equivalent to the Appin and Southern Highland groups of the Dalradian. The Yell Sound Division, which occurs adjacent to the Walls Boundary Fault and contains Lewisian inliers, is considered to be a tectonised slice of Moine basement provisionally correlated with the Glenfinnan Division of the Northern Highlands (Flinn, 1985; 1988). The islands of Unst and Fetlar include two ophiolite nappes emplaced after regional metamorphism of the East Mainland Succession at about 526 Ma, but prior to the climax of regional metamorphism in mainland Scotland (Flinn et al., 1972; 1979) at about 490 Ma (G Rogers et al., 1989). The offshore continuation of this basement succession, albeit undifferentiated, has been confirmed by sea-bed sampling to the east of Shetland (BGS Shetland Solid Geology sheet).

On the North Shetland Platform (Figure 12), the nature of the basement remains ambiguous. BGS borehole 81/17 recovered tremolitic amphibolite which yielded a K-Ar date of 697 ± 13 Ma, although the significance of the date is unclear (Ritchie et al., 1987). To the north-east, well 220/26-1 proved foliated metabasite that was unsuitable for dating, but similar to that from intrusions within the Dalradian of mainland Scotland (Hitchen and Ritchie, 1987). On the Erlend Platform, well 209/12-1 sampled granitic basement (see below), with xenoliths of garnetiferous schist which Ritchie et al. (1987) regarded as being of Moinian aspect.

Granites

Large granitic bodies intrude both the Moine and Dalradian successions, and are traditionally classified as 'Older' and 'Newer' granites. The former includes early intrusive bodies and migmatitic complexes related to the peak of regional metamorphism at about 490 Ma (Harris, 1983; G Rogers et al., 1989), as well as the late Grampian granites intruded between 490 and 470 Ma (Brown, 1991). The 'Newer' granites were intruded after the main metamorphic recrystallisation and deformation of the country rocks. Their intrusion spanned the closure of the Iapetus Ocean in Silurian to Early Devonian times (435 to 390 Ma), and they include post-tectonic granites related to uplift and relaxation after the closure (Brown, 1991).

In the Moine, 'Older' granites occur adjacent to the report area only near Reay (Figure 12), where the Strath Halladale Granite, dated at about 650 Ma (Johnstone and Mykura, 1989), intrudes an older migmatitic complex. The nature of the granitic basement on Orkney (see above) remains ambiguous. Offshore to the north-east of Shetland, well 210/4-1 on the Margarita Spur (Figure 12) yielded an Ar-Ar (biotite) age of 442 ± 4 Ma from biotite-granite/gneiss pebbles within ?Permo-Triassic sediments (Frost et al., 1981). The pebbles are thought to be derived from a nearby granite mass. The age spectrum derived from a biotite concentrate from the sample was interpreted by Frost et al. (1981) to indicate an 'Older' granite origin overprinted by later Caledonian events.

The 'Newer' granites, whilst generally referred to as granite, comprise a calc-alkaline suite ranging from appinite and basic diorite to granite (Johnstone and Mykura, 1989). Although abundantly developed in the Grampian Highlands, the 'Newer' granites are sparse to the north-west of the Great Glen Fault (Harris, 1983). Offshore, evidence of 'Newer' granites has been found in commercial wells north of Shetland. On the Erlend Platform, well 209/9-1 (Figure 12) penetrated the Rendle Granite (Hitchen and Ritchie, 1987; BGS Miller Solid Geology sheet), and recovered a crudely foliated granodiorite. This has been interpreted as a 'Newer' granite on the basis of a K-Ar (biotite) age of 392 ± 6 Ma (Ritchie et al., 1987), and a Rb-Sr age of 411 ± 4 Ma obtained by the Britoil oil company. To the south-west, well 209/12-1 sampled a foliated biotite-granite for which a late Caledonian intrusive age is inferred from K-Ar dates of 360 ± 3 Ma (Ritchie et al., 1987) and 394 ± 3 Ma (Marathon oil company). Comparable ages have been determined from granitic plutons on Shetland east of the Walls Boundary Fault (Miller and Flinn, 1966). Acidic plutons in and around Shetland west of the Walls Boundary Fault represent slightly younger, Mid- to Late-Devonian postorogenic intrusions (see Chapter 5).

4   Post-Caledonian structural development

The area to the north and west of Scotland has a complex structural history; the structural framework reflects the strongly anisotropic nature of the pre-Devonian rocks, which is dominated by north-easterly trending lineaments with subordinate north-westerly fractures (Figure 17). These were formed during Proterozoic and Caledonian orogenesis. Since the Caledonian orogeny, or in some cases before, this basement structure has exerted a significant control on basin development. The accumulation of Torridonian, Devonian to Lower Carboniferous (Old Red Sandstone), Upper Carboniferous, Permian and Mesozoic strata in intracratonic rift basins resulted from intermittent reactivation of pre-existing orogenic structures during phases of regional crustal extension. However, the offshore record of pre-Carboniferous basin history is fragmentary, with basinal areas only crudely defined from remnants on platforms and ridges. Consequently, most of the known offshore basin history relates to Permian and younger rocks (Figure 18).

Following the Late Carboniferous Variscan orogeny, compressional stresses were replaced by crustal extension and rifting throughout the Arctic–North Atlantic region. During Permian and early Mesozoic times, basin formation was closely linked to the evolution of the Norwegian–Greenland Sea rift system, which had propagated southwards into the Faeroe–Rockall–north-west Scottish area by the Late Carboniferous or Early Permian (Ziegler, 1988). Extensional faulting and half-graben development led to the accumulation of thick Permo-Triassic clastic sequences in continental basins throughout the report area, although by the Early Jurassic, a marine connection with the Tethys rift system had formed.

Since Mid-Jurassic times, basin development has been mainly concentrated on the outer part of the Hebrides and West Shetland shelves, and within the Rockall Trough, Faeroe–Shetland Basin and Møre Basin (Figure 18). Basinal subsidence was largely governed by stresses related to the northward propagation of the Central Atlantic sea-floor-spreading system. This culminated in the opening of the North-East Atlantic Ocean in the early Tertiary as the spreading axis shifted from the Labrador Sea, in the North-West Atlantic, to the area between Greenland and Rockall. A change in the style of subsidence is evidenced by the switch from intrabasinal faulting in Late Jurassic and Early Cretaceous times to passive thermal subsidence during the Late Cretaceous. In the early Tertiary, a renewed phase of fault activity and widespread volcanism accompanied the formation of the North-East Atlantic Ocean. Continental break-up ultimately occurred on the western flank of the Rockall Plateau and the Faeroe and Møre platforms (Figure 17).

As a precursor to North Atlantic spreading, tensional stresses led to extreme crustal attenuation across the Rockall Trough, Faeroe–Shetland Basin and Møre Basin. These structures form part of a pre-Tertiary proto-North Atlantic rift zone which can be traced from the Vøring Plateau off central Norway to the Porcupine Bank (Figure 1) region west of Ireland (Smythe, 1989). The present configuration of the rift zone developed during an abortive attempt at continental break-up. Post-rift thermal subsidence occurred in response to extreme crustal thinning beneath the rift zone, and this influenced the development of the deep-water area which currently separates the Hebrides and West Shetland shelves from the Rockall Plateau, Faeroe Shelf and intervening banks (Figure 1).

The report area can be divided on the basis of post-Variscan tectonics and sedimentation into three broad structural provinces: the west Orkney–Hebrides Shelf region, the West Shetland Shelf, and the Rockall Trough–Faeroe–Shetland Basin–Møre Basin rift zone (Figure 19). The basins beneath the west Orkney and Hebrides Shelf region are largely tilted to the west, controlled by east-dipping faults. In contrast, easterly tilted basins bounded by west-dipping faults underlie the West Shetland Shelf. In both provinces, basins developed on the inner shelf contain a Permo-Triassic to Lower Jurassic sediment fill, whereas basins on the outer shelf are filled by Permo-Triassic to Tertiary sequences (Figure 18). The Rockall Trough, Faeroe–Shetland Basin and Møre Basin have, as far as is known, a predominantly Cretaceous and Tertiary sediment fill. This may reflect maximum extension and crustal thinning across the rift zone at that time, although a rift system or chain of basins may have existed along this axis since the Late Palaeozoic (Scrutton, 1986; Smythe, 1989). It should be noted that a number of the structural elements described in this report have been discussed by other authors using different nomenclatures, as indicated in Figure 20.

STRUCTURE OF THE LITHOSPHERE

The lithosphere consists of the uppermost mantle and crust, which are separated by a seismic discontinuity termed the Mohorovičić Discontinuity, or Moho. North and west of Scotland, the depth to the Moho, as determined from refraction-seismic and gravity data, varies widely (Figure 21). Beneath the Hebrides and West Shetland shelves, the Moho generally occurs at a fairly constant depth of 25 to 30 km, despite variation in upper-crustal structure associated with Late Palaeozoic and Mesozoic basin development (Smith and Bott, 1975; Jones, 1978; Bott et al., 1979). The Moho rises significantly beneath the rift zone to a minimum depth of about 12 km in the Rockall Trough at 56°N (Scrutton, 1972), and about 15 km in both the Faeroe–Shetland Basin at 61°N (Bott, 1984) and the Møre Basin at 63°N (Smythe et al., 1983). There is considerable variation within the rift zone; in the Rockall Trough between 57° and 58°20'N, the Moho appears to dip westwards from about 17 km depth on the eastern margin of the basin to 20 to 24 km adjacent to the Rockall Plateau (Roberts et al., 1988). A more constant depth of about 14 km was recorded across the trough at 56°30'N by Neish (1990), and west of Ireland the Moho occurs at 16 to 17 km depth (Makris et al., 1991). Beneath the Wyville–Thomson Ridge, the Moho has been depressed to about 26 km (Roberts et al., 1983). The depth to the Moho below the Rockall Plateau, and the Faeroe and Møre platforms, varies from 22 to 31 km (Scrutton, 1972; Bott et al., 1974; Hamar and Hjelle, 1984).

Reflectivity of the uppermost mantle and the Moho

On deep seismic-reflection profiles, the upper mantle in the report area is generally nonreflective, although isolated, high-

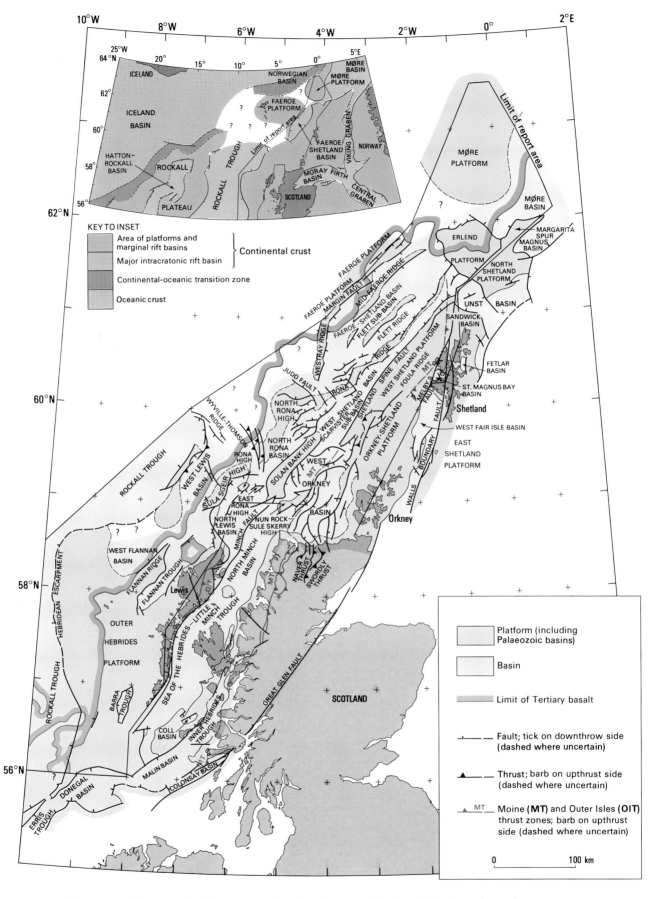

Figure 17 The structural framework of the area north and north-west of Scotland. The inset shows the megatectonic setting of the north-west UK Continental Margin, highlighting the major Mesozoic rift system. Compiled from BGS maps, Hamar and Hjelle (1984), Andrews (1985), Coward and Enfield (1987), Duindam and Van Hoorn (1987), Mudge and Rashid (1987), Ritchie et al. (1987), Coward et al. (1989), Earle et al. (1989), Andrews et al. (1990) and Roberts et al. (1990).

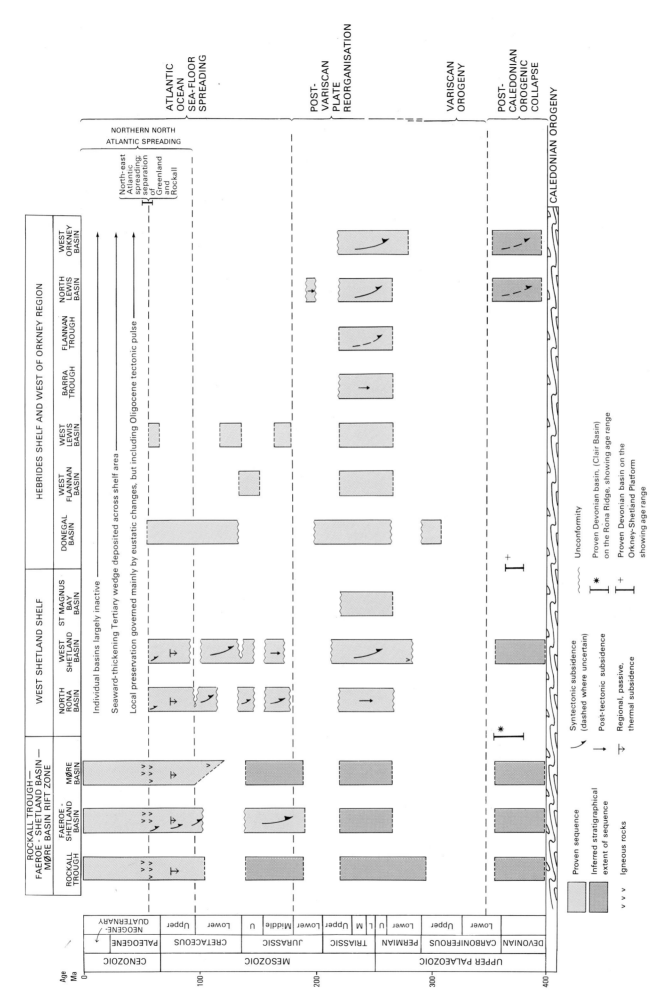

Figure 18 Conceptual stratigraphical chart relating basinal sequences to the regional tectonic framework.

23

ly reflective mantle structures have been imaged beneath the Hebrides Shelf (Brewer and Smythe, 1986). The most striking feature is the easterly dipping Flannan structure (Figure 22), which can be traced rising at an angle of 25° to 30° from a depth of at least 80 km up to about 15 to 18 km in the lower crust, where it appears to become subhorizontal after crossing the Moho without significant offset (Brewer and Smythe, 1986; Flack and Warner, 1990). This reflector has been interpreted as a shear zone formed during the Caledonian orogeny (Warner and McGeary, 1987; Snyder and Flack, 1990). At about 50 km depth, a subhorizontal reflector branches off the Flannan structure; gravity modelling suggests that this is a result of density stratification within the lithosphere. The reflector is possibly a remnant of the base of the Caledonian crust now offset by the Flannan structure (Snyder and Flack, 1990).

The acoustic character of the Moho displays lateral variability ranging from a bright, continuous, subhorizontal reflector to a more-discontinuous seismic boundary (Brewer and Smythe, 1984, 1986; McGeary and Warner, 1985; Stein and Blundell, 1990). This change in character is locally abrupt where the Moho is cut by crust-penetrating faults or shear zones such as the Flannan structure, or by the Walls Boundary Fault north of Shetland (Figure 22).

Crustal structure

Seismic-refraction data suggest that the sedimentary basins of the Hebrides and West Shetland shelves are underlain by a two-layer continental crust ranging from about 22 to 30 km thick (Figure 21). An upper-crustal layer with an interval velocity of 5.8 to 6.4 km/s has been distinguished from a lower-crustal layer of 6.45 to 7.1 km/s; the mid-crustal discontinuity lies between 2 and 17 km depth (Smith and Bott, 1975; Roberts et al., 1988), although it is not present everywhere (Bott et al., 1979; Jones et al., 1984; Hughes et al., 1984). The lower layer has been inferred to consist of Lewisian granulites of Scourian type, and the upper layer to be lower-grade Lewisian (Laxfordian) or Caledonian metamorphic rocks (Smith and Bott, 1975). Fluctuations in depth to the mid-crustal refractor coincide with changes in upper-crustal structure related to the formation of Late Palaeozoic and Mesozoic basins.

Deep-seismic reflection profiles across the Hebrides and West Shetland shelves (Figure 22) image the upper crust as an acoustically transparent layer overlying a highly reflective lower crust (McGeary et al., 1987; Flack and Warner, 1990). Where upper-crustal reflections are observed, the basement is usually cut by relatively low-angle faults and/or is overlain by sedimentary basins. The thickness of the reflective zone in the lower crust varies from 1 to 5 s TWTT, that is about 3 to 15 km (Brewer and Smythe, 1986: McGeary, 1989). There is considerable variation in reflection character and continuity; this may relate to changes in the regional strike of the crustal structure arising from polyphase deformation (Brewer and Smythe, 1986; Cheadle et al., 1987).

Crust of greatly reduced but variable thickness occurs beneath the rift zone (Figure 21). In the Rockall Trough, refraction-seismic and gravity data indicate that the thickness of the crust underlying the sediment fill generally increases northwards from about 6 km immediately south-west of the report area to 18 km at the northern end of the Rockall Trough (Scrutton, 1972; Bott et al., 1979). An asymmetry has been suggested, with the thinnest crust occurring on the eastern margin of the trough (Roberts et al., 1988), although more symmetric models have also been proposed (Figure 21) by Neish (1990; 1992). The transition from the thicker crust

underlying the Hebrides Shelf to the thinned crust beneath the trough appears to be fairly abrupt, occurring over a distance of about 40 to 80 km on the outer part of the shelf (Roberts et al., 1988; Smythe, 1989). In the Faeroe–Shetland and Møre basins, crustal thicknesses of 6 to 8 km and 8 to 20 km respectively have been estimated (Bott and Smith, 1984; Smythe et al., 1983). West of Shetland (Figure 17), crustal thinning occurs beneath the western flank of the Rona Ridge (Bott and Smith, 1984).

The nature of the crust flooring the rift zone remains problematic in the absence of conclusive data. The discovery of thin crust beneath the rift zone (e.g. Scrutton, 1972) was taken to imply that it was oceanic in origin. This was seemingly supported by the interpretation of linear magnetic anomalies in the southern Rockall Trough, together with axial intrusions and sills in the Faeroe–Shetland and Møre basins (Ridd, 1981, 1983; Roberts et al., 1981; Hanisch, 1984; Price and Rattey, 1984). These were taken as being indicative of sea-floor spreading, but these characteristics may equally be interpreted in terms of highly attenuated continental crust heavily intruded by igneous material (Smythe, 1989; Bentley and Scrutton, 1987; Joppen and White, 1990). The latter form is favoured by interpreters of recent seismic-refraction data from the northern Rockall Trough (Figure 21), who describe a two-layer continental crust consisting of a 5.8 to 6.2 km/s upper crust and a 6.45 to 6.6 km/s lower crust (Roberts et al., 1988; Neish, 1990). This subdivision is poorly imaged on the deep seismic-reflection profile of Stein and Blundell (1990) shown in Figure 22.

Seismic-reflection data from the Faeroe–Shetland Basin image several easterly dipping, low-angle reflectors beneath the basin floor; these are interpreted as Caledonian thrusts cutting continental crust (Mudge and Rashid, 1987). In the Møre Basin, gravity, magnetic and seismic-reflection data lend no support for the presence of oceanic crust (Bukovics et al., 1984).

West of the rift zone, gravity modelling (Hamar and Hjelle, 1984) suggests that continental crust up to 20 km thick exists beneath the Møre Platform. The crust beneath the Faeroe Platform is estimated to be between 27 and 38 km thick (Bott et al., 1974; Bott 1984); this is comparable with the Rockall Plateau to the south-west, where Scrutton (1972) identified a two-layer continental crust.

STRUCTURE OF THE WEST ORKNEY AND HEBRIDES SHELF REGION

West of Orkney

West of Orkney, sedimentary basins have formed preferentially by the reactivation of normal faults in the hanging-wall blocks of earlier, easterly dipping thrust zones, such as the Moine and Outer Isles thrust zones. The Moine thrust zone is a late Caledonian structure stretching from western Scotland to the north of Shetland (Andrews, 1985; Enfield and Coward, 1987; Ritchie et al., 1987). West of Orkney, the Moine thrust zone, and the Naver and Swordly thrusts, are imaged on deep seismic-reflection profiles (Figures 17 and 22) as a series of easterly dipping, upper-crustal reflection packages (Brewer and Smythe, 1984; Snyder, 1990). These thrusts dip at 20° to 25° in the upper crust, but have a lesser gradient where deeper than 17 to 20 km as they flatten or terminate in a zone of mid-crustal reflectors.

The Outer Isles thrust zone extends from the eastern coast of the Outer Hebrides on to the northern Hebrides Shelf. Seismic-reflection profiles show that it dips eastwards at

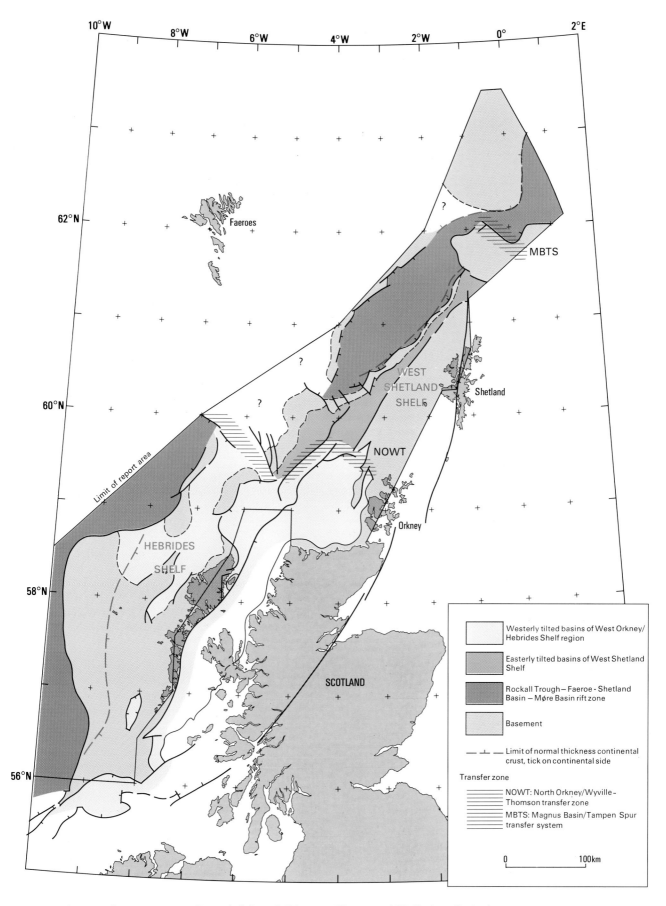

Figure 19 Structural province map. Compiled from BGS maps, Hamar and Hjelle (1984), Andrews (1985), Coward and Enfield (1987), Duindam and Van Hoorn (1987), Mudge and Rashid (1987), Ritchie et al. (1987), Coward et al. (1989), Earle et al. (1989), Andrews et al. (1990) and Roberts et al. (1990).

Figure 20 Structural nomenclature used for the report.

	This Report	Previous variations
BASINS	WEST ORKNEY BASIN	Includes Stack Skerry Basin of Duindam and Van Hoorn (1987), Earle et al. (1989) and BGS Rona Solid Geology sheet Includes Stormy Bank and Noup basins of BGS Rona and Orkney Solid Geology sheets
	NORTH LEWIS BASIN	Part of North Minch Basin of Naylor and Shannon (1982) Part of West Orkney Basins of Duindam and Van Hoorn (1987) Outer Isles Basin of Coward and Enfield (1987) Outer Hebrides Basin of Earle et al. (1989)
	WEST SHETLAND BASIN	'Basin Margin' of Bailey et al. (1987) Includes Foula Basin of Bailey et al. (1987) and Meadows et al. (1987)
	NORTH RONA BASIN	Sula Sgeir Basin of Duindam and Van Hoorn (1987) and Earle et al. (1989) Includes Solan Basin of Bailey et al. (1987) and Meadows et al. (1987) Includes West Rona Basin of Earle et al. (1989)
	FAEROE–SHETLAND BASIN	Faeroe Basin of Ridd (1981, 1983), Bailey et al. (1987), Blackbourn (1987), Duindam and Van Hoorn (1987), Larsen (1987), Meadows et al. (1987), Mudge and Rashid (1987) and Nelson and Lamy (1987)
PLATFORMS	SOLAN BANK HIGH	Stack Skerry Horst of Duindam and Van Hoorn (1987) Rona Ridge of Earle et al. (1989)
	WEST SHETLAND PLATFORM	Includes Papa Bank and North Shoal Highs of BGS Orkney Solid Geology sheet
	MARGARITA SPUR	Nordfjord High of Nelson and Lamy (1987) Nordfjord Horst of Larsen (1987)
	NORTH RONA HIGH	North Lewis Platform of Mudge and Rashid (1987)
TRANSFER ZONES	NORTH ORKNEY/WYVILLE–THOMSON TRANSFER ZONE	~ Wyville–Thomson Transfer Zone of Duindam and Van Hoorn (1987) ~ Orkney–Faeroe Alignment of Earle et al. (1989)
	MAGNUS BASIN/TAMPEN SPUR TRANSFER SYSTEM	Includes Magnus Transfer Zone of Duindam and Van Hoorn (1987)

about 25° (Figure 22) before flattening out in the lower crust (Brewer and Smythe, 1986; McGeary et al., 1987), although Peddy (1984) has suggested that the thrust zone continues into the upper mantle, displacing the Moho by 2 to 3 km. In contrast to the Moine and adjacent eastern thrusts, the Outer Isles thrust zone may have been initiated during the early Proterozoic (Lailey et al., 1989).

Extensional reactivation of these thrusts, by footwall withdrawal and hanging-wall collapse, resulted in the development of the westerly tilted, asymmetric half-grabens of the West Orkney and North Lewis basins. The three-dimensional shape of these basins is further constrained by the geometry of the thrust zones, which are locally offset by steep, west to north-westerly trending transfer faults. These faults have probably utilised existing Precambrian lines of weakness, and have led to the compartmentalisation of the basins. This is demonstrated by the arcuate nature of the basin-controlling faults.

The West Orkney Basin is a broad basinal complex bordered by structural highs, and is separated by tilt-block highs (Figure 17) into a number of sub-basins (Figures 22 and 23). In the east, sub-basin development was controlled by planar, domino-type faulting, whereas listric faulting predominated in the west (Enfield and Coward, 1987). These sub-basins developed largely in the hanging wall of the Moine and related eastern thrusts, although the main basin-bounding fault on its north-western margin bordering the Solan Bank High may be the northern continuation of the Minch Fault, which developed above the Outer Isles Thrust (Stein, 1988; Coward et al., 1989).

The deepest of the component sub-basins formed adjacent to the bounding fault (Figure 23), where up to 8000 m of synrift Permo-Triassic strata may be preserved (Kirton and Hitchen, 1987; Earle et al., 1989). The West Orkney Basin shallows to the south-east, where a thinner Permo-Triassic sequence may overlie 2000 to 3000 m of Old Red Sandstone (ORS) strata;

Figure 21 Crustal structure beneath the Hebrides Shelf, the West Shetland Shelf, the Rockall Trough, and the Faeroe–Shetland Basin. Sections are based on seismic-refraction data, except the western half of Section 2 which is based on gravity data, leading to a slight mismatch. Section 1 from Smith and Bott (1975); Section 2 from Roberts et al. (1983) and Bott (1984); Section 3 from Roberts et al. (1988); Section 4 from Neish (1990).

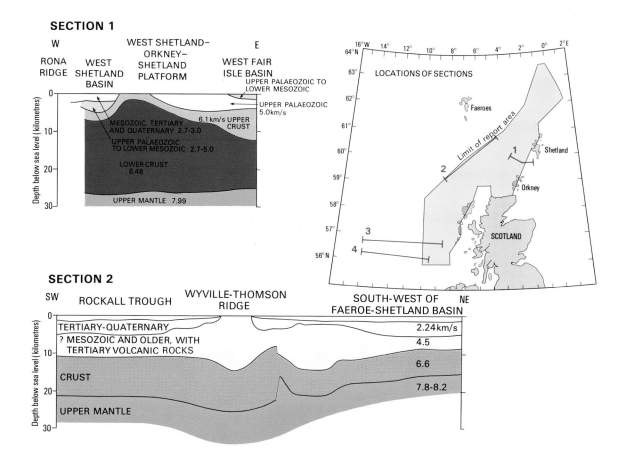

SECTION 1

W

RONA RIDGE — WEST SHETLAND BASIN — WEST SHETLAND–ORKNEY–SHETLAND PLATFORM — WEST FAIR ISLE BASIN

E

UPPER PALAEOZOIC TO LOWER MESOZOIC

UPPER PALAEOZOIC 5.0km/s

6.1 km/s UPPER CRUST

MESOZOIC, TERTIARY AND QUATERNARY 2.7-3.0

UPPER PALAEOZOIC TO LOWER MESOZOIC 2.7-5.0

LOWER CRUST 6.48

UPPER MANTLE 7.99

Depth below sea level (kilometres)

LOCATIONS OF SECTIONS

Limit of report area

Faeroes

Shetland

Orkney

SCOTLAND

SECTION 2

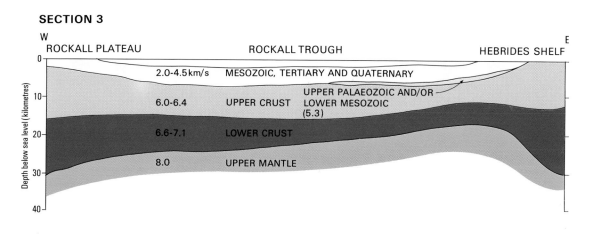

SW — ROCKALL TROUGH — WYVILLE-THOMSON RIDGE — SOUTH-WEST OF FAEROE-SHETLAND BASIN — NE

TERTIARY-QUATERNARY — 2.24km/s

? MESOZOIC AND OLDER, WITH TERTIARY VOLCANIC ROCKS — 4.5

6.6

CRUST — 7.8-8.2

UPPER MANTLE

Depth below sea level (kilometres)

SECTION 3

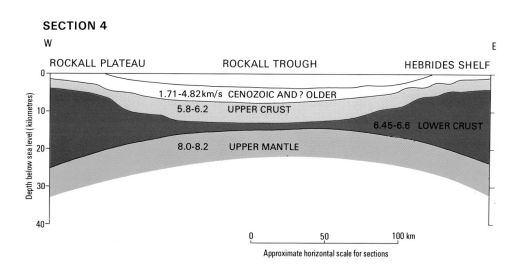

W — ROCKALL PLATEAU — ROCKALL TROUGH — HEBRIDES SHELF — E

2.0-4.5km/s MESOZOIC, TERTIARY AND QUATERNARY

UPPER PALAEOZOIC AND/OR LOWER MESOZOIC (5.3)

6.0-6.4 UPPER CRUST

6.6-7.1 LOWER CRUST

8.0 UPPER MANTLE

Depth below sea level (kilometres)

SECTION 4

W — E

ROCKALL PLATEAU — ROCKALL TROUGH — HEBRIDES SHELF

1.71-4.82km/s CENOZOIC AND ? OLDER

5.8-6.2 UPPER CRUST

6.45-6.6 LOWER CRUST

8.0-8.2 UPPER MANTLE

Depth below sea level (kilometres)

0   50   100 km

Approximate horizontal scale for sections

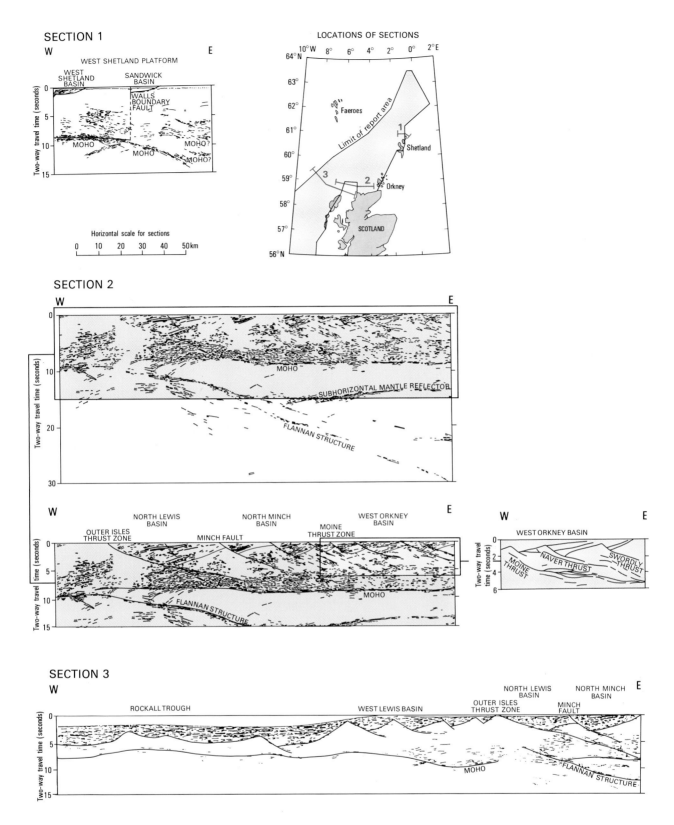

Figure 22 Deep seismic-reflection profiles across the report area. Section 1, the UNST profile, from McGeary (1989); Section 2, the DRUM profile, taken from McGeary et al. (1987) and Snyder (1990); Section 3 (GECO MP-1) from Stein and Blundell (1990).

these are similarly interpreted as synrift sediments (Coward et al., 1989; Earle et al., 1989). The ORS strata crop out on the adjacent Orkney–Shetland Platform (Figure 3).

The North Lewis Basin (Figure 17) formed in the hanging-wall of the Outer Isles thrust zone, in an area where the zone is offset by a north-west-trending fault (Stein, 1988). The basin is separated from the North Minch Basin by the

Minch Fault, and developed as a result of the change in strike of the Outer Isles thrust zone (Stein, 1988). The North Lewis Basin contains 4000 to 5000 m of Permo-Triassic and Lower Jurassic sediments (BGS Lewis Solid Geology sheet). The Permo-Triassic strata accumulated as a synrift sequence (Kirton and Hitchen, 1987), but preservation of the Lower Jurassic sediments is a result of postdepositional, intrabasinal fault activity. The discovery of Torridonian strata beneath Permo-Triassic sediments in the adjacent North Minch Basin (Fyfe et al., 1993) suggests that pre-Devonian basin development cannot be discounted.

A major north-east-trending horst, the Solan Bank High, forms the north-western margin of the West Orkney Basin (Figure 17). The high is a north-easterly plunging block of Precambrian basement partially overlain by thin Tertiary sediments (Figure 3); it marks the northern limit of reactivated thrust movement in the area west of Orkney. The area to the north and north-west of the high, the West Shetland Shelf, is dominated by listric normal faults downthrowing to the north-west (Kirton and Hitchen, 1987). Another prominent high, the Sula Sgeir High (Figure 17), occurs at the north-western margin of the North Lewis Basin, where it forms an exposed basement platform crosscut by north-westerly trending faults.

Hebrides Shelf

The structure of the Hebrides Shelf, particularly the outer shelf, is poorly understood. This is largely due to the masking effect of lower Tertiary basalts which, on seismic profiles, obscure the underlying framework. On the inner shelf, the Flannan Trough (Figure 17) is an elongate half-graben controlled by a south-easterly dipping fault on its north-west margin (Figure 23) and restricted to the south-west by northwest-trending faults related to pre-existing Precambrian lineaments (Jones, 1981). It is also partly faulted on its southeastern margin, but the north-eastern end of the basin remains poorly defined. The thickest basin fill is estimated to be 1000 to 2000 m (Figure 23) adjacent to the bounding fault (Jones, 1978; 1981); it consists of Permo-Triassic redbeds, the asymmetry of which may indicate some degree of synsedimentary faulting.

The West Lewis Basin occurs on the outer, northern part of the Hebrides Shelf, where it is broadly defined from gravity anomalies (Figure 4). Its structural style and basin history remain unclear, but it has been interpreted as a westerly tilted half-graben controlled by a large listric fault on its north-west margin, and separated from the Rockall Trough by a narrow, north-east-trending ridge (Earle et al., 1989). Westerly dipping strata have been identified on seismic-reflection profiles across the eastern margin of the basin, where there are Permo-Triassic, Middle Jurassic and Lower Cretaceous sediments of unknown thickness. The western part of the basin and adjacent ridge are buried beneath a seaward-thickening wedge of Tertiary sedimentary and volcanic rocks. The north-eastern end of the West Lewis Basin is marked by a set of north-west-trending thrusts generated by transpression, and probably coalescing at depth to form a strike-slip fault (Earle et al., 1989). Phases of reverse movement are thought to have occurred at the western side of the basin (Figure 23); this contractional deformation has been attributed to minor Late Cretaceous and Paleocene inversion, and major Oligocene inversion in response to Alpine and Pyrenean stresses (Roberts, 1989). The opposite-facing thrusts (Figures 17 and 23) are inferred to be part of a positive flower structure of Oligocene age (Earle et al., 1989).

To the south-west of the West Lewis Basin, the West Flannan Basin may display a similar geometry (Roberts, 1989), although evidence of faulting has only been identified on its south-eastern margin (Figure 23). Gravity modelling suggests that up to 4000 m of westerly dipping strata may be present in the central part of the basin (BGS Lewis and Geikie Solid Geology sheets); these include Permo-Triassic, Upper Jurassic and Lower Cretaceous sediments. A basement

ridge may separate the West Flannan Basin from the northern Rockall Trough, although the structural detail remains uncertain (Figure 17).

A large part of the southern Hebrides Shelf consists of the Precambrian basement high of the Outer Hebrides Platform, which includes the Flannan Ridge and the Outer Hebridean islands (Figures 15 and 17). This platform has probably been a significant structural high since at least the Late Palaeozoic, as an isostatic response to Permian and Mesozoic extensional reactivation of the Outer Isles thrust zone, and basinal subsidence to the east (Brewer and Smythe, 1986). The platform is broadest between 57° and 58°40'N, and forms a distinct outer-shelf bulge despite the western part of the platform being underlain by thinned continental crust (Figure 19). The persistence of this bulge has probably been due to the remnant thermal buoyancy of the early Tertiary Geikie and St Kilda igneous centres (Evans et al., 1989). The fault-controlled Hebridean Escarpment, which marks the western edge of the platform, displays a variable trend (Figure 17). As the positive influence of the Geikie igneous centre decreased through the Tertiary, the western part of the platform subsided from a hinge near the limit of the thinned crust. This became overlain by a seaward-thickening wedge of Tertiary strata (Figure 23).

On the inner part of the Outer Hebrides Platform in the south, the Barra Trough occurs as a small, fault-bounded basin containing an unknown, but probably limited thickness of Permo-Triassic redbeds (Figure 23). The southern limit of the platform is marked by the Stanton Banks Fault.

To the south, the Donegal Basin (Figure 17) forms the northernmost part of a narrow linear belt of half-grabens, including the Slyne and Erris basins, that have developed on the north-west Irish Shelf (Tate and Dobson, 1989a). The Donegal Basin is controlled at its western margin by listric faults which may represent reactivated splays of the Great Glen fault system (Shannon, 1991). The basin contains up to 3000 m of Permo-Triassic and younger sediments, mainly Early Cretaceous and early Tertiary in age, although Upper Carboniferous strata encountered in the north suggest that basin development began prior to the Permian. Early Carboniferous deposits in the adjacent Erris Trough are comparable with those preserved onshore in Ireland, which may suggest that the north-west Irish basins had not been separately initiated at that time (Shannon, 1991).

STRUCTURE OF THE WEST SHETLAND SHELF

The inner part of the West Shetland Shelf is largely underlain by Precambrian and Caledonian basement. This crops out on the Orkney–Shetland and West Shetland platforms, as well as on the Foula Ridge, and continues to the north of Shetland where it forms the North Shetland Platform and Margarita Spur (Figures 3 and 17). These basement rocks are overlain by, or faulted against, Devonian sedimentary and volcanic rocks which represent remnants of the ORS Orcadian and Sandwick basins. Together, these structural elements constitute a major post-Variscan structural high that extends north-eastwards from Scotland to the north-east of Shetland, and separates the basins of the northern North Sea from those to the north and north-west of Scotland.

Several major faults transect the platform area, including the Moine thrust zone and the Walls Boundary Fault. The former has been traced northwards across the northern part of the Orkney–Shetland Platform, the West Shetland Platform, and the Foula Ridge. Off the north coast of Scotland the thrust is imaged on seismic-reflection profiles to

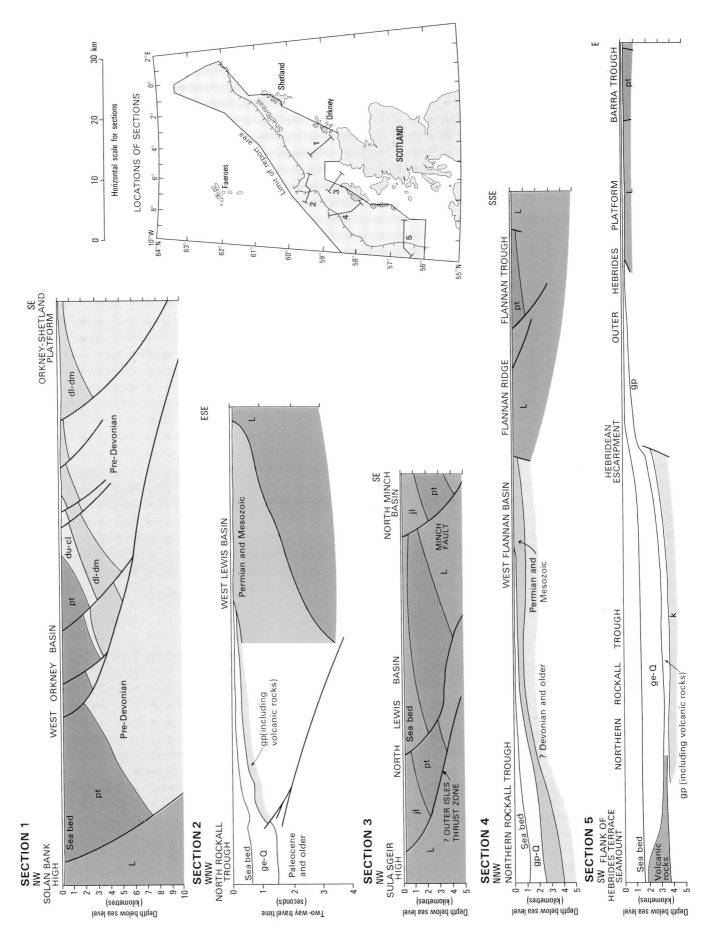

Figure 23 Cross-sections across the west Orkney and Hebrides Shelf region, and the Rockall Trough. After Earle et al. (1989) and BGS maps. For key to stratigraphical abbreviations, see Figure 3.

a depth of about 14 km as a prominent, middle- to upper-crustal, planar reflection that dips east to south-eastwards at 26°. It steepens northwards to dip at 35° near Shetland (Andrews, 1985). In the extreme north-west of Shetland, the thrust zone may continue as the Wester Keolka shear, which separates foreland Lewisian basement from metamorphosed Caledonian rocks (Flinn et al., 1979). North of Shetland, the Moine thrust zone has not been identified on seismic profiles, but isotopic dating of basement rocks suggests it may have a northerly trend (Ritchie et al., 1987). South-west of the Foula Ridge, a thrust has been identified at the south-western end of the West Shetland Platform (Figure 17), although basement–cover relationships (see Chapter 3) suggest that it is structurally higher than the Moine thrust zone, which, by implication, must occur farther to the west.

The Walls Boundary Fault represents a northward continuation, or splay, of the Great Glen fault system, which is a major zone of transcurrent faulting that was initiated during Caledonian orogenesis (Watson, 1984). Deep seismic-reflection profiles north of Shetland (Figure 22) indicate that the Walls Boundary Fault penetrates through the crust, perhaps offsetting a highly reflective Moho (McGeary, 1989). Farther south between Shetland and Fair Isle, there is no abrupt change in crustal thickness across the fault, although easterly dipping Caledonian structures, including the Moine thrust zone, appear to be truncated by the fault (Andrews, 1985: McGeary, 1989).

Left-lateral offset of the West Shetland Platform north of Shetland (Ritchie et al., 1987) implies that net displacement on the Walls Boundary Fault is sinistral, and perhaps not less than 100 km (Roddom et al., 1989), although Ritchie et al. (1987) estimated a shift of only 15 km. It remains unclear whether this movement occurred in response to late Caledonian (Watson, 1984; Ritchie et al., 1987) or Variscan (Roddom et al., 1989) stresses. Post-Devonian dextral displacement of between 60 and 95 km has however been estimated for the Walls Boundary Fault; this movement is generally regarded as Mesozoic in age, with the latest major episode dated as Late Jurassic (Flinn, 1977a; Mykura, 1991; Miller and Pye, 1987; D A Rogers et al., 1989). A post-Triassic, westerly, dip-slip component is suggested by the juxtaposition of the Permo-Triassic infill of the West Fair Isle Basin against basement and Devonian strata of the East Shetland Platform.

Large, post-Devonian, dextral, strike-slip motions proposed for the Melby Fault in the extreme west of Shetland (Mykura, 1991) are more probably of limited extent (D A Rogers et al., 1989), as the fault plane has evidence of only reversed movement (Flinn, 1977a). The Melby Fault forms the western edge of the small and shallow St Magnus Bay Basin (Figures 17 and 24), which is infilled with Permo-Triassic sediments (BGS Shetland Solid Geology sheet).

The western margin of the West Shetland Platform is marked by the Shetland Spine Fault, a major, north-west-hading, listric, normal fault (Figures 17 and 24). It may have been initiated as a strike-slip fault in Devonian times, but was later reactivated as a normal fault during the Permian and Mesozoic (Mudge and Rashid, 1987). Intermittent movement on the Shetland Spine Fault has controlled sedimentation in the adjacent West Shetland Basin, which is a narrow, elongate, south-easterly tilted, north-easterly trending basin showing a half-graben geometry. The throw on the fault is greatest in the south-west, where up to 8000 m of sediments may be preserved, including 4000 m of Permo-Triassic strata restricted by syndepositional faulting to this part of the basin (Duindam and Van Hoorn, 1987; Hitchen and Ritchie, 1987). From the Jurassic to the end of the Early

Cretaceous, differential movement occurred along the length of the fault, but during the Late Cretaceous, the depocentre moved north-westwards away from the fault as tensional subsidence was succeeded by passive, thermal subsidence (Haszeldine et al., 1987). During the early Paleocene, a further tectonic pulse reactivated the bounding fault and caused the development of local depocentres such as the Scarvister Sub-Basin (Figure 17; Hitchen and Ritchie, 1987).

To the south-west of, and partially offset from the West Shetland Basin, lies the North Rona Basin (Figure 17). This is an easterly tilted half-graben with local sub-basins (Figure 24). The formation of the North Rona Basin was initially controlled by a listric bounding fault on the western flank of the Solan Bank High. This fault was probably initiated in the Early Jurassic, and is responsible for the preservation of about 5000 m of parallel-bedded Permo-Triassic strata (Kirton and Hitchen, 1987). In the north-eastern part of the basin, listric faulting was largely superseded by a series of planar, rotational faults which developed through migration to the south-east by footwall collapse (Figure 24). These faults were active intermittently from the Mid-Jurassic to the Paleocene, and resulted in the deposition of sedimentary wedges in a number of sub-basins.

The West Shetland Basin is bordered to the north-west by the Rona Ridge, and the North Rona Basin by the North Rona High (Figure 17). The Rona Ridge consists of Lewisian basement locally overlain by Devono-Carboniferous sediments that are the remnants of the ORS Clair Basin (Figure 18). At its narrower north-eastern end, the ridge takes the form of the crestal part of a south-easterly dipping, tilted, fault block (Hitchen and Ritchie, 1987). To the south-west, it broadens and develops into a complex series of horsts and fault slices in which the basement is severely fractured (Ridd, 1981). The Rona Ridge acted as a structural high throughout most of the Mesozoic, but its influence waned during the late Mesozoic and Cenozoic as the ridge was buried. Crustal thinning occurred beneath the western flank of the ridge (Bott and Smith, 1984), where normal faults that were initiated during the Mid-Jurassic, and were particularly active in the Late Cretaceous, have a vertical throw of 5000 m.

The North Rona High (Figure 17) is a north-easterly plunging basement high, cut by a dense network of faults and fractures (Duindam and Van Hoorn, 1987), and buried by up to 2000 m of Mesozoic and Cenozoic strata. The north-eastern limit of the high is the north-westerly trending Judd Fault, a transfer fault which appears to have offset the high relative to the Rona Ridge, and which has a dip-slip component (Figure 24) of about 2000 m at basement level (Kirton and Hitchen, 1987). This fault was probably initiated in Mid- to Late Jurassic times, when the major faults of the Rona Ridge developed, and continued to be intermittently active until the Eocene (BGS Judd Solid Geology sheet).

Both the Rona Ridge and the North Rona High are locally offset by north to north-westerly trending fractures (Figure 17). The boundary between the easterly tilted basins of west Shetland and the westerly tilted basins to the south is indistinct, and probably coincides with the North Orkney/Wyville–Thomson transfer zone (Figure 19). The north-west-trending fractures are probably a partial expression of this zone.

STRUCTURE OF THE ROCKALL TROUGH–FAEROE–SHETLAND BASIN–MØRE BASIN RIFT ZONE

The Rockall Trough is a north to north-easterly trending basin that forms the most southerly and widest part of the

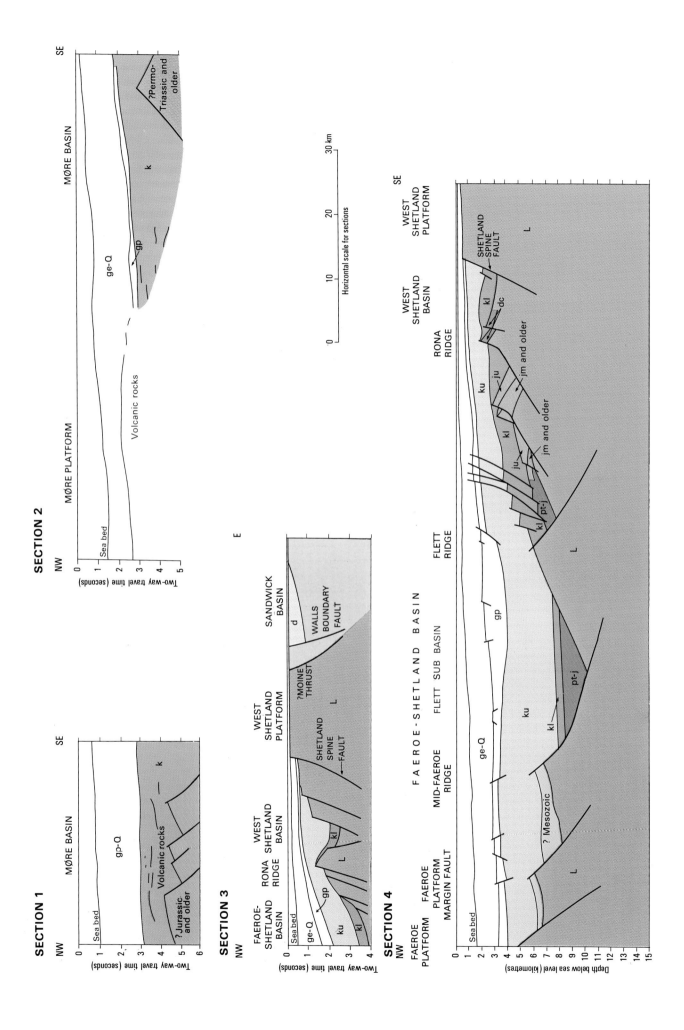

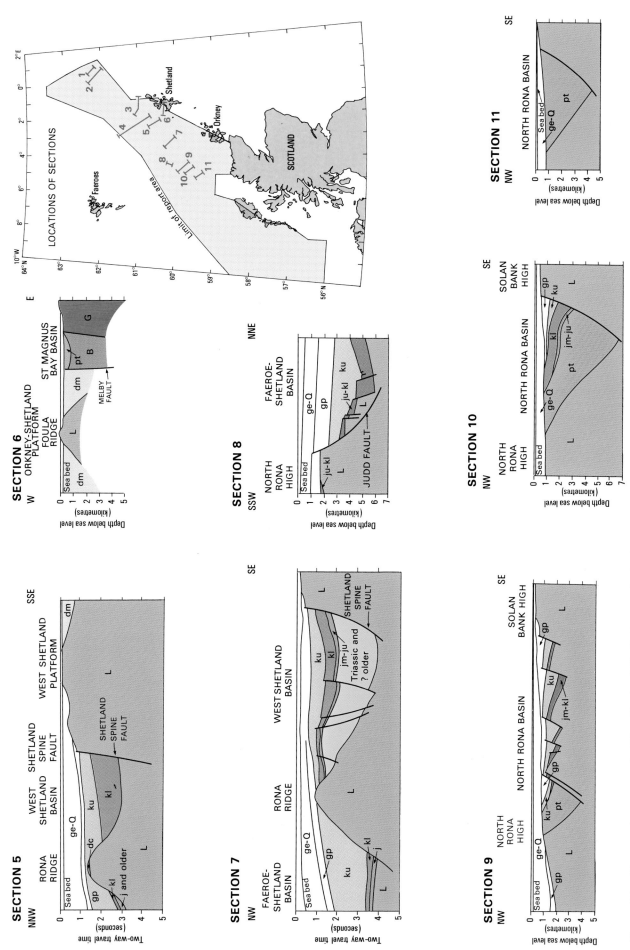

Figure 24 Cross-sections across the West Shetland Shelf, Faeroe–Shetland Basin, and Møre Basin and Platform. Note difference in vertical scales. Sections taken from BGS maps and adapted Smythe et al. (1983), Bøen et al. (1984), Haszeldine et al. (1987), Kirton and Hitchen (1987), and Mudge and Rashid (1987). For key to stratigraphical abbreviations, see Figure 3.

'proto-North Atlantic' rift zone (Smythe, 1989). It is coincident with the present-day deep-water basin of the same name (Figure 5). The report area includes the north-eastern part of the trough, which is bounded on its eastern margin by the fault-controlled Hebridean Escarpment, although structural detail is largely obscured beneath lower Tertiary basalts (Figure 17). On the opposing western flank of the trough, seismic-reflection profiles have imaged westerly tilted sub-basins adjacent to the Rockall Plateau (Joppen and White, 1990).

The Rockall Trough contains about 5000 to 6000 m of sedimentary and volcanic rocks, the bulk of which consist of Tertiary strata up to 3000 m thick (Scrutton, 1986). Refraction-seismic data have been used to suggest that the pre-Tertiary succession may include Torridonian, Upper Palaeozoic or lower Mesozoic sediments (Roberts et al., 1988); this would be consistent with the proven occurrence of Carboniferous, Permo-Triassic, Jurassic and Cretaceous sediments in rift basins on the adjacent Hebrides and Irish shelves. Thus, a likely model for the formation of the Rockall Trough is that it developed through intermittent continental rifting and subsidence that began in the Late Palaeozoic, with the final, major phase of extension in latest Jurassic to Early Cretaceous time (Scrutton, 1986; Earle et al., 1989; Smythe, 1989). This was followed by predominantly passive, thermal subsidence during the Late Cretaceous and Tertiary. The latter was largely a time of subsidence without sedimentation keeping pace; at least 2500 m of post-early Tertiary subsidence is indicated by the relative displacement of the lower Tertiary basalts between the Hebrides Shelf and the Rockall Trough, assuming extrusion at or near sea level (Stoker et al., 1988). Some differential movement along the eastern margin of the Rockall Trough has been attributed to reverse movement on the basin-bounding fault due to Late Cretaceous to Oligocene inversion on the Hebrides Shelf (Earle et al., 1989; Roberts, 1989).

The bathymetric boundary between the Rockall Trough and the Faeroe–Shetland Channel is marked by the Wyville–Thomson Ridge (Figure 5), but this feature may not mark a structural boundary between the Rockall Trough and the Faeroe–Shetland Basin. The ridge is probably a relatively superficial feature consisting mainly of an anomalously thick pile of lower Tertiary lavas (see Chapter 10), whose location and linear form may have been controlled by an underlying fracture zone (Roberts et al., 1983). The form of the ridge may have been further accentuated by early Tertiary differential movement on its faulted margins (Wood et al., 1987).

The Westray Ridge (Figure 17), interpreted as Lewisian basement overlain by Devono-Carboniferous strata (Duindam and Van Hoorn, 1987; Mudge and Rashid, 1987), may constitute a more satisfactory structural boundary between the Rockall Trough and the Faeroe–Shetland Basin, although its northerly orientation is unusual. The area between the Westray and Wyville–Thomson ridges is partially covered by basalts and is poorly understood. Within this area, a cumulative 90 km dextral offset between the south-eastern margins of the Rockall Trough and the Faeroe–Shetland Basin has been inferred, with displacement accommodated by north-west-trending faults such as the Judd Fault (Earle et al., 1989).

The Faeroe–Shetland Basin is a broad, north-east-trending basinal complex bordered by structural highs both to the north-west and south-east (Figures 17 and 24). At the sub-Upper Cretaceous level, it consists of a number of westerly tilted sub-basins with half-graben geometry that are separated by Precambrian tilt-block highs, such as the Flett and Mid-Faeroe ridges. There appears to be a contrast in tectonic style between the central and north-western parts of the basin: sub-basin development in the north-west may have been controlled by low-angle, south-easterly dipping faults (Mudge and Rashid, 1987), whereas the south-eastern part of the basin is characterised by steeper, westerly dipping faults (Haszeldine et al., 1987). The relationships between the faults are unclear; activity on both sets may have occurred intermittently since the Late Palaeozoic, resulting in the deposition of Permo-Triassic, Jurassic, and Lower Cretaceous sediment wedges.

The Faeroe–Shetland Basin was a major depocentre during the Late Cretaceous, when sedimentation was partly controlled by the Faeroe Platform Margin Fault (Figure 17), adjacent to which in excess of 5000 m of sediment accumulated. In Paleocene times, up to 3000 m of sediment were deposited in association with growth faulting (Duindam and Van Hoorn, 1987; Mudge and Rashid, 1987) in the central part of the basin, termed the Flett Sub-Basin (Hitchen and Ritchie, 1987). A maximum post-Devono-Carboniferous sediment thickness of about 8000 m was deposited between the Flett and Mid-Faeroe ridges.

The Faeroe–Shetland Basin is bordered to the north-west by the Faeroe Platform, an extensive Precambrian basement high overlain by a cover of Upper Cretaceous to Tertiary sediments and lavas (Mudge and Rashid, 1987). A spur from the Faeroe Platform appears to continue southwards as the Westray Ridge (Figure 17), which plunges to the south and terminates against the Judd Fault. However, the precise location of the basin margin remains unclear due to the cover of early Tertiary basalts; interpretation of seismic-refraction data has suggested that it occurs much closer to the Faeroe Islands (Bott et al., 1974).

To the north-east of the Faeroe–Shetland Basin, the Erlend Platform (Figure 17) is an area of basement between the Faeroe–Shetland and Møre basins that lies at the fairly shallow depth of 2 to 3 km (Duindam and Van Hoorn, 1987). The Erlend Platform appears to be bounded by faults on all sides, and is downfaulted on its south-eastern margin against the Caledonian metamorphic basement highs of the North Shetland Platform and Margarita Spur. The Erlend Platform probably remained emergent until the Late Cretaceous, when it subsided following the main phase of rifting.

The Møre Basin is a north-easterly trending, approximately symmetrical graben which extends north-eastwards from the report area (Figure 17) on to the mid-Norwegian continental margin to about 65°N (Gabrielsen et al., 1984). On its south-eastern margin, the basin is separated from the Norwegian landmass by the Møre/Trøndelag fault complex, which consists of numerous tilted fault blocks composed of Precambrian intrusives and/or Early Palaeozoic metasediments (Hamar and Hjelle, 1984). The north-western margin of the basin is marked by the Møre Platform, although the margin framework is largely obscured beneath the cover of lower Tertiary volcanic rocks which extends for 50 to 110 km beyond the edge of the platform.

The Møre Basin was a major centre of deposition during the Cretaceous and Tertiary, when up to 8000 m of sedimentary and volcanic rocks accumulated in its central part. Pre-Cretaceous structural highs (Figure 24) have been interpreted as fault blocks of Late Jurassic or older age (Smythe et al., 1983; Bøen et al., 1984). A maximum sediment thickness of about 1300 m has been inferred from gravity modelling (Hamar and Hjelle, 1984). It seems likely that the basin is a Late Palaeozoic or Mesozoic rift basin subsequently filled by Cretaceous and Tertiary sediments, mainly during thermal subsidence (Bukovics et al., 1984; Hamar and Hjelle, 1984; Eldholm and Mutter, 1986; Roberts et al., 1990).

The Møre Platform lacks positive bathymetric expression, and plunges north-westwards into the Norwegian Basin (Figure 17). It is covered by lower Tertiary volcanic rocks which are onlapped and overstepped by a north-westerly prograding Eocene and younger clastic wedge (Figure 24). Below the volcanic rocks, pre-Tertiary sediments may continue uninterrupted from the Møre Basin onto the platform (Hamar and Hjelle, 1984; Smythe et al., 1983). The western margin of the platform marks the boundary between continental and oceanic crust.

STRUCTURAL DEVELOPMENT OF THE REPORT AREA

The area to the north and north-west of Scotland displays marked regional variations in crustal structure and structural style. The most significant difference is the transition from continental crust of normal thickness beneath the Hebrides–West Shetland Shelf region to highly extended and thinned crust below the Rockall Trough–Faeroe–Shetland Basin–Møre Basin rift zone. The present consensus of opinion (Hamar and Hjelle, 1984; Mudge and Rashid, 1987; Roberts et al., 1988; Joppen and White, 1990; Neish, 1990, 1992; Makris et al., 1991) favours the concept of the rift zone as an intracontinental structure.

The gross structural framework of the area developed through intermittent activity on long-lived tectonic lineaments within the anisotropic Precambrian and Caledonian basement. Proterozoic and Caledonian low-angle thrusts were particularly susceptible to reactivation as normal faults in tensional stress fields, and the orientation of many of the basin-controlling faults was governed by the trend of the underlying thrusts.

The regional framework also highlights the change in polarity of the extensional basins between the Hebrides Shelf–west Orkney region and the West Shetland Shelf. This switch in basin polarity suggests the existence of a major orthogonal transfer-fault zone, the North Orkney/Wyville–Thomson transfer zone (Figure 19) separating these tectonic provinces (Kirton and Hitchen, 1987; Earle et al., 1989). Such fault zones are a feature of continental extensional terranes (Gibbs, 1984).

Mechanisms of lithospheric extension

Two main hypotheses have been developed to explain the way that continental lithosphere extends: the pure-shear model of McKenzie (1978), and the simple-shear model of Wernicke (1985). The former involves brittle failure of the upper crust and ductile stretching of the lower crust and mantle lithosphere to produce a symmetrical lithospheric cross-section. In the latter, extension is concentrated along low-angle shear zones, possibly affecting the whole of the lithosphere. A markedly asymmetric lithospheric cross-section is produced, with thinning in the upper lithosphere laterally offset from thinning in the lower lithosphere. Hybrid models incorporating elements of both pure and simple shear have also been developed (Etheridge et al., 1989).

In the report area, several contrasting models of lithospheric stretching have been proposed (Figure 25). The lithospheric profile proposed by Neish (1990) for the central Rockall Trough is symmetrical (Figure 25C), and pure-shear deformation has been invoked here by Joppen and White (1990) and Makris et al. (1991). The suggestion of crustal asymmetry across the Rockall Trough by Roberts et al. (1988) led Earle et al. (1989) to invoke a simple-shear model of lithospheric extension between Orkney and the Rockall Plateau (Figure 25A). They inferred that major detachment

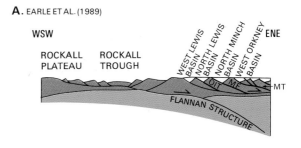

A. EARLE ET AL. (1989)

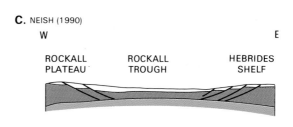

B. STEIN AND BLUNDELL (1990)

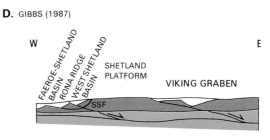

C. NEISH (1990)

D. GIBBS (1987)

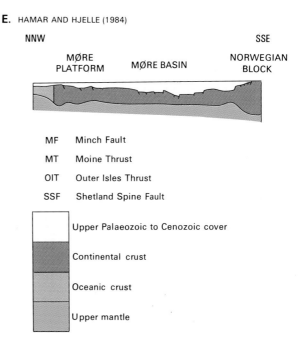

E. HAMAR AND HJELLE (1984)

MF	Minch Fault
MT	Moine Thrust
OIT	Outer Isles Thrust
SSF	Shetland Spine Fault

Upper Palaeozoic to Cenozoic cover

Continental crust

Oceanic crust

Upper mantle

Figure 25 Schematic sections across the Rockall Trough–Faeroe–Shetland Basin–Møre Basin rift zone, showing proposed models of basin development. Sections A and B conceptually represent an early stage of Mesozoic rifting in the Rockall Trough.

levels have strongly influenced extensional basin development in this area; one represents the basal detachment to the reactivated thrusts beneath the Hebrides Shelf–west Orkney region, and is considered to have controlled half-graben development during the Late Palaeozoic to early Mesozoic interval. Another more speculative detachment surface below the Rockall Trough is considered to link into the Flannan structure, and is envisaged to have been most influential during late Mesozoic rifting in the Rockall Trough.

An alternative model, combining pure- and simple-shear deformation, has been proposed by Stein and Blundell (1990), who suggested that a region of crust/mantle decoupling occurs beneath the Outer Isles Thrust (Figure 25B). Basins to the east developed through passive collapse of the hanging-wall block above an actively moving footwall block. To the west, lithospheric extension was accomplished by simple shear in the upper crust and upper mantle, by movement along faults including the Flannan structure, with bulk pure-shear occurring in the lower crust along a network of anastomosing ductile shears. Basin development occurred through block rotation in the upper crust.

West of Shetland, lithospheric stretching has been considered in terms of the simple-shear model (Figure 25D). The steep, westward-dipping faults, including the Shetland Spine Fault, are interpreted as being antithetic to major east-dipping extensional detachments (Duindam and Van Hoorn, 1987; Gibbs, 1987). Ridges such as the Rona and Flett ridges are envisaged as fault blocks overlying eastward-dipping, lithosphere-penetrating detachments that probably belong to the same set as those underlying the North Sea Viking Graben, and which continue below the Norwegian margin (Gibbs, 1987). The implications of this model remain unclear for the Møre Basin (Figure 25E), which is underlain by an approximately symmetric basement structure (Hamar and Hjelle, 1984).

Role of transfer faults

Major normal faults in extensional terranes are commonly terminated by orthogonal cross-faults which allow 'leakage' between faults with variable slip rates. These faults are commonly referred to as transfer faults (Gibbs, 1984). On a regional scale, systematic variation in basin polarity may be indicative of a major transfer fault or zone dividing the extending terrane into segments or provinces (Figure 19). In the report area, the compartmentalisation of the basins has been accomplished by the reactivation of steep, west to north-westerly trending zones of weakness perpendicular to the strike of the basins (Stein and Blundell, 1990). Faults such as the Judd Fault probably formed as an integral part of the extension system (Kirton and Hitchen, 1987).

The switch in polarity observed between the basins of the Hebrides Shelf–west Orkney region and the West Shetland Shelf can be attributed to the presence of a significant cross-cutting tectonic element, the North Orkney/Wyville–Thomson transfer zone. Although the precise location of this structure is ill defined (Figure 19), it may extend into the lower crust, and probably originated during or before the Permian (Earle et al., 1989). Whereas many transfer faults in the report area are only of local extent, this zone of transfer may have been controlled by a more fundamental basement lineament, the Tornquist Zone, established prior to the late Precambrian and extending across western and eastern Europe (Pegrum, 1984).

A second major zone of transfer, the Magnus Basin/Tampen Spur transfer system of Roberts et al. (1990), may occur in the area of the Margarita Spur and Magnus Basin

(Figure 19). According to Roberts et al. (1990), extension in the Møre Basin is resolved southwards into two components by transferring displacement into both the Viking Graben and the Faeroe–Shetland–West Shetland basin systems. North-west-trending faults on the southern margin of the Erlend and North Shetland platforms may be associated with this transfer zone (Duindam and Van Hoorn, 1987).

Summary of post-Caledonian history

The conceptual chronostratigraphical chart showing basin development in the area (Figure 18) indicates that the post-Caledonian history is far from being fully understood. Seven main phases occurred: during the Devonian, Carboniferous, Permo-Triassic, Jurassic, Early Cretaceous, Late Cretaceous to early Tertiary, and late Tertiary to Quaternary.

DEVONIAN

Following the Caledonian orogeny, strike-slip or extensional tectonism caused the formation of fault-bounded, molasse basins; these were possibly controlled by pre-existing lines of crustal weakness. The postorogenic Orcadian and Clair basins were infilled with thick ORS sequences derived from adjacent uplifted areas of the Caledonian mountain chain. Deposition took place in alluvial, fluvial, and lacustrine environments. The area of ORS deposition possibly extended as far as the Rockall Trough, Faeroe–Shetland Basin and Møre Basin. In the Clair Basin, continental sedimentation persisted into Early Carboniferous times (Blackbourn, 1987).

CARBONIFEROUS

Continental-clastic deposition was terminated in the Clair Basin by a Viséan marine transgression which has been cited as evidence that the Faeroe–Shetland Basin and Rockall Trough had subsided by the latter part of the Early Carboniferous (Haszeldine and Russell, 1987). A large part of the report area may have remained an essentially upland region supplying sediment to the fluviodeltaic systems to the south, in the Midland Valley of Scotland and beyond. Basins bordering the southern part of the area, such as the Donegal Basin, which contains volcanic and coal-bearing Upper Carboniferous strata (Tate and Dobson, 1989a), may have developed individually in Late Carboniferous times.

PERMO-TRIASSIC

Late Carboniferous to Early Permian crustal extension and alkaline volcanism is seen to represent the onset of a 'proto-North Atlantic' rifting episode that affected regions from the Norwegian–Greenland Sea to the Bay of Biscay–Porcupine Bight (Smythe, 1989). Large-scale, synsedimentary faulting occurred throughout the report area, and the ensuing basins developed upon an inherited set of crustal weaknesses which controlled subsidence throughout Permo-Triassic times. The extensional reactivation of east-dipping, low-angle thrusts resulted in the formation of westerly tilted half-grabens over a large part of the Hebrides Shelf–west Orkney area, possibly including the Faeroe–Shetland Basin. However, on the West Shetland Shelf, the easterly tilted West Shetland Basin was controlled by a steep, north-westerly hading fault which probably formed antithetically to east-dipping crustal detachments. The switch in basin polarity has been taken to indicate that the major transfer zone segmenting the shelf already existed at this time (Earle et al., 1989).

The basins were infilled largely by thick, continental redbeds. Repeated levels of conglomerate adjacent to faults suggest periodic tectonic activity and rejuvenation of upland areas throughout Permo-Triassic times. However, the Late

Permian may have been a time of tectonic quiescence as the report area was partly inundated by a marine incursion from the north, resulting in the deposition of carbonates and evaporites. The preservation of Permo-Triassic sequences in post-depositionally faulted basins, such as the North Rona Basin, implies that the area of deposition extended beyond the present basin network (Kirton and Hitchen, 1987).

JURASSIC

In latest Triassic times, tectonic activity declined and a markedly diachronous marine transgression occurred. During the Early Jurassic, a first connection between the Arctic and Tethys seas may have been established through the Hebrides–Rockall–Faeroe–Møre area (Ziegler, 1988). Consequently, Lower Jurassic sediments were probably deposited over a large part of the report area. Lower Jurassic rocks are preserved in the North Lewis and Donegal basins, but renewed uplift and faulting in Mid-Jurassic times led to their removal from the West Shetland area, excepting the deeper parts of the Faeroe–Shetland Basin (Haszeldine et al., 1987). Reworked Lower Jurassic microfossils have been recovered from the basin in well 208/19-1 (Hitchen and Ritchie, 1987). By implication, Lower Jurassic strata are also likely to occur in the Rockall Trough and Møre Basin.

During Mid-Jurassic times, a shallow-marine to nearshore environment was established in the West Shetland Basin, with the accumulation of a thin sandstone-dominated succession (Hitchen and Ritchie, 1987). Active faulting on the Rona Ridge caused talus slopes to develop on its north-western margin, and resulted in the deposition of turbiditic sandstones in the deeper-water Faeroe–Shetland Basin (Haszeldine et al., 1987). Additionally, syntectonic sediment wedges accumulated in the North Rona Basin.

During the Late Jurassic, fault activity declined west of Shetland, and basinal subsidence accompanied by a rising sea level led to the deposition of fine-grained clastic sediments which onlapped much of the underlying topography. Local faulting and coarse-grained, clastic deposition occurred adjacent to pre-existing structural highs such as the Rona Ridge. During the Volgian, some basins west of Shetland accumulated black shales under anoxic conditions.

Throughout Mid- and Late Jurassic times, the Rockall Trough, Faeroe–Shetland Basin and Møre Basin probably remained as a narrow, epicontinental seaway (Ziegler, 1988). Middle and Upper Jurassic rocks are preserved in the adjacent West Lewis and West Flannan basins, but the fragmentary nature of the Jurassic record beyond the west Shetland region gives no indication of the overall tectonic control on deposition.

EARLY CRETACEOUS

Uplift and erosion during latest Jurassic times probably marked the onset of a major Early Cretaceous rifting episode concentrated along the axis of the Rockall Trough, Faeroe–Shetland Basin and Møre Basin. Eastward-dipping faults were reactivated in the Faeroe–Shetland Basin, and syntectonic sediment wedges were deposited in its half-graben sub-basins (Mudge and Rashid, 1987). Extreme crustal attenuation occurred beneath the rift zone, where estimates of extension of the prerift crust range from 100 to 200 per cent in the Møre Basin (Hamar and Hjelle, 1984; Roberts et al., 1990) to over 500 per cent in the central Rockall Trough (Joppen and White, 1990). Although the rift zone may have been locally very close to continental break-up, current opinion favours a rift zone floored by greatly thinned and heavily intruded continental crust (Hamar and Hjelle, 1984; Mudge and Rashid, 1987; Roberts et al., 1988;

Joppen and White, 1990; Neish, 1990, 1992; Makris et al., 1991).

Extension across the rift zone caused differential uplift and erosion on its margins. West of Shetland, active faulting occurred on existing faults, and structural highs such as the Rona Ridge and West Shetland Platform were uplifted and became partly emergent. Sediment was shed from these highs into the adjacent West Shetland and North Rona basins. West of Orkney, westerly tilted half-grabens were not reactivated, and these basins were part of a wide, uplifted platform (Earle et al., 1989). However, Lower Cretaceous sediments are present in basins marginal to the Rockall Trough. In particular, the Donegal Basin accumulated a thick carbonate sequence, with a significant clastic input during synsedimentary fault activity (Tate and Dobson, 1989b). Movement on the North Orkney/Wyville–Thomson transfer zone caused a dextral displacement of the rift margin (Earle et al., 1989). A similar sense of displacement probably occurred between the Faeroe–Shetland and Møre basins (Roberts et al., 1990).

LATE CRETACEOUS TO EARLY TERTIARY

By mid-Cretaceous times, active extension across the rift zone had largely ceased, and was replaced by passive thermal subsidence, with faulting confined to basin margins. The Faeroe–Shetland Basin subsided as a single basin controlled by the Faeroe Platform Margin Fault (Mudge and Rashid, 1987). In contrast, subsidence in the Møre Basin was accomplished with minimal fault control on the basin (Roberts et al., 1990). In the West Shetland Basin, movement on the Shetland Spine Fault ceased, and the depocentre moved north-westwards into the centre of the basin.

Sea level rose throughout the Late Cretaceous, and the basins became starved of clastic input. Upper Cretaceous successions in the north consist of thick, extensive, shale-dominated sequences with thin limestones and dolomites. By Maastrichtian times, sea level had reached a maximum, and Upper Cretaceous sediments had overlapped many of the structural highs in the area. The seaway connection to the south remained open, and an Upper Cretaceous succession is inferred for the Rockall Trough. The Hebrides Shelf–west Orkney region may have remained emergent (Ziegler, 1988), although carbonate sedimentation continued in the Donegal Basin.

During Campanian to Maastrichtian times, a minor tectonic pulse accompanied by limited igneous activity caused uplift of some structural highs, including the Rona Ridge. This pulse preceded a renewed phase of rifting in the Paleocene, associated with continental break-up along the western side of the Rockall Plateau and Faeroe and Møre platforms; this led to the formation of the North-East Atlantic Ocean. Thermal uplift caused reactivation of existing faults, including transpressive movement on the North Orkney/Wyville–Thomson transfer zone (Earle et al., 1989). Paleocene deltaic and marine sediments accumulated in fault-controlled sub-basins within the West Shetland and Faeroe–Shetland basins (Hitchen and Ritchie, 1987). Voluminous and widespread flood basalts were extruded subaerially over a large part of the report area, and there was intrusive activity, which peaked in late Paleocene to early Eocene times following the onset of sea-floor spreading (Knox and Morton, 1988; Wood et al., 1988; White, 1988).

The post-Paleocene history of the report area was mainly dominated by tectonic quiescence and regional, thermal subsidence that far exceeded sedimentation. The Wyville–Thomson Ridge may have briefly formed a land bridge between the Hebrides and Faeroe shelves during Paleocene times, but was transgressed during the late Paleocene to mid-

Eocene (Berggren and Schnitker, 1983; Stoker et al., 1988). A vigorous bottom-current circulation during the mid-Tertiary caused major erosion in the deep-water basins. The effects of this erosion may have been accentuated by a phase of Oligocene inversion, particularly along the eastern margin of the Rockall Trough; this occurred in response to Pyrenean collision and the suturing of the Iberian and European plates (Roberts, 1989). A widespread unconformity effectively separates the lower and upper Tertiary sequences.

LATE TERTIARY TO QUATERNARY

Since mid-Tertiary times, sedimentation in the deep-water basins has been mostly controlled by bottom-current activity, resulting in mounded sediment drifts that are particularly well developed in the Rockall Trough. Quaternary ice sheets influenced sedimentation along the eastern margin of the Rockall Trough, Faeroe–Shetland Basin and Møre Basin, eroding the shelf areas and depositing substantial, prograding, slope-front sequences. The morphological expression of the Møre Basin and Platform is obscured by an overlying upper Tertiary to Quaternary clastic wedge, and the Norwegian margin presently slopes gently down into the Norwegian Basin (Bukovics et al., 1984). The axis of the Faeroe–Shetland Basin has shifted north-westwards, and the present basin is generally referred to as the Faeroe–Shetland Channel. The development of the slope aprons has been locally modified by intermittent failure of the slope.

5 Devonian to Lower Carboniferous (Old Red Sandstone)

The term Old Red Sandstone (ORS) refers to the continental facies of the Devonian in northern Britain. Lower, Middle and Upper ORS subdivisions are broadly equivalent in age to the Lower, Middle and Upper Devonian marine sequences of southern Britain and continental Europe. However, the upper limit of the ORS is poorly defined as the facies is diachronous across the Devonian–Carboniferous boundary (House et al., 1977). Its lower limit is also questioned (Marshall, 1991).

ORS sediments have been proved in two regions north of Scotland: the Orkney–Shetland Platform, and the Rona Ridge (Figure 26). The deposits are predominantly Mid- to Late Devonian in age, although Early Carboniferous sediments form the top of the ORS sequence on the Rona Ridge (Figure 27). These deposits probably accumulated in separate basins (Figure 26); the Orkney–Shetland Platform occurs on the western margin of the Orcadian Basin (Donovan et al., 1976), whereas the Rona Ridge sequence was deposited in the Clair Basin farther to the north-west (Blackbourn, 1987; Earle et al., 1989). ORS sediments have also been postulated to be present in the Sandwick Basin north of Shetland (Hitchen and Ritchie, 1987), and in the deeper parts of the West Orkney, North Lewis and North Minch basins (Coward et al., 1989). However, the overall north-westward extent of ORS basin development remains unknown.

These basins developed at the end of the Caledonian orogeny, following the collision of the Laurentian–Greenland and Fennoscandian–Russian continental plates during late Silurian to Early Devonian times (Ziegler, 1988). This resulted in the formation of a single large landmass, the 'Old Red Sandstone' supercontinent. Following plate collision, the tectonic regime changed from one dominated by compression to one controlled either by strike-slip or extensional faulting, resulting in the development of fault-bounded, molasse basins.

According to Ziegler (1988), a complex wrench-fault system transected the Arctic–North Atlantic Caledonides during the Devonian and Early Carboniferous. In this tectonic setting, the development of the Orcadian and Clair basins has been attributed to sinistral strike-slip motion on the Great Glen fault system (Anderton et al., 1979; Blackbourn, 1987). However, D A Rogers et al. (1989) argued that any post-collision strike-slip motion on this fault system had ceased by the late Emsian, and that basin development in Emsian to Frasnian times (Figure 27) was associated with extensional tectonism. Crustal extension may have been driven by the collapse of the overthickened Caledonian orogen, with basin formation resulting from the reactivation of existing lines of crustal weakness (McClay et al., 1986; Norton et al., 1987; Seranne, 1992). The present juxtaposition of ORS sequences across the Walls Boundary Fault (Figure 26) may be related to Late Palaeozoic, dextral, strike-slip displacements on the Great Glen fault system (Coward et al., 1989).

During Mid-Devonian to Early Carboniferous times, northern Britain occupied a low-latitude position in the southern hemisphere, and was drifting northwards from about 20°S to 10°S (Woodrow et al., 1973; Faller and Briden, 1978; Tarling, 1985). The climate was warm to hot and generally semiarid (Allen, 1979), although a gradual change from tradewind desert conditions to those associated with the equatorial rain belt took place at the beginning of the Carboniferous (Tarling, 1985).

The basinal deposits consist largely of continental-facies assemblages, including alluvial, fluvial and lacustrine deposits. These were derived locally from adjacent uplifted areas of the Caledonian orogenic belt. Fluviatile sediments deposited on the north-western margin of the Orcadian Basin were coeval with shallow, lacustrine deposits to the south, although the lake sporadically transgressed northwards on to the alluvial plain (Mykura, 1991).

In the Clair Basin, alluvial facies were replaced by a predominantly fluvial system as tectonic activity declined (Blackbourn, 1987). Probable marine deposits at the top of the Clair sequence (Meadows et al., 1987) may indicate an Early Carboniferous marine transgression (Haszeldine and Russell, 1987), thereby terminating continental ORS deposition.

Sedimentation in the Orcadian Basin was accompanied by limited tholeiitic to calc-alkaline and alkaline volcanism during Mid- and Late Devonian times (Thirlwall, 1981; Mykura, 1991). This volcanism has been attributed to the effects of plate subduction (Thirlwall, 1981), although in the post-collision, intra-plate context of the ORS basins, magma generation most likely occurred above a remnant slab of subducted material (Astin, 1983; Thirlwall, 1983).

ORKNEY–SHETLAND PLATFORM

The ORS succession preserved on the Orkney–Shetland Platform was deposited on the western margin of the Orcadian Basin, mainly during the Mid-Devonian. Along the western and northern edge of the platform, the sediments are partly faulted against, and partly unconformably overlie, the basement of the West Shetland Platform (Figures 24 and 26), although in the south-west the ORS may extend westwards into the West Orkney Basin. The eastern margin of the platform is effectively bounded by the Walls Boundary and Melby faults, which have respectively juxtaposed the platform sequence with structurally separate ORS deposits of the Fair Isle Ridge and the highly deformed Lower to Middle Devonian strata of the Walls Peninsula (Figure 26).

Gravity modelling (Bott and Browitt, 1975; BGS Orkney Solid Geology sheet) suggests that the ORS sequence is 3000 to 5000 m thick beneath much of the platform, being thickest adjacent to the Walls Boundary Fault (Figure 26). The nature of the succession is best established from the onshore exposures; up to 4000 m of strata occur in Caithness, and over 2000 m in Orkney. Although the bulk of the succession consists of Middle ORS sediments, both Lower and Upper ORS deposits are present (Figure 27).

In Caithness, the outcrop of Lower ORS becomes discontinuous towards the north coast (Figure 26); the isolated outcrops consist of valley-fill deposits of conglomerates, massive to cross-bedded arkoses, and some thin, red mudstones (Johnstone and Mykura, 1989) dated by Collins and Donovan (1977) as Emsian (Figure 27). On Orkney, the only outcrop of Lower ORS is at Yesnaby (Figure 26), where alluvial-fan sediments are faulted against medium-grained, yellowish, aeolian sandstones and fluviatile deposits (Mykura, 1976; 1991).

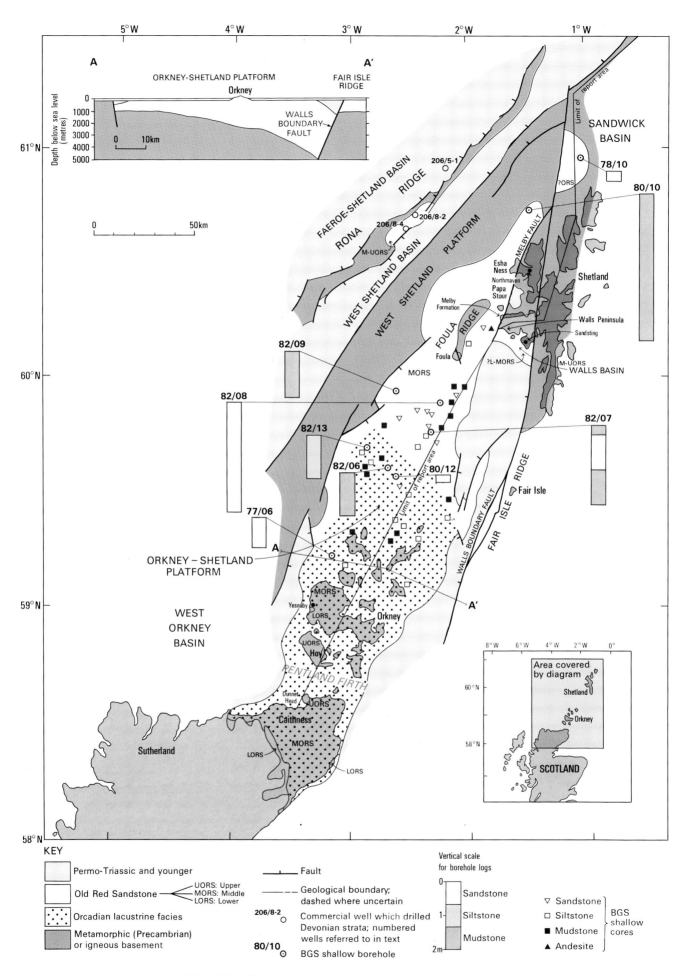

Figure 26 Geological setting of the Old Red Sandstone around Orkney and Shetland.

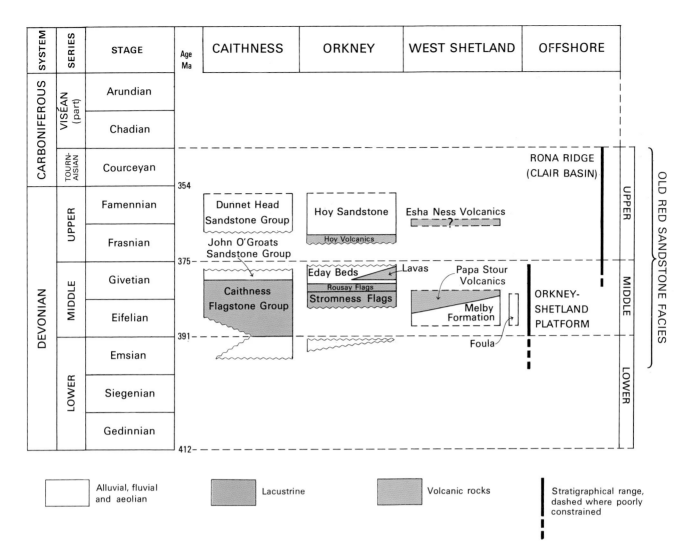

SYSTEM	SERIES	STAGE	Age Ma	CAITHNESS	ORKNEY	WEST SHETLAND	OFFSHORE		
CARBONIFEROUS	VISÉAN (part)	Arundian							OLD RED SANDSTONE FACIES
		Chadian							
	TOURN-AISIAN	Courceyan	354				RONA RIDGE (CLAIR BASIN)	UPPER	
DEVONIAN	UPPER	Famennian		Dunnet Head Sandstone Group	Hoy Sandstone	Esha Ness Volcanics ?			
		Frasnian	375	John O'Groats Sandstone Group	Hoy Volcanics				
	MIDDLE	Givetian		Caithness Flagstone Group	Eday Beds — Lavas	Papa Stour Volcanics	ORKNEY-SHETLAND PLATFORM	MIDDLE	
		Eifelian	391		Rousay Flags Stromness Flags	Melby Formation			
	LOWER	Emsian				Foula		LOWER	
		Siegenian							
		Gedinnian	412						

Alluvial, fluvial and aeolian

Lacustrine

Volcanic rocks

Stratigraphical range, dashed where poorly constrained

Figure 27 Stratigraphical-range chart of the Old Red Sandstone in and around the report area. The onshore stratigraphy is based on Mykura (1976; 1991) and Marshall (1988). Timescale after McKerrow et al. (1985).

In both Caithness and Orkney, the base of the Middle ORS is strongly diachronous, the sediments becoming progressively younger to the west where they rest with angular discordance on Lower ORS and older strata (Johnstone and Mykura, 1989; Coward et al., 1989). The lower part of the Middle ORS is represented by the Caithness Flagstone Group and the Stromness and Rousay flags (Figure 27). These consist of cyclical, upward-coarsening, carbonate-rich, lacustrine sequences of siltstones, shales and fish beds with subordinate fine-grained, fluviatile sandstones (Mykura, 1991; Parnell, 1988). Fluvial deposits increase in abundance in the upper part of the succession, where the flagstones are overlain (Figure 27) by the John O'Groats Sandstone Group in Caithness, and by the Eday Beds in Orkney; these were deposited from north-eastward-flowing rivers (Mykura, 1991). This facies change may have occurred in response to a phase of Mid-Devonian faulting (Wilson et al., 1935; Enfield and Coward, 1987). The Middle ORS on Foula and Shetland, to the west of the Melby Fault (Figures 26 and 27), is composed of a largely fluvial facies that consists of up to 1800 m of red and buff, cross-bedded sandstones with subordinate red siltstones and mudstones deposited from the west-north-west (Mykura, 1976; 1991). However, two prominent lacustrine beds in the Melby Formation are directly correlatable with the flagstone sequences to the south, and imply periodic northward transgression of the Orcadian lake.

The sediments of the Melby Formation are overlain by rhyolites which may be contiguous with the predominantly basaltic and rhyolitic volcanic sequences of Papa Stour and Esha Ness (Mykura, 1991), although these sequences are not correlatable on geochemical grounds (Thirlwall, 1979; 1983). The Papa Stour volcanic sequence (Figure 27) has been dated as mid-Eifelian to early Givetian (Marshall, 1988), and is comparable in age with the volcanic rocks in the Walls Basin (Marshall in Astin, 1983). However, a rhyolitic ignimbrite at Esha Ness (Figure 27) yielded a Rb-Sr date of 365 ± 2 Ma (Flinn et al., 1968; Mykura, 1991), implying a Late Devonian age (Odin, 1985; Harland et al., 1990).

On Orkney, ash in the Upper Stromness Flags is of similar age to the Papa Stour volcanics, but the two are not directly correlatable. The younger Eday Lavas (Figure 27) consist of thin, laterally impersistent, olivine-basalt flows of calc-alkaline affinity (Thirlwall, 1979).

Upper ORS strata crop out on either side of the Pentland Firth at Dunnet Head and on Hoy (Figures 26 and 27). The Hoy Sandstone unconformably overlies gently folded and faulted Middle ORS rocks (Mykura, 1991); the sediments consist of cross-bedded, locally pebbly, medium- to coarse-grained, fluvial sandstones deposited from braided rivers flowing from the west or south-west (Johnstone and Mykura, 1989). It has been suggested (D A Rogers in Astin, 1990)

41

that the Hoy Sandstone is a lateral equivalent of the Middle Devonian Eday Beds and John O'Groats Sandstone. The Hoy Sandstone is underlain by volcanic rocks which include airfall tuffs and olivine-basalts of alkaline affinity (Thirlwall, 1979; Mykura, 1991). The lavas have been dated as approximately 370 Ma (Halliday et al., 1977). In west Shetland, to the east of the Melby Fault, the Sandsting and Northmaven plutonic complexes (Figure 26) were intruded between 370 and 359 Ma (Mykura, 1976; 1991). The Sandsting complex was intruded into the ?Lower to Middle ORS sediments of the Walls Basin, following two episodes of intense deformation of these deposits.

The ORS unconformities have previously been attributed to major compressive or transpressive tectonic events (cf. Ziegler, 1988), but are now interpreted as more localised features resulting from normal faulting and tilting during extension (D A Rogers et al., 1989). Coward et al. (1989) have noted that the general basin architecture, as well as the parallel-bedded nature and sedimentology of the Middle ORS flagstone succession, is more typical of passive, regional subsidence than of fault-controlled growth.

Offshore, sparker profiles image the ORS sequence as varying from acoustically well bedded to structureless, the latter texture being generally associated with more resistant and upstanding parts of the platform (BGS Orkney Solid Geology sheet). The extensively sampled (Figure 26) sediments consist of red-brown to grey-green, flat- to cross-bedded and massive sandstones as well as grey, calcareous, rippled and laminated siltstones and brownish purple to grey-green, calcareous mudstones. Miospore assemblages indicative of an Eifelian to Givetian age (Figure 27) include *Ancyrospora ancyrea* (Eisenack) Richardson, *Auroraspora macromanifestus* Richardson, *Hystricosporites corystus* Richardson, and *Rhabdosporites langi* (Eisenack) Richardson (B Owens, written communications, 1980–83).

Organic residue recovered in BGS borehole 80/10, on the northernmost part of the platform (Figure 26), is dominated by cuticular debris and structured wood fragments indicative of a terrestrial source. By contrast, deposition in algal-rich waters is suggested by the pale yellow amorphogen that characterises the deposits recovered farther south in BGS borehole 82/13 and adjacent shallow cores. This is consistent with the facies distribution in the adjacent correlatable onshore sequences. Red andesite recovered in a gravity core west of the Walls Peninsula may represent southward continuation of the West Shetland volcanic suite.

North of Orkney, the platform sediments have been gently folded about north- to north-east-trending axes that are parallel to onshore structures such as the Eday Syncline. Deformation was probably associated with basin inversion, following about 1 km of burial which may have occurred in response to mid- to Late Carboniferous, dextral, strike-slip reactivation of the Great Glen fault system (D A Rogers et al., 1989; Seranne, 1992).

RONA RIDGE

To the north-west of the Orcadian Basin, the Clair Basin (Figure 26) was a smaller depocentre during Mid-Devonian to Early Carboniferous times (Blackbourn, 1987). Interpretation of seismic-reflection data suggests that this basin developed as a north-easterly trending, westward-dipping half-graben (Earle et al., 1989). It was the site for deposition of a succession of predominantly Middle to Upper ORS sediments now preserved on the Rona Ridge, a north-easterly trending structural high separating the Faeroe-

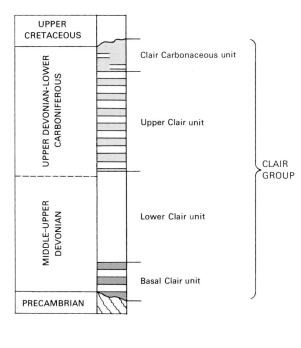

Figure 28 Generalised stratigraphical succession for the Clair Group. After Blackbourn (1987). For details of a more recent stratigraphy, see Allen and Mange-Rajetsky (1992).

Shetland and West Shetland basins (Figures 24, 26 and 27). Its relative structural elevation has been a consequence of Late Palaeozoic and Mesozoic fault activity.

Wells on the ridge (Figure 26) have recovered an ORS sequence unconformably overlying Precambrian crystalline basement, and buried beneath Cretaceous to Quaternary deposits. The thickness of the sequence is highly variable; in well 206/8-4 it reaches its known maximum of nearly 1000 m, but it is absent along the north-western flank of the Rona Ridge. Although this variation may partly reflect an irregular depositional surface, its present thickness was strongly controlled by postdepositional, pre-Cretaceous faulting (Ridd, 1981). A provisional stratigraphy for the sequence, termed the Clair Group, has been established by Blackbourn (1987), who divided it into four units (Figure 28). This stratigraphy has since been revised by Allen and Mange-Rajetsky (1992). Although Blackbourn (1987) considered the sequence to represent continuous sedimentation from the Givetian or Frasnian to the late Courceyan (Figure 27), Allen and Mange-Rajetsky (1992) report a widespread unconformity that does not necessarily correspond to the Devonian–Carboniferous boundary.

Direct correlation of the Clair and Orcadian successions is not possible at present, but Middle Devonian sporomorphs derived from the Rona Ridge, and typical of the flagstone successions of Caithness and Orkney, occur in Jurassic sediments near the Rona Ridge in well 206/5-1 (Figure 26). The Clair sediments may represent a transitional facies between the fluviolacustrine sediments of the Orcadian Basin and a montane environment that may have existed to the north-west (Hitchen and Ritchie, 1987).

Basal Clair unit

This unit overlies Lewisian basement and ranges from 30 to 120 m in thickness, increasing to the north-east. It consists of proximal to mid-fan conglomerates interbedded with flat to cross-bedded and pebbly, sheetflood sandstones, and thin red mudstones deposited in inter-fan lakes. Its interbedded nature implies overlapping of adjacent fans along a fault-controlled margin (Meadows et al., 1987).

Lower Clair unit

The Lower Clair unit is at least 325 m thick and rests with sharp but conformable contact on the Basal Clair unit. It consists mostly of poorly sorted, very fine- to medium-grained, braided-fluvial sandstones with rare pebble lag and fine-grained overbank deposits. Horizontal lamination, trough cross-lamination and cross-bedded sets are abundant, the latter commonly forming stacked sequences 10 to 20 cm thick. Thin aeolian sandstones towards the top of the unit were probably deposited as small-scale dunes. Fish scales similar to *Holoptychus nobilissimus*, which ranged from the Emsian to the Courceyan, have also been found near the top of the unit (Ridd, 1981; Blackbourn, 1987).

Upper Clair unit

The Upper Clair unit is at least 334 m thick, and conformably overlies the Lower Clair unit, although in the north-west it locally rests directly on Lewisian basement. The unit consists mainly of interbedded sandstones and red, calcrete-bearing mudstones with minor conglomerates. The unit is interpreted as a fluvial sequence deposited in a meandering river system as the basin filled and the surrounding landscape was reduced in relief.

Clair Carbonaceous unit

The Upper Clair unit passes transitionally into the Clair Carbonaceous unit, which is over 100 m thick and consists of red, green and brown, carbonaceous mudstones, siltstones and fine-grained sandstones; these were deposited in a fluvio-deltaic or lacustrine environment. The absence of calcrete and the increasing abundance of carbonaceous detritus suggest that, compared to the underlying deposits, a more humid climate prevailed during their deposition. Miospores recovered from these sediments are comparable with a late Courceyan assemblage in the Midland Valley of Scotland (Blackbourn, 1987). In well 206/8-2 (Figure 26), the unit is capped by Viséan marine sediments (see Chapter 6: Meadows et al., 1987).

SANDWICK BASIN

The Sandwick Basin is a small half-graben located to the north of Shetland, and bounded on its western margin by the Walls Boundary Fault (Figure 26). The basin contains at least 2000 m of westerly dipping sediments which unconformably overlie basement (Hitchen and Ritchie, 1987). BGS borehole 78/10 recovered a very small sample of friable, moderately sorted, medium-grained, red, feldspathic sandstone of presumed Devonian age, although a Permo-Triassic age cannot be ruled out.

The redbed sediment fill of the Sandwick Basin, together with its areally restricted nature, suggests a depositional setting possibly analogous to the Clair Basin. Its present proximity to the northern margin of the Orcadian Basin is misleading, as up to 95 km of post-ORS dextral displacement may have occurred on the Walls Boundary Fault (cf. D A Rogers et al., 1989).

OTHER OCCURRENCES

North and west of Shetland, reworked Devonian microfossils have been found in sediments ranging from Late Jurassic to early Tertiary in age (Hitchen and Ritchie, 1987), suggesting that Devonian strata may be more widespread than currently proven.

Coward et al. (1989) considered that the Orcadian Basin was part of a much larger, linked, basin system which extended westwards to include the West Orkney, North Minch and North Lewis basins (Figure 17). Although Permian and Mesozoic sediments comprise the upper part of these basin fills, a considerable thickness of Devonian sediment may occur at depth (Figure 23); an average of 3000 to 4000 m has been estimated in the West Orkney Basin (Coward and Enfield, 1987; Enfield and Coward, 1987). This estimate was based on inferred structural continuity between the West Orkney Basin, north-west Orkney, and a series of conglomerate and sandstone outliers on the north Sutherland coast (Figure 26) that some authors consider to be of Devonian age (Blackbourn, 1981; O'Reilly, 1983). However, the latter have more recently been assigned a Permo-Triassic age consistent with adjacent offshore data (BGS Sutherland Solid Geology sheet). Furthermore, well 156/17-1, in the North Minch Basin (Figure 12), has proved Permo-Triassic sediments resting directly on Torridonian, with no Devonian or Carboniferous rocks present (Fyfe et al., 1993). In their interpretation of the West Orkney Basin succession, Earle et al. (1989) envisaged a Lower Devonian to Lower Carboniferous sequence to be present, but restricted to the eastern part of the basin (Figure 23).

The westward and southward extent of ORS basins remains unknown. Outcrops of Lower ORS strata along major faults occur in the Kerrera–Firth of Lorne area of western Scotland (Mykura, 1991; Stoker, 1982; BGS Argyll and Tiree Solid Geology sheets), and at Ballymastocker Bay in north-west Ireland (Pitcher et al., 1964). Their presence indicates that ORS sediments on the southern Hebrides Shelf and Irish Shelf cannot be discounted, particularly adjacent to major faults.

Interpretation of seismic-reflection data from the southern end of the Faeroe–Shetland Basin suggests that Devono-Carboniferous sediments may be preserved on basement highs such as the Westray Ridge (Figure 17) in a manner analogous to that of the Rona Ridge (Duindam and Van Hoorn, 1987). In the Rockall Trough, seismic-refraction data have been interpreted as indicating that Upper Palaeozoic deposits (Devonian to ?Permian) may form a basal sediment wedge along the eastern margin of the trough (Roberts et al., 1988). To the north-east, Hamar and Hjelle (1984) have inferred that up to 4000 m of Devono-Carboniferous clastics may be present in the Møre Basin.

6 Carboniferous

This chapter deals with Carboniferous strata which are of different lithological and biotic character, from the poorly dated fluviatile sandstones of Old Red Sandstone (ORS) facies which were deposited through the Devonian into Early Carboniferous times (see Chapter 5). Such deposits have been proven in two widely separated parts of the report area: in the Clair Basin on the Rona Ridge, and in the Donegal Basin (Figures 29 and 30). Reworked Carboniferous miospores found in younger sediments from the intervening area, together with isolated outliers in western and southwestern Scotland, suggest a formerly more widespread occurrence of Carboniferous rocks across northern Scotland, north-west Ireland and the adjacent shelf.

During Carboniferous times, northern Britain and the adjacent offshore areas were located on the southern marginal shelf of Laurasia, which formed part of the foreland region to the north of the Rheic Ocean (Ziegler, 1988). Palaeogeographic reconstructions (Anderton et al., 1979; Ziegler, 1988) generally depict the whole of the area off north-west Britain as an upland region bordering major basinal systems both to the south and north. These basins, which include the Midland Valley Graben of Scotland, may have developed in response to rifting (Haszeldine and Russell, 1987; Tate and Dobson, 1989a) and/or strike-slip faulting (Leeder, 1988) in the proto-North Atlantic region. According to Ziegler (1988), Early Carboniferous wrench deformation gave way to Late Carboniferous regional crustal extension associated with the initiation of a major rift system in the Norwegian–Greenland Sea; this rift system propagated southward into the area west of Shetland by Westphalian times.

The terrestrial, semiarid conditions associated with ORS deposition gave way to a more humid, tropical climate as Britain drifted northwards across equatorial latitudes during the Carboniferous (Smith et al., 1981). By the end of the Carboniferous, northern Britain occupied a position at about 10°N, and had reverted to a semiarid climate (Anderton et al., 1979; Torsvik et al., 1990).

Throughout most of the Carboniferous, the north-west shelf may have existed mainly as a sourceland supplying clastic detritus to the Midland Valley Graben of Scotland and its south-westwards extension into Ireland (Anderton et al., 1979). This basin was transgressed by periodic marine incursions during the Dinantian, and the sea may have penetrated at least as far north as the Clair Basin. Coal-bearing deltaic facies which characterise the Silesian of the UK are preserved in the Donegal Basin (Figure 30), where sedimentation accompanied by pyroclastic volcanism continued into Stephanian times. This contrasts with onshore Britain and Ireland, where Carboniferous sedimentation essentially ceased by the end-Westphalian terminal phase of the Variscan orogeny.

RONA RIDGE

The bulk of the Lower Carboniferous sequence deposited in the Clair Basin on the Rona Ridge is of ORS facies. However, in well 206/8-2 (Figure 29) the Upper ORS is conformably overlain by a 27 m-thick sequence of Viséan marine sediments comprising grey, argillaceous siltstone in-

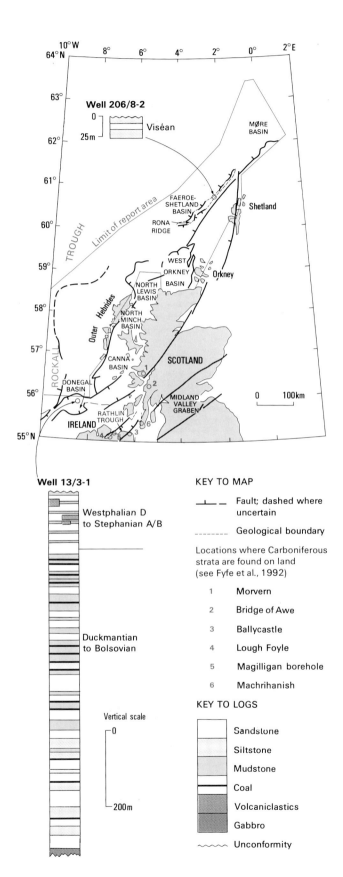

Figure 29 Distribution of Carboniferous rocks, with graphic representations of wells 206/8-2 and 13/3-1. The latter well is taken from Tate and Dobson (1989a).

terbedded with subordinate, fine-grained, carbonaceous, ripple cross-laminated sandstone (Meadows et al., 1987). Intense *Chondrites*-type bioturbation occurs throughout the sequence, which Meadows et al. (1987) considered to have been deposited in a marine, middle-shoreface environment. The presence of acritarchs in these deposits supports a marine interpretation (Allen and Mange-Rajetsky, 1992).

DONEGAL BASIN

The Donegal Basin (Figure 29) is the most northerly of a series of major depocentres which developed on the western and north-western Irish Shelf during Carboniferous times. Although the distribution and total thickness of Carboniferous strata in the basin is unknown, well 13/3-1, on the northern margin of the basin immediately outside the report area, penetrated 949 m of Upper Carboniferous sediments overlying, and variably metamorphosed by, an undated tholeiitic gabbro (Tate and Dobson, 1989a).

The lower 796 m of the succession represent a delta-top assemblage of alternating white to grey, laminated, carbonaceous sandstone, siltstone and mudstone with up to 50 coal beds. It is dated as Duckmantian to Bolsovian (Westphalian B to C). These are overlain by 153 m of Westphalian D to Stephanian B, white to grey, carbonaceous sandstone and grey, silty mudstone, which accumulated in a marginal-marine to freshwater environment, probably a low-lying, muddy, alluvial swamp. Common volcaniclastic intervals in the upper 60 m of the section are Stephanian, and broadly contemporaneous with the Late Carboniferous to Early Permian volcanism of southern Scotland (Francis, 1991) and north-east Ireland (Penn et al., 1983).

To the south-west in the Erris Trough (Figure 17) and Main Porcupine Basin, upper Namurian to Stephanian sediments unconformably overlie upper Tournaisian to lower Namurian deposits (Tate and Dobson, 1989a). The presence of a similar succession beneath the gabbro in the Donegal Basin cannot be discounted.

OTHER OCCURRENCES

Up to 1000 m of Carboniferous strata may be preserved in the Rathlin Trough, at the south-western end of which Viséan to Namurian sediments are exposed at the head of Lough Foyle, and are proved in the Magilligan borehole (Figure 29; BGS Malin Solid Geology sheet). A similar Lower to Upper Carboniferous sequence forms a complex faulted outlier on the Highland Border Ridge around Ballycastle on the south-eastern margin of the trough. A Dinantian to Westphalian succession occurs on Kintyre at Machrihanish.

Upper Carboniferous rocks also crop out at Morvern and near Bridge of Awe (Johnstone and Mykura, 1989). Reworked Carboniferous miospores occur in Permo-Triassic sediments in the North Lewis and West Orkney basins

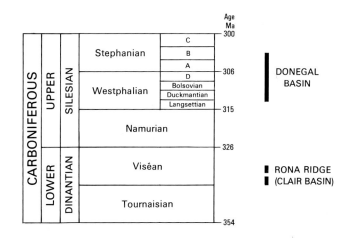

Figure 30 Stratigraphical-range chart for the Carboniferous, showing the relative ages of the Clair and Donegal basin successions. Timescale after McKerrow et al. (1985) and Hess and Lippolt (1986).

(Figure 29); these include *Lycospora* spp.,which ranged from latest Tournaisian to late Westphalian (Neves et al., 1973). A similar fauna has been recovered in sea-bed samples east of the Outer Hebrides (Eden et al., 1973; Owens and Marshall, 1978; Chesher et al., 1983), and Carboniferous erratics have been found on the Outer Hebrides (Jehu and Craig, 1934).

These occurrences, together with the succession in the Donegal Basin, suggest that a more extensive Carboniferous cover may once have existed across much of Scotland and the shelf adjacent to Ireland, at least in regions marginal to the major depocentre of the Midland Valley Graben.

Stein (1988) has proposed that the first major phase of post-Caledonian Hebridean basin development, including the initiation of the North Lewis Basin, began during the Carboniferous. His interpretations of seismic profiles across the North Minch Basin and the Sea of the Hebrides–Little Minch Trough (Figure 17) suggest that Carboniferous deposits may be present beneath Mesozoic and Tertiary strata (Stein, 1988), although drilling in the North Minch Basin has indicated that Carboniferous rocks are absent there (Fyfe et al., 1993). Significantly, perhaps, these basins are contiguous with the Donegal and west Irish basins to the south-west, which are known to contain Lower to Upper Carboniferous rocks (Tate and Dobson, 1989a). Furthermore, the Lower Carboniferous marine sediments preserved in the Clair Basin have been cited as evidence that the adjacent Faeroe–Shetland Basin had subsided by Early Carboniferous times, and that it was connected to the Rheic Ocean by a chain of basins which may have included the Rockall Trough (Haszeldine and Russell, 1987). To the north-east, the Møre Basin (Figure 17) has been inferred to contain up to 1000 m of Carboniferous sediments; these were predicted to be of continental-clastic facies (Hamar and Hjelle, 1984).

7 Permian and Triassic

Redbeds of known or inferred Permian and Triassic age are widely distributed in the Hebridean and west Shetland regions (Figure 31). Strata assigned to either the Permian or the Triassic are generally lithologically indistinguishable; they consist predominantly of locally conglomeratic sandstones, mudstones and claystones. In rare instances, they include carbonates and evaporites. All these rocks generally exhibit well-bedded acoustic character on both deep- and shallow-seismic profiles, making it difficult to differentiate between them in the subsurface. Moreover, palaeontological evidence is extremely sparse, and rarely enables even the broadest subdivision between deposits of Permian and Triassic age. The term 'New Red Sandstone' (NRS) has therefore continued to be applied to these sequences of predominantly continental facies in the Scottish region (Warrington et al., 1980).

Following the Late Carboniferous Variscan orogeny, northern Britain lay within the arid hinterland of the newly formed Pangaean supercontinent. Compressive orogenic uplift was superseded by a tensional stress regime that led to the development of intracratonic basins, causing fragmentation of the Variscan fold belt and its northern foreland (Anderton et al., 1979). The main rifts developed in the Norwegian–Greenland Sea and in the Bay of Biscay–Porcupine Bight area, but may have also included the Rockall–Faeroe area where crustal extension may have occurred as early as the Late Carboniferous (Ziegler, 1988). In the Hebridean and west Shetland regions, extensional basins resulted from the localised reactivation of earlier (Precambrian/Caledonian) structures. These basins accommodate wedge-shaped sediment packages that incorporate conglomeratic intervals, as well as some associated ?Early Permian volcanic rocks. However, although some basins were actively subsiding during the Permo-Triassic, the infill of others appears to reflect local preservation as a result of post-depositional faulting.

During the Late Carboniferous and Early Permian, northern Britain drifted northwards out of an equatorial position into the northern tradewind belt (Ziegler, 1982). Between the Late Permian and the Late Triassic, the area moved from about 15°N to approximately 35°N (Lovell, 1991). A hot, arid, desert climate prevailed throughout most of Permo-Triassic times (Anderton et al., 1979).

The Permo-Triassic rocks were formed at a time of major overall eustatic regression, and are represented almost entirely by continental redbeds. These were derived from adjacent uplifted areas, including the Scottish mainland, which remained a mostly stable, upland area (Lovell, 1991). Coarse-grained, water-lain breccias and conglomerates were deposited adjacent to active fault scarps, and as valley-fill accumulations in the deeply dissected landscape (Steel and Wilson, 1975). Away from the upland areas, sandstones, siltstones, mudstones and claystones were deposited in fluviatile, lacustrine and aeolian environments. The Hebrides and west Shetland areas may have been partly submerged by Arctic Seas during the Late Permian Zechstein transgression (Ziegler, 1988), but fully marine conditions were only established over large areas of the UK during the latest Triassic Rhaetian transgression, which advanced from the south (Anderton et al., 1979).

Permo-Triassic sedimentation was accompanied by limited volcanism in both the Early Permian and the Late Triassic.

The Early Permian volcanism was 'within plate' and 'continental' in character (Francis, 1991), and was probably related to the first phase of post-Variscan continental disintegration (Ziegler, 1988). The Late Triassic volcanism indicates a subsequent episode of synrift igneous activity west of Britain and Ireland (Tate and Dobson, 1989b).

PERMO-TRIASSIC SEDIMENTS

The greatest thickness of Permo-Triassic strata proved in the report area is 2931 m in well 202/19-1 in the West Orkney Basin (Figure 31). Borehole data exist for many of the basins, but stratigraphical control is poor or lacking, as the redbeds are commonly devoid of age-diagnostic fossils. Seismic and well evidence show that the thickest sequences occur in the West Orkney and West Shetland basins, but they are also found in the Donegal Basin and in basins on the Hebrides Shelf (Figure 32). The occurrence of Permo-Triassic strata in the Rockall Trough, Faeroe–Shetland and Møre basins remains largely a matter of conjecture.

West Orkney Basin

The West Orkney Basin (Figure 31) consists of a series of half-graben sub-basins formed by the relaxation of former Caledonian thrusts (Brewer and Smythe, 1984; Snyder, 1990). The sub-basins contain westerly dipping sediments which form wedge-shaped packages (Figures 23 and 33) indicative of syndepositional tectonism (Kirton and Hitchen, 1987).

The total extent and thickness of the Permo-Triassic basin fill remains unclear. Along the north coast of Sutherland, which corresponds essentially with the southern margin of the basin, several undated outliers previously regarded as Devonian (Blackbourn, 1981; O'Reilly, 1983), have been assigned a Permo-Triassic age (Johnstone and Mykura, 1989). Outliers around Kirtomy and Tongue (Figure 31) are composed mainly of coarse-grained, valley-fill conglomerates and breccias up to 300 m thick overlying metamorphic basement. Bright red, fluvial sandstones up to 120 m thick are also developed (Blackbourn, 1981; Johnstone and Mykura, 1989). North of Tongue, Eilean nan Ròn consists almost entirely of up to 500 m of coarse-grained, grey-brown conglomerates derived from the west or north-west (Johnstone and Mykura, 1989). These sediments were probably deposited on the proximal part of an alluvial fan; their thickness suggests fault-controlled sedimentation (Blackbourn, 1981).

Offshore, BGS shallow boreholes indicate that Permo-Triassic rocks exist at or near sea bed across the basin. Enfield and Coward (1987) proposed that the Permo-Triassic sediments merely form a veneer capping a predominantly Old Red Sandstone (ORS) basinal succession. However, well 202/19-1 (see Figure 34), drilled in the deepest and most north-westerly sub-basin (Figures 31 and 33), proved a 2931 m-thick sequence of NRS redbeds and evaporites.

The basal 613 m of the sequence in well 202/19-1 consist of red-brown, anhydritic, slightly sandy mudstone and claystone with a few thin limestones and traces of halite towards the top. These beds are overlain by an 819 m-thick evaporitic

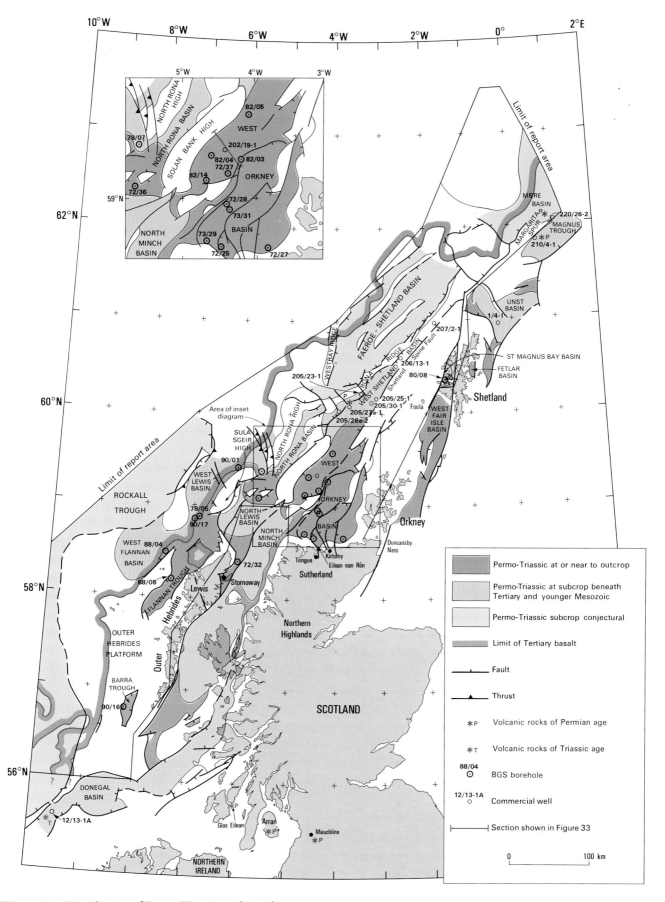

Figure 31 Distribution of Permo-Triassic rocks in the report area.

unit comprising beds of halite up to 6 m thick interbedded with sandy, anhydritic mudstone and claystone. There are sporadic limestone and dolomite beds, and thin sandstones are present, particularly in the upper part of the unit. The geophysical-log characteristics of this interval display highly serrated gamma-ray and sonic traces; the high interval velocity and corresponding low gamma-ray response are typical of halite. On seismic-reflection profiles, this interval is marked by a series of high-amplitude reflections (Figure 33). The overlying 1500 m of sediment consists predominantly of red-brown and grey, occasionally purple, very fine- to fine-grained, moderately sorted sandstone with subordinate red-brown to grey-green, locally halite-bearing, anhydritic and dolomitic mudstone, claystone, siltstone, and thin conglomerate. The evaporitic unit may be stratigraphically equivalent to the Upper Permian Zechstein and Bakevellia sequences, as described by Smith et al. (1974) for the North Sea and Irish Sea basins respectively. Although evaporites are also present in Triassic strata of the East Irish Sea Basin and Northern Ireland (Warrington et al., 1980; Penn et al., 1983; Jackson et al., 1987), current regional palaeogeographic interpretations (Ziegler, 1988) suggest that their occurrence is unlikely in the West Orkney Basin. It is however possible that the redbeds overlying the evaporitic unit are of Triassic age (Figure 34).

Seismic interpretation tied into well 202/19-1 indicates that NRS deposits comprise almost the whole of the sedimentary fill of this sub-basin (Figure 33). Earle et al. (1989) have inferred that the deeper, western half of the West Orkney Basin is occupied only by Permo-Triassic strata; these overlie tectonised basement (Figure 23) and may exceed 8000 m in thickness adjacent to the bounding fault. The 200 to 300 millisecond-thick package of prominent reflectors beneath the termination of well 202/19-1 may also consist of sedimentary and/or volcanic rocks of Permo-Triassic age. To the east, the Permo-Triassic probably thins and rests unconformably on ORS strata which may predominate in the shallower, eastern part of the West Orkney Basin (Earle et al., 1989).

Clastic sediments lithologically similar to the upper part of the sequence in well 202/19-1 have been recovered in 9 BGS shallow boreholes located throughout the basin (Figure 31). In the south, boreholes have sampled red, friable, slightly muddy and pebbly sandstones, dark red conglomeratic sandstones and red and green, silty mudstones. Across the northern half of the basin, up to 22 m of interbedded, dark reddish brown, moderately well-sorted, medium- to fine-grained, fluviatile sandstones, siltstones and mudstones were proved in BGS boreholes 82/03, 82/04 and 82/05; borehole 82/14 recovered breccia with angular pebbles of microcrystalline dolomite.

In contrast to the redbeds, borehole 72/37 (Figure 31) sampled 3.5 m of purple to pale grey, bioturbated, partially recrystallised, sandy, micritic limestone with fossil remains including bivalve and bryozoan fragments. Palynological analysis yielded *Circulina* sp. and *Classopollis torosus* (Reissinger) Balme, the latter indicative of a Late Triassic (Rhaetian) to Cretaceous age (G Warrington, written communication, 1972). The sediments were deposited in an intertidal to subtidal environment.

Donegal Basin

The Donegal Basin (Figure 31) lies at and beyond the southern margin of the report area, and is the most northerly of a series of depocentres that evolved on the West Irish Shelf during Permian and Triassic times (Tate and Dobson,

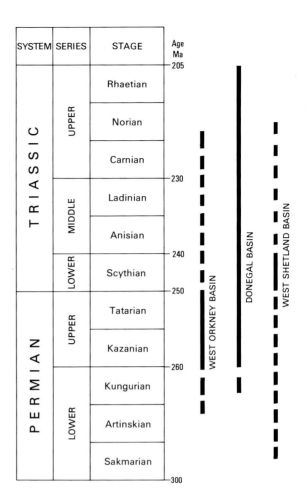

Figure 32 Stratigraphical-range chart of the Permian and Triassic successions in the West Orkney, Donegal and West Shetland basins. Timescale after Forster and Warrington (1985) and Hess and Lippolt (1986).

1989b). Although the total thickness of Permo-Triassic sediment in the basin is unknown, well 12/13-1A penetrated at least 686 m of Upper Permian to Upper Triassic strata subdivided into three lithostratigraphical units (Tate and Dobson, 1989b). These were assigned Late Permian, undifferentiated Triassic, and Rhaetian (Late Triassic) ages (Figure 35), on the basis of correlation with strata in the North Porcupine and Erris basins.

The Upper Permian deposits, which are considered to be equivalent to the Zechstein of the North Sea Basin, rest unconformably on red-brown sandstone of uncertain age. The sequence consists of 19 m of interbedded, reddish brown, calcareous siltstone and white to pale grey anhydrite and dolomite; it probably accumulated in a sabkha-type environment.

The unconformably overlying Triassic sediments consist of 599 m of red-brown, calcareous sandstone with scarce volcaniclastic detritus, siltstone, claystone and sporadic limestone. There is thinly bedded, cryptocrystalline dolomite and dolomitic claystone in the lower part of the succession, and interbeds of anhydrite in the upper part. Sedimentation occurred in a continental setting; the interbedded dolomite and redbed clastics were probably laid down in a low-lying playa plain or lake subjected to influxes of coarse-grained detritus.

At the top of the sequence, sediments of Rhaetian age mark a sharp, but conformable, change to marine deposition.

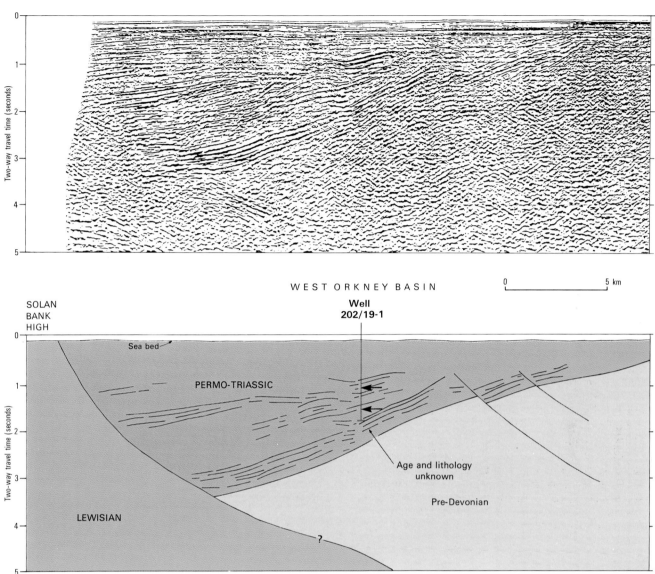

Figure 33 Seismic profile and interpretation from the West Orkney Basin, showing the structural position of well 202/19-1. The evaporitic interval in the well lies between the arrows. For location see Figure 31.

A 68 m-thick unit of red-brown, calcareous mudstone, claystone and dolomite signifies the establishment of marginal-marine to sabkha or lagoonal environments. A further 119 m of shallow-marine limestone, dolomite and claystone were identified on the original well log as occurring within the Rhaetian, but have been reassigned to the Lower Jurassic by Tate and Dobson (1989b). The Triassic–Jurassic boundary remains poorly constrained, but Tate and Dobson (1989b) indicate that limestones become more abundant as the boundary is approached, reflecting marine transgression associated with the Rhaetian eustatic sea-level rise.

West Shetland Basin

The West Shetland Basin is a major, easterly tilted depocentre underlying the outer part of the West Shetland Shelf. During Permo-Triassic times, the south-western end of the basin was actively subsiding, controlled by the Shetland Spine Fault to the east (Figures 24 and 31). Up to 4000 m of continental-clastic Permo-Triassic sediments may have accumulated adjacent to this fault, where their base occurs at a depth of 6000 to 7000 m (Browitt, 1972; Haszeldine et al.,

1987). The sequence thins north-westwards against the Rona Ridge, and also north-eastwards along the axis of the basin until it pinches out at about 60°30'N (Hitchen and Ritchie, 1987). Well 207/2-1 (Figure 31) proved Cretaceous sediments resting directly on metamorphic basement.

The thickest succession of Permo-Triassic sediments has been penetrated in well 205/27a-1 (Figure 36), drilled on a south-easterly dipping fault block. The oldest part of the sequence is an undated, 280 m-thick unit comprising red, sandy siltstone interbedded with conglomerate containing volcanic clasts. This is succeeded by 738 m of interbedded, red-brown sandstones and reddish purple, calcareous and anhydritic claystones, the upper 64 m of which have been dated as Scythian (earliest Triassic). On this basis, it seems probable that at least part of the underlying sequence is of Permian age. The former existence of Permian strata in this basin is supported by the presence in well 206/13-1 (Figure 31) of a rich Permian microflora reworked into Late Cretaceous/Danian sediments (Hitchen and Ritchie, 1987).

The Scythian interval in well 205/27a-1 is overlain by 1416 m of undated, red-brown sandstone and pebbly sandstone with some interbedded conglomerate, siltstone and

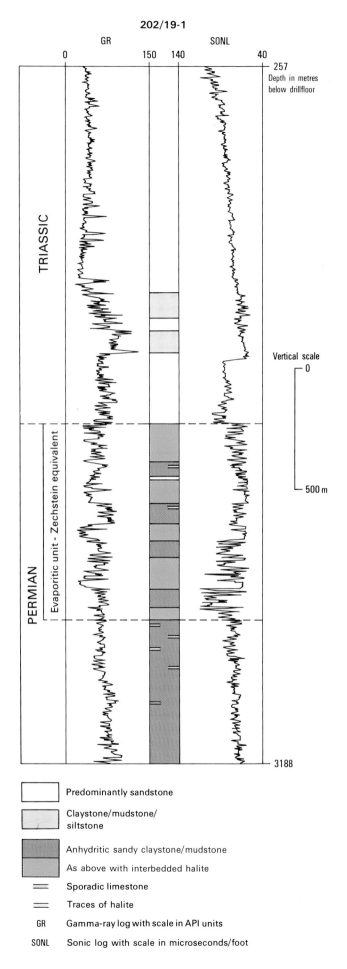

Figure 34 Simplified log of the Permo-Triassic succession in well 202/19-1, from the West Orkney Basin. For location see Figure 31.

claystone. Lithologically comparable, unfossiliferous successions proven in wells 205/23-1, 205/25-1, 205/26a-2 and 205/30-1 (Figure 31) have been assigned undifferentiated Permo-Triassic ages.

In wells 205/25-1 and 205/27a-1 (Figure 36), thick breccias and conglomerates, containing fragments up to boulder-size and mainly of granitic aspect, provide evidence of rapid deposition adjacent to active faults, including the Shetland Spine Fault. However, the bulk of the basin fill consists of sandstones which are very variable in character, but commonly red-brown, medium- to coarse-grained, poorly sorted and containing angular grains. They are either friable, or well cemented with calcite or silica. A braided or anastomosing fluviatile setting is suggested by graded bedding, cross-bedding, ripple cross-lamination, horizontal lamination with primary lineation, dewatering structures, and intraformational claystone clasts. In addition, the sandstone in well 205/23-1 (Figure 31) includes frosted quartz grains indicative of aeolian action.

Subordinate siltstones, mudstones, claystones and shales occur in all wells throughout the basin. In wells 205/26a-2 and 205/27a-1, thin anhydrite and argillaceous limestone occur sporadically within these lithologies, and there are locally developed calcium carbonate nodules of probable early diagenetic origin. The suggestion of an overbank-floodplain or lacustrine environment is supported by the presence of synaeresis cracks.

Other basins on the Hebrides Shelf

Small outliers of NRS redbeds in western Scotland (Steel, 1974; Steel and Wilson, 1975) represent the marginal expression of the adjacent, larger, offshore basins, including the North Lewis Basin (Fyfe et al., 1993). The lithological characteristics of these sequences provide an indication of the nature of the sedimentary infill in the offshore Permo-Triassic basins.

The North Lewis Basin (Figures 23 and 31) consists of several westerly tilted, half-graben sub-basins containing over 2500 m of Permo-Triassic sediments, the base of which occurs at about 4 to 5 km depth (BGS Lewis Solid Geology sheet). The maximum thickness of Permo-Triassic sediment occurs adjacent to contemporaneously active faults (Kirton and Hitchen, 1987), although the sequence has also been affected by later fault movements. Outside the report area, the southern part of the basin extends onshore at the east coast of Lewis, where the infill comprises the Stornoway redbed succession. This consists of thick, red-brown conglomerates, with subordinate sandstones, rare siltstones, and incipient cornstones; it was deposited as a series of overlapping alluvial fans along the foot of actively retreating fault scarps (Steel and Wilson, 1975; Johnstone and Mykura, 1989). Smith (1976) suggested that the succession is of Lower Permian aspect, but palaeomagnetic work (Storetvedt and Steel, 1977) indicates a Late Permian to Triassic age.

The nature of the offshore sediments in the North Lewis Basin is less well known. Red sandstone was sampled in BGS borehole 72/32 north-east of Stornoway, and red marl was recovered in the northern part of the basin at borehole 72/36 (Figure 31). A sparse miospore assemblage from borehole 72/36 is indicative of a latest Triassic to Jurassic age (G Warrington, written communication, 1972).

The Flannan Trough to the west of Lewis (Figures 23 and 31) is an asymmetric, westerly tilted basin possibly containing up to 2000 m of Permo-Triassic sediment adjacent to its main bounding fault (BGS Lewis Solid Geology sheet; Jones, 1978, 1981; Jones et al., 1986b). On the western margin of the basin, BGS borehole 88/08 recovered undated, red-brown, fine-grained, micaceous, fluviatile sandstone with intraformational mudstone clasts. The asymmetry of the sedimentary fill may reflect some degree of syndepositional faulting.

The Permo-Triassic succession in the West Lewis Basin, a westerly tilted half-graben (Earle et al., 1989), is largely obscured beneath an extensive cover of Paleogene basalts (Figures 23 and 31). Seismic-reflection data from the eastern margin of the basin indicate that a north-westerly dipping sequence of unknown thickness rests unconformably on the Lewisian of the Sula Sgeir High; these strata may lie in tectonic contact with the basement ridge of the North Rona High (Earle et al., 1989). This sequence was sampled by BGS borehole 90/01, which penetrated up to 11 m of undated, red-brown to grey-green, fine- to medium-grained sandstone and muddy sandstone deposited in a fluviatile environment. Carbonate nodules of probable pedogenic origin are common.

Up to 4000 m of westerly dipping, Permian and Mesozoic deposits are estimated to be present in the largely basalt-covered West Flannan Basin (Figure 31). The bulk of the sediments are considered to be of Permo-Triassic age (BGS Lewis and Geikie Solid Geology sheets); these may have been deposited in a half-graben analogous to the West Lewis Basin (Roberts, 1989). On the eastern margin of the basin, BGS borehole 88/04 penetrated 8 m of undated, white to greenish grey, poorly sorted, fine- to very coarse-grained and slightly pebbly, fluviatile sandstone.

On the western flank of the West Lewis Basin, the Permo-Triassic sequence has been tested by BGS boreholes 78/05 and 90/17 (Figure 31). These penetrated up to 26 m of undated, red, yellow and grey, very fine- to fine-grained sandstones, with scattered carbonate nodules; there are also interbedded yellow-brown to dark brown and grey-green, slightly micaceous siltstones and mudstones, and a few plant fragments.

The Barra Trough is an isolated, fault-bounded basin on the southern part of the Outer Hebrides Platform (Figure 31). Seismic profiles indicate predominantly westerly dipping reflectors which become synclinally disposed along the western margin of the basin, probably as a result of post-depositional faulting (BGS Peach Solid Geology sheet). BGS borehole 90/16 penetrated 13 m of red sandstone and pebbly sandstone in stacked, upward-fining cycles; carbonate nodules also occur.

Other basins on the West Shetland Shelf

The St Magnus Bay Basin is a small, partly fault-bounded trough (Figures 24 and 31) that may contain up to 1000 m of Permo-Triassic strata (BGS Shetland Solid Geology sheet). BGS borehole 80/08 sampled 13 m of undated, reddish purple, calcareous sandstone interbedded with pinkish white, laminated, anhydritic siltstone and coarse-grained, well-rounded conglomerate. These deposits, together with those of the adjacent West Fair Isle, Fetlar and Unst basins (Figure 31; Andrews et al., 1990; Johnson et al., 1993), are possibly remnants of a more extensive Permo-Triassic cover that may have existed in the Shetland region. In the Unst Basin for example, well 1/4-1 penetrated 3600 m of redbeds that have yielded palynological evidence for a Late Permian age in the middle part of the sequence (Johns and Andrews, 1985).

The North Rona Basin is an easterly tilted half-graben which contains up to 5000 m of Permo-Triassic strata (Figures 24 and 31; BGS Rona Solid Geology sheet). A number of sub-basins are present at the north-eastern end of the basin, where Permo-Triassic strata are restricted to the most north-westerly sub-basin. The sediments are largely buried beneath a variable thickness of Mesozoic and Cenozoic de-

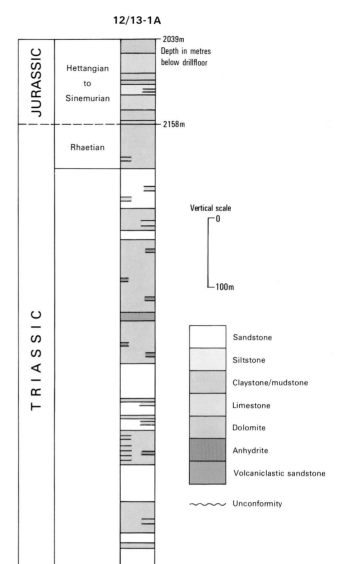

Figure 35 Simplified log of Permo-Triassic and Lower Jurassic strata in well 12/13-1A from the Donegal Basin. For location see Figure 31.

posits, although they occur at or near sea bed at the extreme south-west where BGS borehole 78/07 recovered undated, reddish brown to grey-green, ripple-laminated, fluviatile sandstone and mudstone. Seismic-reflection data image the Permo-Triassic deposits as south-easterly dipping, parallel-bedded strata; this suggested to Kirton and Hitchen (1987) that faulting and basin formation took place after deposition of the redbed sediments.

Rockall Trough–Faeroe–Shetland Basin–Møre Basin rift zone

There are no published accounts of Permo-Triassic rocks being proved in this rift zone: opinion as to whether or not they occur depends largely on perception of the regional structure and palaeogeography. Ziegler (1988) tentatively shows a rift persisting from the latest Carboniferous through Permo-Triassic times. This rift accommodated mainly continental and lacustrine sands and shales, except during the Late

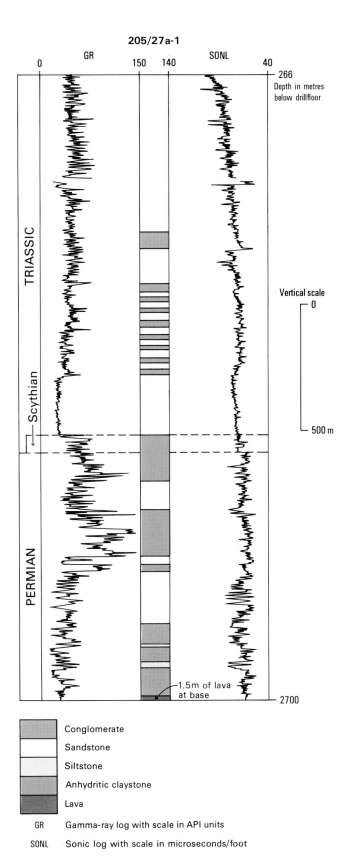

205/27a-1

Conglomerate
Sandstone
Siltstone
Anhydritic claystone
Lava

GR   Gamma-ray log with scale in API units

SONL   Sonic log with scale in microseconds/foot

Figure 36 Simplified log of Permo-Triassic rocks in well 205/27a-1 from the West Shetland Basin. For location see Figure 31.

Permian when a marine incursion from the north may have resulted in the deposition of evaporites, carbonates and nearshore, shallow-marine clastics.

Roberts et al. (1988) suggested, on the basis of seismic-refraction data, that Upper Palaeozoic or lower Mesozoic

(?Permo-Triassic) strata may be present locally on the eastern margin of the Rockall Trough. This is supported by a gravity interpretation across the outer part of the Hebrides Shelf, which suggests that the Permo-Triassic and younger Mesozoic sediments of the West Flannan Basin extend seawards into the Rockall Trough (Figure 23; BGS Lewis and Geikie Solid Geology sheets).

To the north-east, Haszeldine et al. (1987) inferred that the West Shetland and Faeroe–Shetland basins were probably affected by the same tensional stress field throughout their development. If so, because Triassic and probably Permian sediments occur in the West Shetland Basin, sediments of similar ages should exist in the Faeroe–Shetland Basin (Haszeldine et al., 1987). Interpretation of seismic data across the Faeroe–Shetland Basin supports this view, and suggests that Permo-Triassic sequences are preserved in half-graben sub-basins (Figure 24; Mudge and Rashid, 1987). Duindam and Van Hoorn (1987) postulated the occurrence of Devonian to Triassic redbeds on the Westray Ridge, at the southern end of the basin (Figure 31).

Hamar and Hjelle (1984) proposed that up to 3500 m of Permo-Triassic continental and marine deposits may be preserved in the Møre Basin, with Triassic strata forming the bulk of the succession. Triassic redbeds and evaporites are known to occur on the eastern margin of the basin in Norwegian waters (Bukovics et al., 1984), although the presence of Permian deposits has not been established. However, Zechstein (Upper Permian) evaporites, largely anhydrite, overlying Rotliegend (Lower Permian) siltstone that is commonly volcaniclastic, have been drilled in well 220/26-2 on the flank of the Margarita Spur (Figure 31). In the Magnus Trough immediately south of the Møre Basin, well 210/4-1 penetrated 913 m of Permo-Triassic sediments. The lowermost 40 m consist of Lower Permian conglomeratic sandstone with volcanic rocks overlain by ?Zechstein limestone and claystone with anhydrite. These are succeeded by predominantly red sandstone assigned to the Cormorant Formation, which is of Triassic age.

IGNEOUS ROCKS

Extrusive, alkaline, volcanic rocks of probable Permian age occur in association with redbeds in the West Shetland Basin and on the flanks of the Magnus Trough and Møre Basin adjacent to the Margarita Spur (Figure 31). These may be stratigraphically equivalent to the extensive suite of Early Permian volcanic rocks preserved in south-west Scotland and north-east Ireland. This volcanic suite includes basaltic lavas and tuffs on Arran and at Mauchline (Smith et al., 1974), basaltic lavas on Glas Eilean in the Sound of Islay (Pringle, 1944; Upton et al., 1987), and lavas and pyroclastic rocks in the Larne No. 2 borehole in Northern Ireland (Penn et al., 1983). No offshore equivalents have been identified of the slightly older, Permo-Carboniferous camptonite-monchiquite dyke swarms of Orkney and the Outer Hebrides (Johnstone and Mykura, 1989), or the Permian volcanic necks on Orkney (Mykura, 1976) and at nearby Duncansby Ness (MacIntyre et al., 1981).

At the south-western end of the West Shetland Basin, well 205/27a-1 recovered 1.5 m of red, weathered, amygdaloidal (calcite-filled) alkali-basalt below a thick succession of redbeds (Figures 31 and 36). Although the latter are poorly dated, Early Triassic (Scythian) miospores have been identified from sediments about 960 m above the lavas (company log), for which a Permian age therefore seems probable.

On the north-west margin of the Magnus Trough (Figure 31), well 210/4-1 encountered within Lower Permian redbeds a 6 m-thick, highly altered, fine-grained, feldspathic rock with pyroxene phenocrysts pseudomorphed by carbonate and serpentine. This may originally have been a moderately evolved member of an alkali-basalt-trachyte series such as a hawaiite or a mugearite (Dixon et al., 1981). On the flank of the Margarita Spur, the volcaniclastic Lower Permian siltstone encountered in well 220/26-2 is underlain by at least 5 m of fine-grained, trachyandesitic lavas.

Although there is no evidence for Triassic volcanism on mainland Britain, well 12/13-1A in the Donegal Basin (Figures 31 and 35) recovered a pale grey to red-brown, fine- to very fine-grained volcaniclastic sandstone about 15 m thick containing fragments of basic igneous rock (Tate and Dobson, 1989b). Stratigraphically equivalent volcaniclastic-sandstones and conglomerates up to 37 m thick also occur in the Erris and North Porcupine basins to the south. These have been interpreted in terms of a Late Triassic episode of synrift igneous activity along this graben chain.

8 Jurassic

The known distribution of Jurassic strata (Figure 37) largely reflects the extent of commercial exploration activity across the report area. West of Shetland, where numerous wells have been drilled, a widespread, albeit fragmented Jurassic succession has been proved within the West Shetland, North Rona and Faeroe–Shetland basins. Although a Jurassic stratigraphy is well established onshore in the Hebridean region, its extension into the West Orkney–Hebrides Shelf region is poorly constrained. In the Rockall Trough and the Møre Basin, the presence of Jurassic rocks remains conjectural, although peripheral borehole data, together with regional palaeogeographic considerations, suggest that they may occur.

The Arctic–North Atlantic and Tethys rift systems remained tectonically active throughout the Jurassic Period (Ziegler, 1988). In the Early Jurassic, crustal extension west of Britain, combined with rising sea level, may have established the first seaway linking the Arctic and Tethys seas via the Hebrides–Rockall–Faeroe–Møre area. During Mid-Jurassic times, regional extension intensified across the Arctic–North Atlantic rift system, largely as a consequence of the onset and northward propagation of sea-floor spreading in the Central Atlantic. A broad east–west zone of uplift developed between the Irish Shelf and the Irish Sea, causing rapid subsidence in the basins to the north (Earle et al., 1989; Tate and Dobson, 1989b). This may have been coeval with thermal uplift of a rift dome in the central North Sea, although in contrast to the latter, there is limited evidence for associated volcanism to the west of Britain. Although tectonic activity declined during the Late Jurassic, local faulting continued adjacent to pre-existing structural highs, particularly west of Shetland.

During the Early Jurassic, a major marine transgression which began in Rhaetian (latest Triassic) times affected most of Europe, transforming the area into a shallow, epicontinental sea (Anderton et al., 1979). Although a transgressive regime persisted throughout most of the Jurassic, significant regressive phases occurred in Mid-Jurassic and latest Jurassic to Early Cretaceous times (Hallam, 1975). Sedimentation across most of the report area was characterised by the deposition of shallow-shelf, marine carbonates and argillites, with a terrestrial influence in the east. A succession of Lower and Middle Jurassic, shallow-marine sediments overlain by Upper Jurassic deep-water strata is inferred to be preserved in the Rockall Trough–Faeroe–Shetland Basin–Møre Basin rift zone. A coarser-grained clastic succession may be preserved along the rift margin, where sedimentation was largely controlled by contemporaneous fault activity (Hitchen and Ritchie, 1987; Ziegler, 1988).

A change from the arid climate of the Triassic to a humid climate in the Jurassic (Hallam, 1981) is evidenced by the presence of thin coals, lignites and abundant plant debris in Jurassic strata. This change coincided with the northward drift of the area during the Jurassic from about 35°N to 45°N (Anderton et al., 1979).

The Jurassic succession (Figures 38 and 39) is punctuated by unconformities which reflect intervals of uplift and erosion that accompanied phases of rifting (Trueblood and Morton, 1991). Thus, despite the overall eustatic sea-level rise, there were tectonically induced lowstands. There are considerable lateral and vertical thickness and facies variations, with the regressive facies fringing areas of contemporaneous uplift. During the Mid-Jurassic, uplift and shallowing west of Britain may have temporarily severed open-marine connections between the Arctic and Tethys seas (Ziegler, 1988). Similarly, in Late Jurassic to Early Cretaceous times, a major rifting pulse affected the entire Arctic-North Atlantic rift system, generating a major regional unconformity that is sometimes termed the late-Cimmerian unconformity (Ziegler, 1988).

Over 2500 m of Jurassic strata have been estimated to occur in the North Lewis and North Minch basins (BGS Lewis Solid Geology sheet), but stratigraphical control in these basins, and in the adjacent West Lewis and West Flannan basins, is largely limited to BGS shallow boreholes. In the Donegal, West Shetland and North Rona basins, the Jurassic succession is fragmentary and rarely exceeds 100 m in thickness. A more complete succession is preserved in the Faeroe–Shetland Basin, where well 206/5-1 penetrated 1054 m of Jurassic sediments (Figure 37). Up to 2000 m of Jurassic strata have also been inferred to be present in the Møre Basin (Hamar and Hjelle, 1984).

No lithostratigraphical breakdown is available for the offshore Jurassic. This contrasts with the relatively well-documented sequences in the Hebridean region (Figure 39), where a cumulative thickness of over 1300 m of Jurassic strata is preserved (Morton et al., 1987).

LOWER JURASSIC

Lower Jurassic rocks have a restricted distribution in the report area due either to nondeposition or pre-Mid-Jurassic erosion. Their greatest proven extent and thickness are in the North Minch and North Lewis basins (Figure 37). These form part of the Hebridean region, where the almost complete Lower Jurassic succession onshore between Mull and northern Skye (Figure 39) has a cumulative thickness of about 400 m (Hallam, 1991; Morton et al., 1987). The change from continental to marine conditions near the base of the Jurassic is diachronous from south to north.

Onshore, Hettangian to early Sinemurian nearshore limestones, shales and sandstones of the Blue Lias and Broadford Beds formations are unconformably overlain by the Sinemurian to early Toarcian, upward-coarsening, shallow-marine clastic sediments of the Pabba Shale and Scalpa Sandstone formations (Figure 39). The latter is abruptly but conformably overlain by fully marine sediments of the early Toarcian Portree Shale Formation. The top of the sequence is marked by the early to late Toarcian Raasay Ironstone Formation, a condensed unit which consists of chamositic ironstone with locally developed, phosphatic, stromatolitic hardgrounds. A major unconformity separates these formations from the overlying Middle Jurassic strata.

The Lower Jurassic in the North Lewis and North Minch basins appears to be comparable with the sediments in the adjacent onshore areas, albeit thicker (BGS Sutherland Solid Geology sheet). In the North Minch Basin, the sequence thickens from about 1000 m in the southern part of the basin up to 2500 m in the north, with the greatest thickness

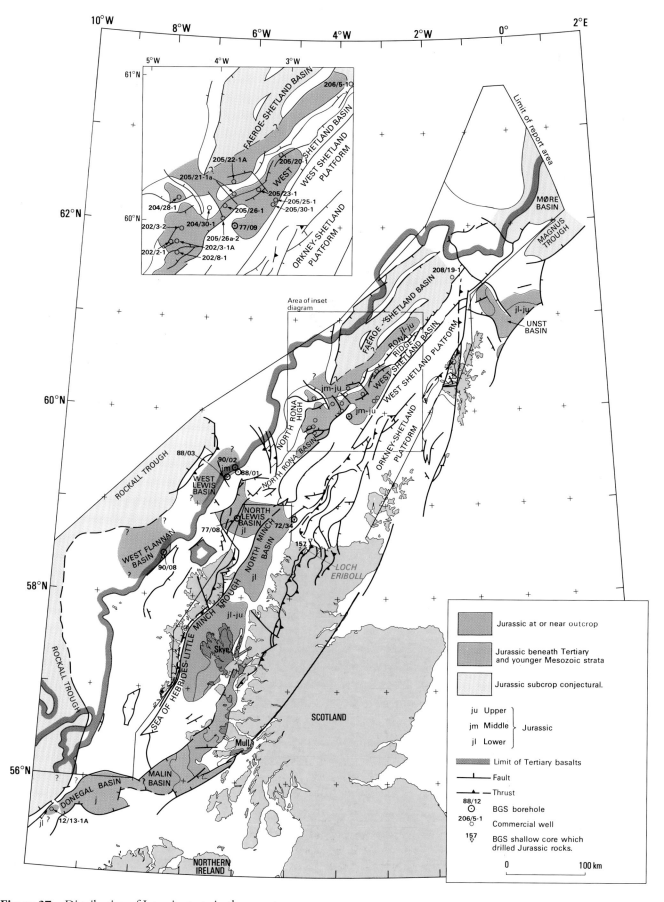

Figure 37 Distribution of Jurassic strata in the report area.

55

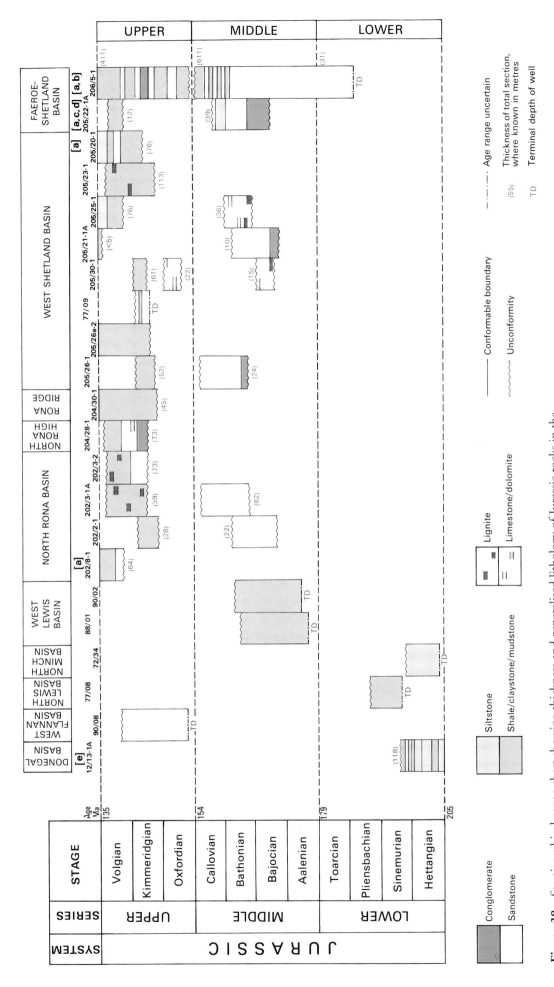

Figure 38 Stratigraphical-range chart showing thickness and generalised lithology of Jurassic rocks in the report area. Information from released well logs, but with modifications as indicated after [a] Bailey et al. (1987), [b] Haszeldine et al. (1987), [c] Meadows et al. (1987), [d] Mudge and Rashid (1987), and [e] Tate and Dobson (1989b). Timescale after Hallam et al. (1985). Locations of wells and boreholes are shown in Figure 37.

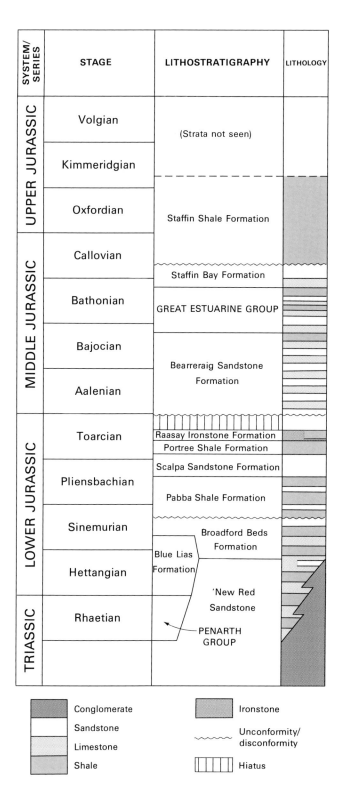

SYSTEM/SERIES	STAGE	LITHOSTRATIGRAPHY	LITHOLOGY
UPPER JURASSIC	Volgian	(Strata not seen)	
	Kimmeridgian		
	Oxfordian	Staffin Shale Formation	
MIDDLE JURASSIC	Callovian	Staffin Bay Formation	
	Bathonian	GREAT ESTUARINE GROUP	
	Bajocian	Bearreraig Sandstone Formation	
	Aalenian		
LOWER JURASSIC	Toarcian	Raasay Ironstone Formation / Portree Shale Formation	
	Pliensbachian	Scalpa Sandstone Formation	
		Pabba Shale Formation	
	Sinemurian	Broadford Beds Formation / Blue Lias Formation	
	Hettangian		
TRIASSIC	Rhaetian	'New Red Sandstone' / PENARTH GROUP	

Legend:
- Conglomerate
- Sandstone
- Limestone
- Shale
- Ironstone
- Unconformity/disconformity
- Hiatus

Figure 39 Generalised stratigraphy and lithology of the onshore Hebridean region between Mull and northern Skye. After Morton et al. (1987).

preserved adjacent to the Minch Fault (Figure 23). In the north-east, BGS borehole 72/34 (Figure 37) proved some 6 m of red, bioturbated, marine, sandy siltstone containing *Ricciisporites tuberculatus* Lundblad and *Tasmanites* cf. *suevicus* (Eisenack) Wall; these were tentatively assigned an Early Jurassic age, but a latest Triassic age is possible (G Warrington, written communication, 1973).

In the North Lewis Basin, Lower Jurassic sediments may exceed 2500 m in thickness adjacent to the line of the reactivated Outer Isles thrust zone (Figure 24). BGS borehole

77/08 (Figure 37) drilled approximately 8 m of the middle part of this basinal sequence, and recovered dark grey, variably micaceous, marine, silty mudstone with small pyritic nodules. The flora and fauna are indicative of a Sinemurian to early Pliensbachian age (BGS Biostratigraphy Group).

To the south-west of the Hebridean region, Lower Jurassic strata are present in well 12/13-1A in the Donegal Basin (Figures 35 and 37), where lower Hettangian to lower Sinemurian deposits are interpreted to rest conformably on the Rhaetic (Tate and Dobson, 1989b). The sequence of 118 m of argillaceous limestone and dolomite, interbedded with grey claystone, mudstone and siltstone, was deposited in a lagoonal to shallow-marine environment, and can be correlated with similar sequences west of Ireland, in the Erris and Slyne troughs and the North Porcupine Basin. In all of these basins, pre-Bathonian regional uplift and erosion (Tate and Dobson, 1989b) has resulted in the Lower Jurassic being unconformably overlain by sediments of either late Mesozoic or Neogene age.

Similarities in sequence stratigraphy and structure between the west Irish and Hebridean sequences suggest that they are interrelated (Trueblood and Morton, 1991), and have comparable structural and depositional histories. Lower Jurassic rocks preserved in the Malin and Loch Indaal basins, and in and around Northern Ireland (Fyfe et al., 1993), give some indication of the former widespread extent of these strata. Futhermore, the preservation of Lower Jurassic rocks in rift basins on the Irish Shelf (Croker and Shannon, 1987; Tate and Dobson, 1989b; Shannon, 1991) suggests that equivalent strata may exist in the Rockall Trough and its eastern margin. Ziegler (1988) inferred that shallow-marine shales were deposited in the trough during the Early Jurassic.

North of the Hebrides Shelf, Lower Jurassic sediments have been recovered only in well 206/5-1, close to the eastern margin of the Faeroe–Shetland Basin (Figures 37 and 40). In this well, the basal, 31 m-thick interval of interbedded, submarine-fan sandstone and mudstone may be partly of Early Jurassic age based on the occurrence of a late Pliensbachian to early Bajocian dinoflagellate cyst (Haszeldine et al., 1987). Seismic data suggest that up to 1000 m of sediment exists between the bottom of this well and Lewisian basement (Haszeldine et al., 1987); the probability that this interval includes Lower Jurassic strata is strengthened by the occurrence in several adjacent wells of reworked Early Jurassic microfossils. In particular, well 208/19-1 (Figure 37) contained an abundant dinoflagellate-cyst assemblage dated as Pliensbachian to Volgian, which according to Hitchen and Ritchie (1987) implies a proximal source of Lower to Upper Jurassic rocks.

It is likely that some Lower Jurassic sediments are preserved in downfaulted basins in the Faeroe–Shetland Basin, and that a thin succession deposited in the West Shetland Basin has been removed by erosion (Hitchen and Ritchie, 1987). Support for a previously more extensive Lower Jurassic cover in this region comes from the Unst Basin north-east of Shetland (Figure 37), where there are 100 m of nonmarine clastic deposits. These are possibly continental equivalents of the Jurassic Dunlin Group of the East Shetland Basin (Johns and Andrews, 1985).

To the north-east of the Faeroe–Shetland Basin, Lower Jurassic shallow- marine clastics are postulated to occur in the Møre Basin (Ziegler, 1988). This is consistent with borehole information from the mid-Norwegian Shelf, flanking the eastern margin of the basin, where probable Hettangian to Pliensbachian alluvial-fan deposits were laid down fringing a shallow- marine basin (Bugge et al., 1984).

MIDDLE JURASSIC

On the Hebrides and West Shetland shelves, the Middle Jurassic is more widely distributed than the Lower Jurassic. Onshore in the Hebridean region, it is more restricted through erosion, but nonetheless the greatest cumulative thickness, up to 770 m, lies here (Morton et al., 1987).

Onshore, the Bearreraig Sandstone Formation (Figure 39) consists of latest Toarcian to late Bajocian shallow-marine clastics and sandy limestones with laminated, marine shales at the top (Hallam, 1991; Morton 1987; Morton et al., 1987). The overlying Great Estuarine Group comprises late Bajocian to late Bathonian sandstones, organic-rich shales, and algal limestones, deposited in deltaic and lagoonal environments (Harris and Hudson, 1980; Hallam, 1991). The early Callovian sandstones and sandy limestones of the Staffin Bay Formation mark a return to more open-marine conditions. The uppermost Middle Jurassic sediments are included within the Staffin Shale Formation, which is an argillaceous, marine sequence ranging from mid-Callovian to early Kimmeridgian in age. A disconformity separates the Staffin Bay and Staffin Shale formations (Hallam, 1991).

Immediately offshore, proven Middle Jurassic sediments occur mainly in the central and northern parts of the Sea of the Hebrides–Little Minch Trough. These sediments range from late Toarcian to Bathonian in age, and include freshwater–brackish and marine facies (Fyfe et al., 1993). The significance of a bedrock sample of grey, shelly, Aalenian limestone (BGS Sutherland Solid Geology sheet) recovered from apparent basement on the southern flank of the West Orkney Basin north of Loch Eriboll (Figure 37) remains unclear; no Middle Jurassic outlier has been identified on seismic profiles.

On the Hebrides Shelf, Middle Jurassic strata have been proved on the eastern flank of the West Lewis Basin (Figure 37). BGS boreholes 88/01 and 90/02 penetrated up to 16 m of organic-rich mudstones deposited under predominantly lacustrine or brackish-water conditions. The presence of the miospores *Callialasporites, Neoraistrickia gristhorpensis* (Couper) Tralau and *Todisporites minor* Couper are diagnostic of an Aalenian to Bathonian age (J B Riding, written communications, 1988 and 1990). In contrast, BGS borehole 88/03 recovered up to 17 m of pale grey, massive and cross-bedded, fluviatile, sandstone, pebbly sandstone and thin conglomerate. The presence of comminuted plant tissue, normally absent in the Triassic of the Hebrides but common in the Jurassic (N Morton, personal communication, 1992), has been cited as evidence of a Mid-Jurassic age (Hitchen and Stoker, in press). However, an older age (?Permo-Triassic) cannot be discounted as Middle Jurassic and Permo-Triassic strata appear to be juxtaposed on the margin of the basin. In the light of this uncertainty, borehole 88/03 is not included in Figure 38.

The preservation of Middle Jurassic sediments on the northern Hebrides and Irish shelves may suggest that equivalent strata occur in the Rockall Trough (Croker and Shannon, 1987; Shannon, 1991). Shallow-marine, clastic sedimentation is inferred to have continued from the Early Jurassic into Mid-Jurassic times, but with a regressive, sandy, fluvial and deltaic succession deposited in the northern part of the trough during Bajocian and Bathonian times. This coarse-grained clastic input may be a result of increased erosion west of Britain following crustal upwarping (Ziegler, 1988; Tate and Dobson, 1989b).

Middle Jurassic sediments sampled in wells both in the northern part of the North Rona Basin, and at the southwestern end of the West Shetland Basin (Figure 37), all rest with a marked unconformity on either Lewisian basement or,

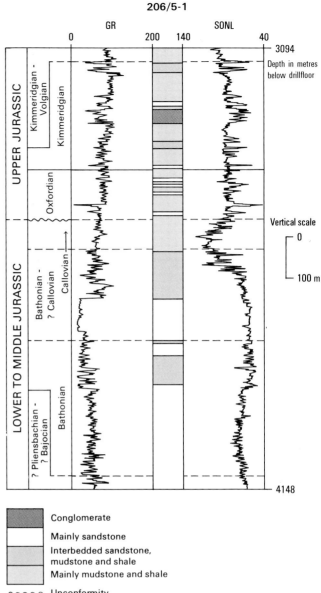

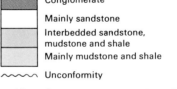

Figure 40 Simplified log of the Jurassic succession in well 206/5-1, from the Faeroe–Shetland Basin. After Haszeldine et al. (1987). For location see Figure 37.

especially in the West Shetland Basin, on Triassic strata. The sequences are thin, ranging from 10 m in well 205/21-1A to 82 m in well 202/3-1A, and have an age range from Bajocian to Callovian (Figure 38). The strata are generally of shallow-marine or coastal-plain origin. They consist mainly of medium- to coarse-grained, poorly sorted, shelly, marine sandstones, with subordinate conglomerates which are most common towards the base of the sequence. In wells 205/25-1 (Figure 41) and 205/30-1, the succession also includes limestone bands, claystone stringers and coals. In contrast, massive, coarse-grained, bioturbated sandstone in well 202/3-1A in the North Rona Basin is interpreted as the product of tectonically induced, episodic, gravity flows which formed shallow-water submarine fans or fan deltas adjacent to active faults (Hitchen and Ritchie, 1987; Meadows et al., 1987). A terrestrial influence has been proposed on the West Shetland–Orkney–Shetland platform area (Hitchen and

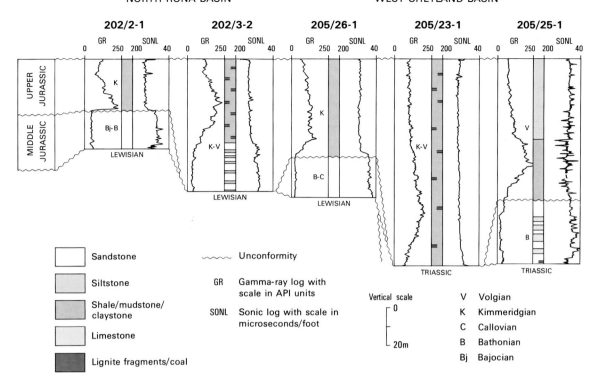

NORTH RONA BASIN   WEST SHETLAND BASIN

Figure 41 Selected wells from the West Shetland and North Rona basins, showing lithology and log response. For locations see Figure 37.

Ritchie, 1987), which formed part of an extensive alluvial plain covering much of the northern North Sea, particularly during the Aalenian to early Bajocian (Richards et al., 1988).

Two wells on the eastern flank of the Faeroe–Shetland Basin (Figure 37) have encountered Middle Jurassic sediments; in well 205/22-1A they rest unconformably on Lewisian basement, whereas the succession in well 206/5-1 is conformable upon Lower Jurassic strata. Well 205/22-1A penetrated 39 m of probable Bajocian to Callovian sandstone, limestone and conglomerate; these are interpreted as the products of submarine fans (Meadows et al., 1987) or talus slopes (Haszeldine et al., 1987). To the north-east, well 206/5-1 drilled an anomalously thick and complete Middle Jurassic succession on a south-easterly dipping, tilted fault block adjacent to the Rona Ridge. The 611 m-thick sequence (Figures 38 and 40) includes 535 m of Bathonian to ?Callovian submarine-fan sandstone with minor interbedded mudstone and shale. These were deposited close to an active fault scarp (Haszeldine et al., 1987), and are overlain by 76 m of Callovian mudstone, shale and minor sandstone, which record submarine-fan abandonment as faulting waned.

According to Ziegler (1988), shallow-marine, clastic sedimentation prevailed in the Møre Basin during the Mid-Jurassic, although coal-bearing, deltaic sediments were deposited on its eastern margin (Bugge et al., 1984). Similar deltaic facies are present in the nearby Unst Basin; these are broadly equivalent to the Brent Group of the northern North Sea, and are probably associated with the progradation of the Brent delta off the East Shetland Platform into the Viking Graben (Johns and Andrews, 1985; Richards et al., 1988)).

UPPER JURASSIC

In the Hebridean region, Upper Jurassic strata are largely restricted to Skye, where they rest conformably on Middle Jurassic sediments. In contrast, west of Shetland the Upper Jurassic is more extensively developed than the Middle Jurassic, and generally overlaps it to lie unconformably on either Triassic rocks or Lewisian basement.

On Skye, the Upper Jurassic is represented by the mid-Callovian to early Kimmeridgian Staffin Shale Formation, which consists of over 140 m of marine shales with minor siltstones and sandstones (Hallam, 1991). Younger Jurassic strata are not found, possibly as a consequence of latest Jurassic to Early Cretaceous basin inversion (Morton et al., 1987). Offshore, Oxfordian to Kimmeridgian, black, silty shales have been recovered from the Sea of the Hebrides–Little Minch Trough (BGS Little Minch Solid Geology sheet; Fyfe et al., 1993).

On the Hebrides Shelf, evidence for Upper Jurassic strata is confined to BGS borehole 90/08 in the eastern part of the West Flannan Basin (Figure 37). This borehole penetrated almost 9 m of fine-grained, muddy, marine sandstone. The presence of the palynomorphs *Hystrichosphaerina orbifera* (Klement) Stover & Evitt and *Systematophora areolata* Klement indicate a probable late Oxfordian to Volgian age (J B Riding, written communication, 1990).

In the adjacent Rockall Trough, there may be strata equivalent to the Upper Jurassic sediments preserved in basins on the Hebrides and Irish shelves (Croker and Shannon, 1987; Shannon, 1991). These are envisaged to consist of deep-water clastics and/or carbonates, but with marginal fluvial and shallow-marine facies (Ziegler, 1988; Shannon, 1991). An overall deepening of the Rockall Trough during the Late Jurassic is portrayed by Ziegler (1988).

On the West Shetland Shelf, the Upper Jurassic rocks in the West Shetland and North Rona basins, and on the Rona Ridge and North Rona High, are highly variable in thickness, ranging from less than 5 m to 113 m (Figure 38). The sediments are predominantly Kimmeridgian to Volgian in age.

At the southern end of the West Shetland Basin, BGS borehole 77/09 (Figure 37) cored 13 m of interbedded sandstone, muddy sandstone and sandy limestone. Diagnostic palynomorphs such as *Systematophora* sp., *Senoniasphaera jurassica* (Gitmez & Sargeant) Leutin & Williams, and *Apteodinium nuciforme* (Deflandre) Stover & Evitt indicate a Kimmeridgian age (R J Davey, written communication, 1977). Wells in, and marginal to, the West Shetland and North Rona basins have recovered dark brown and dark grey to black, subfissile, carbonaceous and partly calcareous, micaceous or pyritic mudstones and claystones, with minor, thin sandstones and limestones (Hitchen and Ritchie, 1987). The mudstones and claystones also contain lignite fragments and sporadic glauconite, together with minor silty beds or partings and marine fossils, including fish remains. In addition, they display a gamma-ray log response (Figure 41) which is usually significantly higher than that from other lithologies in the wells. This facies is directly comparable with the Kimmeridge Clay Formation in the North Sea, which ranges in age from late Oxfordian to Ryazanian (Johnson et al., 1993).

During Kimmeridgian times, possibly in the early Kimmeridgian, a major marine transgression caused the contemporary shoreline in the west Shetland area to shift southeastwards; the shelf, starved of clastic input, became an area of mud-dominated sedimentation. The development of anoxic basins containing much plant debris and inertinite reached its acme in mid- to late Volgian times (Bailey et al., 1987).

In the Faeroe–Shetland Basin, the 12 m-thick argillaceous sequence of Volgian age in well 205/22-1A contrasts with the 411 m-thick Oxfordian to Volgian unit in well 206/5-1 (Figures 38 and 40). Both sequences rest unconformably on Middle Jurassic strata. In well 206/5-1, the sediments consist of black, marine shales with sporadic, thin interbeds of fine-grained, grey sandstone (Haszeldine et al., 1987). The normally high gamma-ray log response is not evident here. Cores taken from within this interval show laminae which are disrupted by slump folds, presumably caused by instability on the palaeoslope (Meadows et al., 1987). A conglomeratic unit contains clasts of quartzofeldspathic gneiss and well-cemented sandstones, the latter being lithologically similar to Devonian sediments described from the adjacent Rona Ridge (Ridd, 1981; Blackbourn, 1987). The conglomerate represents a submarine scree deposit derived from the Rona Ridge as a result of faulting during the Kimmeridgian (Haszeldine et al., 1987). Although local sandstones within the predominantly argillaceous sequence west of Shetland testify to widespread fault movement, the level of activity was relatively minor.

In the Møre Basin, deep-water, marine-clastic sedimentation is inferred for the Late Jurassic (Ziegler, 1988), with these open-marine conditions extending eastwards on to the mid-Norwegian Shelf (Bugge et al., 1984). Borehole information from the mid-Norwegian Shelf has confirmed a marine, argillaceous succession, with the sediments becoming increasingly organic-rich towards the top of the sequence as the depositional environment became increasingly anoxic, as west of Shetland (Bugge et al., 1984).

In the Unst Basin to the north-east of Shetland (Figure 37), the Upper Jurassic is about 680 m thick, and includes over 300 m of Kimmeridge Clay Formation (Johns and Andrews, 1985). Equivalent strata may be present in the Magnus Trough, immediately adjacent to the Møre Basin (Nelson and Lamy, 1987).

IGNEOUS ROCKS

Although there is no direct evidence for Jurassic volcanism in the area, information from adjacent localities suggests that limited volcanic activity probably occurred west of Britain. In the onshore Hebridean region, two possible times of pyroclastic volcanic activity have been identified from Skye; an earlier, Aalenian to Bathonian phase, and a later, stronger, mid-Callovian to early Kimmeridgian phase (Knox, 1977; Andrews, 1987).

To the south of the report area, basaltic andesite flows of Bathonian to Callovian age have been proved in the Goban Spur Basin (Cook, 1987), and Bathonian intrusives occur in the Fastnet Basin (Caston et al., 1981). In addition, pyroclastic airfall deposits have been found within a Bajocian to Kimmeridgian sequence from the Porcupine Basin (MacDonald et al., 1987). To the north-east of the report area, altered pyroclastic debris has been identified in early Callovian to Oxfordian sediments on the eastern margin of the Møre Basin (Bugge et al., 1984).

In the central North Sea, the Forties igneous province represents the most significant known occurrence of Jurassic volcanism on the UK shelf. This province may contain up to 2500 m of predominantly extrusive volcanic rocks dated as Callovian to Oxfordian in age (Ritchie et al., 1988). It may be partly coeval with the later pyroclastic phase in Skye and with that found on the eastern margin of the Møre Basin. An alternative source for the Hebridean ashes may lie to the west of the Hebrides, linked to volcanicity associated with crustal extension in the Rockall–Faeroe area (Knox, 1977).

9 Cretaceous sedimentary rocks

Sedimentary rocks of Cretaceous age are widely distributed throughout the report area (Figures 42 and 43), with the thickest successions probably occurring in the northern Rockall Trough, the Faeroe–Shetland Basin, and the Møre Basin where up to 7000 m of Cretaceous sediments may exist (Nelson and Lamy, 1987). There are thinner successions in the West Shetland, North Rona and Donegal basins. The Upper Cretaceous alone may locally exceed 5000 m in thickness adjacent to the Faeroe Platform Margin Fault (Mudge and Rashid, 1987). Cretaceous rocks crop out at the sea bed only at the south-western end of the West Shetland Basin, and on the south-eastern margins of the West Lewis and West Flannan basins (Figures 3 and 42). Elsewhere they are overlain by a thick Tertiary cover.

Most information is derived from seismic data and deep wells, mainly in the west Shetland area. Cretaceous rocks are apparently absent from the West Orkney Basin, the North Minch Basin and the Flannan Trough, and also from the West Shetland and Hebrides platforms, although latest Cretaceous sediments may have been deposited there prior to removal during Tertiary times. On land, the nearest outcrops occur in the Inner Hebrides region, and more extensively in Northern Ireland (Figure 3; Fletcher, 1977).

The structural evolution of the report area during the Cretaceous was controlled by an extensional regime which caused crustal stretching along the Rockall Trough–Faeroe–Shetland Basin–Møre Basin axis. The origin, timing and extent of this stretching, and possible rifting to produce oceanic crust, remains controversial (see Chapter 4). During the Early Cretaceous, extension across this axis caused uplift on the margins and renewed movement on existing major faults. Structural highs such as the West Shetland Platform and Rona Ridge were rejuvenated to become partially emergent, and to act as sources of sediment. The consequent wide range of water depths has resulted in varied Lower Cretaceous lithologies. Coarse-grained, clastic sediments were shed from the structural highs into the adjacent basins as shallow-water fans, particularly during the Aptian and Albian. In deeper water, shales continued to accumulate.

In mid-Cretaceous times, active faulting and extension gave way to passive thermal subsidence. Major subsidence occurred in the Møre Basin, and especially in the Faeroe–Shetland Basin, where it was partly controlled by movement on the Faeroe Platform Margin Fault (Figure 42). Sea level gradually rose throughout the Late Cretaceous (Hancock and Kaufman, 1979), and had inundated most structural highs by the time it reached its maximum level in the Maastrichtian. Upper Cretaceous strata, which completely blanket all pre-existing structures, usually consist in the north of a very thick, shale-dominated succession with occasional thin limestone or dolomite stringers. Upper Cretaceous successions are generally thicker, more extensive and more uniform than those of the Lower Cretaceous, although a minor tectonic pulse in the Campanian caused local rejuvenation and deposition of proximal sandstones. Some igneous activity also occurred at around this time (see Chapter 10). These events were probably the precursor of the major tectonic and volcanic episode which marked renewed continental rifting, the onset of sea-floor spreading, and the creation of the North-East Atlantic Ocean between Greenland and north-west Europe during the early Tertiary.

LOWER CRETACEOUS

West Shetland Basin

Lower Cretaceous sediments are present throughout the West Shetland Basin, but are absent over the structurally highest parts of the Rona Ridge (Figure 42), which may have been emergent during the Early Cretaceous when it appears to have acted as a source of sediment (Larsen, 1987). The rate of sedimentation largely equalled the rate of subsidence of the basin, resulting in nearshore, shallow-marine, and occasionally deltaic conditions for much of the Early Cretaceous. The subsidence was mainly due to renewed movement on the Shetland Spine Fault (Figure 44); it caused the deposition of thick, coalescing sand wedges, fan deltas and talus slopes adjacent to the fault (Duindam and Van Hoorn, 1987; Hitchen and Ritchie, 1987; Meadows et al., 1987). North-westward progradation of these features may have occurred across the West Shetland Basin, and possibly over the structurally lower parts of the Rona Ridge to supply the south-eastern flank of the Faeroe–Shetland Basin.

The sediments consist of sandstones and conglomerates, interbedded with thin limestones and coals. In well 205/25-1 the Ryazanian to Albian interval is 1140 m thick (Figure 45), whereas in well 205/30-1 there are 565 m of Hauterivian to Albian sediments (Figures 42 and 43). Both wells are close to the Shetland Spine Fault. At the north-eastern end of the West Shetland Basin, wells include thinner, but lithologically similar, Lower Cretaceous clastic sequences (Meadows et al., 1987). At the south-western end of the basin, BGS boreholes 77/09 and 82/02 (Figure 42) recovered greenish grey, calcareous sandstones of possible Early Cretaceous age.

Faeroe–Shetland Basin

Early Cretaceous rifting, differential subsidence, and an abundant sediment supply, resulted in Lower Cretaceous sequences up to at least 2000 m thick in the Faeroe–Shetland Basin (Hitchen and Ritchie, 1987; Mudge and Rashid, 1987). The principal depocentre appears to have been immediately south-east of the Flett Ridge (Figure 42). In wells 206/11-1 and 208/27-1 (Figure 43), there are breccio-conglomerates 124 m and 51 m thick respectively that contain gneissic and schistose rock fragments in a sandy matrix. These are probably the products of the active erosion of the emergent Rona Ridge during the Albian. Overlying the breccio-conglomerate in well 206/11-1 (Figure 43) are 1024 m of Albian sediments which form an overall upward-fining sequence. At the base are inner-fan, coarse-grained, pebbly sandstone and conglomerate overlain by supra-fan, medium-grained sandstone which may be cross-stratified, flat bedded or massive. These are succeeded by fine-grained sandstone and siltstone that are typical of outer-fan to basin-plain sedimentation. Finally there is grey to black mudstone indicative of relatively slow, marine sedimentation (Meadows et al.,

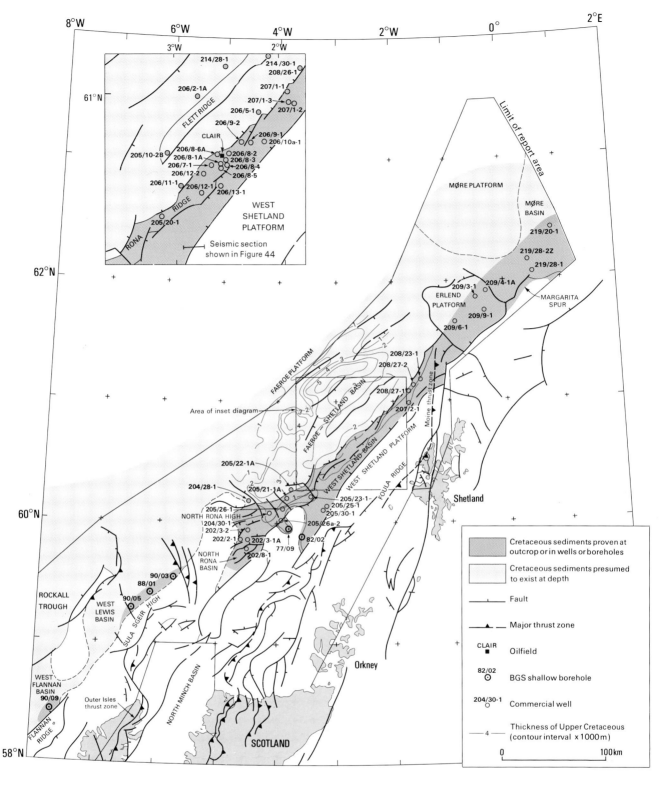

Figure 42 Distribution of Cretaceous strata in the northern part of the report area. In the southern part, the distribution is likely to be similar to that shown in Figure 37 for the Jurassic. Upper Cretaceous isopachs after Mudge and Rashid (1987).

1987). A similar overall upward-fining is demonstrated by the 386 m of Albian sediments in well 208/26-1 (Figure 45). A 162 m-thick, shale-dominated Albian succession comprises the entire Lower Cretaceous in well 206/5-1.

Møre Basin

The Møre Basin was a major centre for Cretaceous deposition (Figure 42). Although the deepest part of the basin has

not been drilled, seismic interpretation suggests that up to 4000 m of Lower Cretaceous sediment may be present in the report area (Nelson and Lamy, 1987). South-east of the basin lies the Margarita Spur, a basement ridge which during Early Cretaceous times probably had considerable submarine relief. Onlap of successively younger Lower Cretaceous sediments against the spur is indicative of a progressive infill of a deep-water basin (Nelson and Lamy, 1987). Furthermore, a strong, flat, seismic reflection from the top of the spur may represent middle to Lower Cretaceous shallow-water carbonates. This is partially corroborated by drilling on the northwest flank of the spur, where well 219/28-1 penetrated 15 m of Hauterivian to Barremian marl and shale with thin limestone, and well 219/28-2Z proved 76 m of Hauterivian to Barremian limestone. Both these sequences overlie metamorphic basement.

North Rona Basin

During the Volgian (Late Jurassic) to Ryazanian (earliest Cretaceous), the northern end of the North Rona Basin (Figure 42) appears to have been relatively stable. Anoxic depositional conditions resulted in the accumulation of black shales which yield a characteristically high gamma-ray log response similar to that of the Kimmeridge Clay Formation over much of the northern and central North Sea. Valanginian to Hauterivian sediments are generally absent, but may be present in well 202/8-1 (Figures 43 and 45). Throughout Barremian to Albian times, episodes of nondeposition or only slow sedimentation are indicated by the presence of early diagenetic calcareous and siliceous nodules, and the replacement of bioclasts by siderite and phosphate (Meadows et al., 1987). Typical lithologies, as in wells 202/3-1A and 202/3-2 (Figure 43), consist of limestones overlain by calcareous mudstones containing disaggregated siliceous sponge spicules. The basin was generally starved of normal siliciclastic shelf sediments, and the rare, thin, interbedded sandstones probably represent storm deposits. This contrasts markedly with the tectonosedimentary environments adjacent to local structural highs in the Faeroe–Shetland Basin and West Shetland Basin to the north-east, where thick sandstones accumulated.

Other occurrences

Mesozoic rocks crop out at the sea bed or beneath Quaternary in a narrow strip between the Sula Sgeir High and the south-eastern margin of the onlapping Tertiary feather edge (Figures 3 and 42). On the flank of the West Lewis Basin, BGS borehole 88/01 proved 4 m of coarse-grained, poorly sorted, calcareous and glauconitic sandstone with abundant lithic and shell fragments; marine and terrestrially derived palynomorphs indicative of a Barremian age were recovered. Nearby borehole 90/05 proved 21 m of dark grey to black, massive or poorly bedded, organic-rich, Ryazanian mudstone, with lignite bands and fragments.

Farther south-west, BGS borehole 90/09 in the West Flannan Basin (Figure 42) proved a Ryazanian succession comprising 11.5 m of grey, fine- to medium-grained, arkosic sandstone overlying 9 m of dark grey to black, organic-rich mudstone. The mudstones in boreholes 90/05 and 90/09 can be directly correlated on palynological and lithological evidence, and lithologies from all three boreholes show that the overall regional pattern of Early Cretaceous deposition here was similar to that in the major basins to the north-east. These results imply that similar and coeval Lower Cretaceous sediments may exist in the adjacent north Rockall Trough. The geochemistry of dacitic lavas sampled in well 163/6-1A (see Figure 46), in the northern Rockall Trough, showed high Ni and Cr contents, which along with other trace elements, are typical of an organic, black-shale facies. Hence, there is the possibility that shales of this nature were assimilated into the dacitic melt. If so, the sediments may have been of Early Cretaceous age, as shales of this age and lithology have been drilled in related tectonic areas of the Bay of Biscay and the Goban Spur (Morton et al., 1988a).

In the Donegal Basin, well 12/13-1A (Figure 37) penetrated 817 m of upper Ryazanian to Albian sediments. The Ryazanian to Hauterivian consists of 167 m of calcareous sandstone, shale and thin, dolomitic limestone. These are overlain by 173 m of calcareously cemented Hauterivian sandstone, succeeded by 310 m of Hauterivian to Albian shale with thin limestone and sandstone. The uppermost 167 m of Lower Cretaceous sediments are Albian, and consist of marl with limestone overlain by argillaceous and dolomitic limestone. The succession suggests consistent accumulation of calcareous-rich sediments interrupted by tectonically controlled hiatuses or intervals of clastic input.

UPPER CRETACEOUS

West Shetland Basin

At the end of the Early Cretaceous, the style of subsidence within the West Shetland Basin changed from that of a half-graben with movement on the Shetland Spine Fault, to passive, thermal-cooling subsidence (Haszeldine et al., 1987). Intrabasinal faulting became less important, and the main depositional centre moved north-westwards towards the centre of the basin (Figure 24). Pre-existing structures became blanketed by Upper Cretaceous sediments, although structurally high areas such as the Rona Ridge and West Shetland Platform retained some influence on sedimentation. Areas close to these highs accumulated proximal successions of mixed lithologies (Hitchen and Ritchie, 1987); well 206/10a-1, located at the narrow north-eastern end of the basin (Figure 45), contains 1163 m of Coniacian to Maastrichtian sandstone, limestone and shale. Adjacent to the Shetland Spine Fault, wells 205/25-1 and 205/30-1 (Figures 43 and 45) proved 635 m and 803 m respectively of a similar proximal facies.

Away from the basin margins, Upper Cretaceous sediments are typically a monotonous sequence of dark grey, marine mudstones and shales with rare, thin, crystalline limestones, dolomites and minor sandstone stringers. Bathyal marine faunas are found in the shales. Meadows et al. (1987) suggested that the Rona Ridge was transgressed by the end of the Coniacian, although lack of Coniacian to Santonian sediments in several wells (Figure 43) suggests that it was not completely overstepped until the Campanian. In the area of the Clair Oilfield, the ridge was covered in Santonian times (Earle et al., 1989). At its south-western end, the ridge may be overlain directly by Paleocene sediments (Haszeldine et al., 1987; Ridd, 1981), perhaps because erosion during the early Tertiary removed any uppermost Cretaceous sediments.

Faeroe–Shetland Basin

The Faeroe–Shetland Basin underwent massive and near-continuous subsidence throughout the Late Cretaceous, a time when sea levels were high (Haq et al., 1987), resulting in the deposition of a huge thickness of Upper Cretaceous sediments. Seismic data show that over 5000 m of Upper Cretaceous sediments exist both close to the Faeroe Platform Margin Fault and to the east of the Westray Ridge (Figure 42), and in excess of 2000 m occur over most of the basin (Mudge and Rashid, 1987). The maximum drilled thickness is in well 205/10-2B (Figure 42), which proved 2279 m of Cenomanian to Maastrichtian sediment on a local high. A near-complete Upper Cretaceous succession is expected in the centre of the basin, whereas some early stages may be ab-

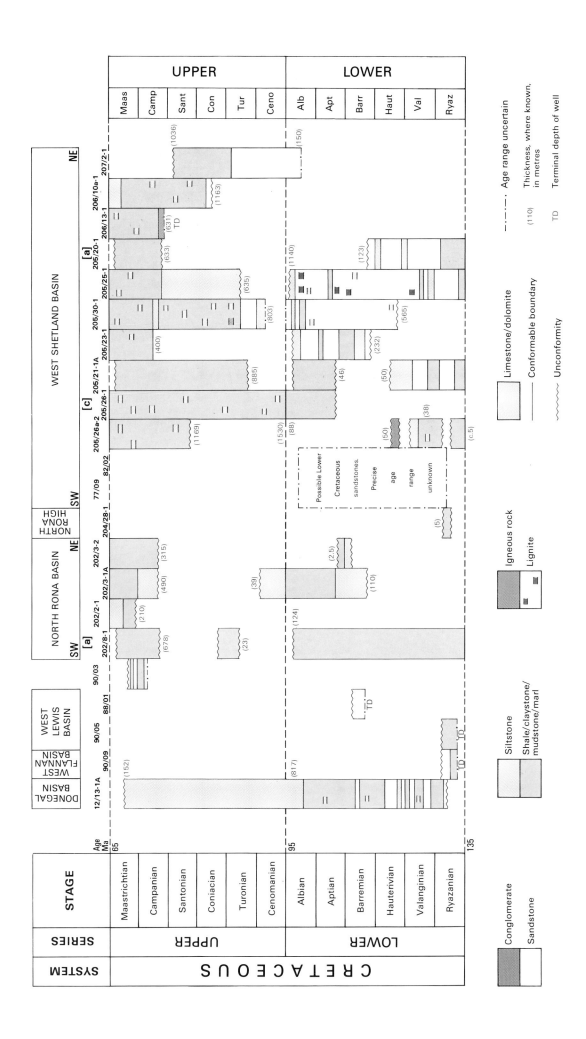

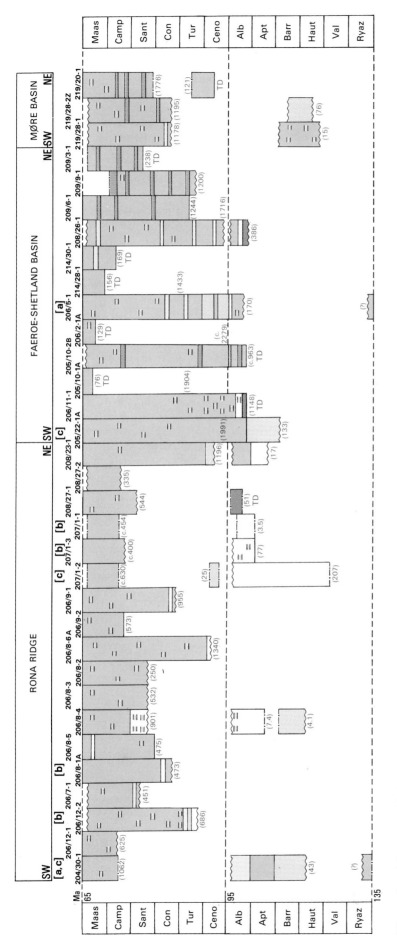

Figure 43 The age and lithology of Cretaceous strata drilled in the report area. Information from released well logs, but with modifications as indicated after: [a] Bailey et al. (1987), [b] Meadows et al. (1987), and [c] Mudge and Rashid (1987). For locations see Figures 37 and 42.

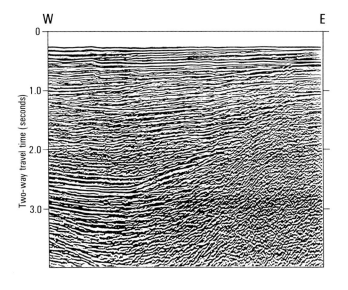

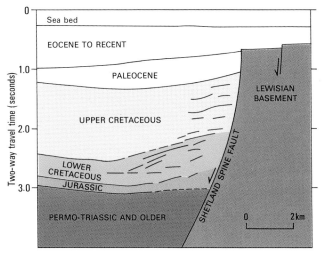

Figure 44 Seismic-reflection line, with interpretation, across the Shetland Spine Fault. For location see Figure 42.

sent on the flanks or close to intrabasinal highs. The sediments comprise a very uniform sequence of grey, marine, basinal shales with rare, thin limestone and dolomite stringers. There are many basic intrusions within the Upper Cretaceous, most of which are of early Tertiary age.

The relative tectonic calm of the Late Cretaceous was disturbed during the Campanian (Hitchen and Ritchie, 1987) by a tectonic pulse probably related to a renewed phase of rifting in the Rockall area. This caused minor rejuvenation of existing structural highs, such as the Rona Ridge, which shed turbidites of carbonate sand into the basin. It also caused overstep of earlier Cretaceous sediments by Campanian to Maastrichtian deposits (Ridd, 1981). Log data show only a minor inflection at this level (Figure 45), as lithologies above and below the disconformity are similar. Earle et al. (1989) reported uplift of an intrabasinal high within the Faeroe–Shetland Basin during Maastrichtian to Danian times, and also showed an intra-Maastrichtian seismic marker; this probably represents the same event, but with a slight discrepancy in the dating.

Møre Basin

The Møre Basin accumulated sediments throughout the Late Cretaceous, reaching an estimated thickness of 3000 to 4000 m at the south-western end of the basin (Nelson and Lamy, 1987; Duindam and Van Hoorn, 1987; Ziegler, 1988). The thickest drilled succession is in well 219/20-1 (Figure 42), which proved 1897 m of shales with numerous Tertiary igneous intrusions, before terminating in the Cenomanian. Wells 219/28-1 and 219/28-2Z, drilled on the south-eastern margin of the basin, proved 1178 m and 1195 m respectively of similar lithologies, although well 219/28-1 did not penetrate any intrusions.

North Rona Basin

In the North Rona Basin (Figures 24 and 42), Upper Cretaceous sediments blanket pre-existing half-graben structures (Kirton and Hitchen, 1987). Proven drilled lithologies include limestones, shales and marls deposited mainly during Campanian to Maastrichtian times, but older sediments may be present in down-dip locations. Drilled thicknesses range from 210 m in well 202/2-1 to 701 m in well 202/8-1.

Other occurrences

A Mesozoic inlier within Tertiary rocks just north-west of the Sula Sgeir High was drilled by BGS borehole 90/03 (Figure 42). This proved a minimum of 82 m of sediment, consisting mainly of claystone interbedded with subordinate siltstone and muddy sandstone, dated from dynoflagellate cysts as ?Campanian to Maastrichtian (R Harland and J B Riding, written communication, 1990). The claystone is typically dark green or grey to black, organic rich, with lignite and some plant remains; accumulation under quiet, stable, nearshore conditions is indicated. The main sandstone interval is 10.5 m thick, poorly sorted and muddy, with lithic fragments of various sedimentary and igneous rocks; it may be the result of the Campanian tectonic pulse identified in the Faeroe–Shetland Basin.

Palaeogeographic reconstructions suggest that Upper Cretaceous sediments in the northern Rockall Trough might be similar to those of the Faeroe–Shetland Basin, for the two basins probably formed a continuous seaway prior to the formation of the Wyville–Thomson Ridge in the early Tertiary; this is partially corroborated by the results of BGS borehole 90/03 (Figure 43). However, although not necessarily typical of the lithologies of the deeper parts of the Rockall Trough, chalk has been reported from both the Anton Dohrn and Rosemary Bank seamounts (Figure 1). It was discovered in boulders dredged from the steep, eastern flank of the Anton Dohrn Seamount by Jones et al. (1974); the chalk either occupies vesicles or occurs as a matrix between basaltic clasts, and nannofossils recovered from it yielded a late Maastrichtian assemblage. On the top of Rosemary Bank (Figures 1 and 5), BGS borehole 90/18 drilled through approximately 1.5 m of recrystallised bioclastic limestone, containing basaltic clasts, immediately overlying the basaltic core of the seamount. Nannofossils again indicate a late Maastrichtian age. This is the most northerly proven occurrence, on the western side of Britain, of the chalk lithofacies which is so typical of the Upper Cretaceous of mainland Britain, Northern Ireland and the central and southern North Sea. In the Donegal Basin, well 12/13-1A (Figure 37) proved 152 m of Cenomanian to Maastrichtian sediment consisting of white to pale grey, partly dolomitic and cherty limestone, that is less argillaceous and dolomitic than the underlying Albian limestone. The sediments proved by this well were deposited in the same carbonate sea which covered a large part of Britain, its surrounds, and much of continental Europe (Ziegler, 1988).

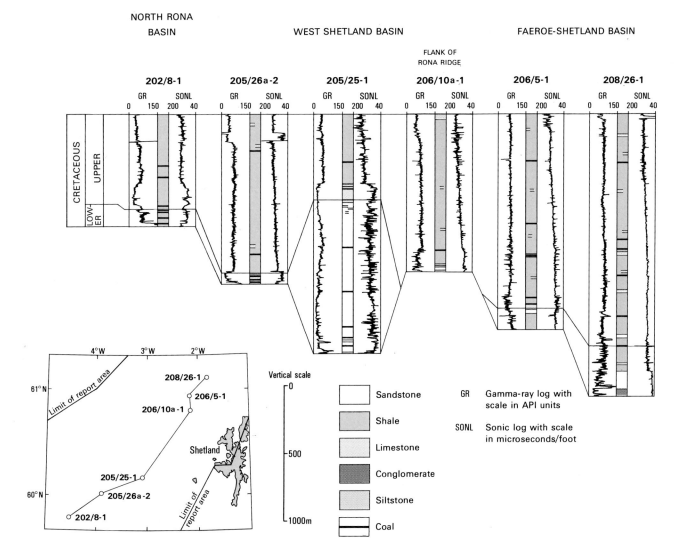

Figure 45 Selected wells from the North Rona, West Shetland and Faeroe–Shetland basins, showing lithology and log response.

10 Cretaceous and Tertiary igneous rocks

The Cretaceous and Tertiary igneous rocks of the report area represent part of the British 'Tertiary' Igneous Province (BTIP). The onshore portion of this province is situated along the west coast of the Scottish mainland, the Inner Hebrides, and parts of Ireland. It is typified by igneous centres with lavas, sills, and radiating dyke swarms. The offshore part of the BTIP extends from the Rockall Trough and Plateau to north of Shetland, and includes both deep-water and shelf areas (Figure 46). Within this region are igneous centres, extensive sill complexes, and widespread flood basalts; some crop out at the sea bed, whereas others are buried by younger sediments.

The BTIP is a part of the much larger volcanic terrane which developed as a direct result of Greenland splitting away from Europe as the North Atlantic Ocean opened during the early Tertiary. Volcanic activity related to this event has been described from Baffin Island, the east and west coasts of Greenland, the Faeroe Islands, as far south as Lundy Island in the Bristol Channel, and eastwards to the Skagerrak (Morton and Parson, 1988).

Within or adjacent to the report area, the first signs of these prolonged and extensive igneous events occurred in the mid- to Late Cretaceous, when thin, tuffaceous layers were deposited, and sills and dykes emplaced. The origin of some igneous centres and seamounts, with their associated outpourings of basic and acidic lavas, may also date from this time. Dating of offshore events has been difficult, mainly due to lack of suitable material; most UK onshore activity of the BTIP took place between 63 and 52 Ma (early Paleocene to early Eocene — Harland et al., 1990), with the acme at 59 Ma (Mussett et al., 1988). Thereafter, activity waned but continued sporadically, possibly into the Oligocene. As the sea-floor spreading continues, active volcanism persists at present outside the report area along the Mid-Atlantic Ridge, notably in Iceland.

The volcanism in the report area resulted primarily from the partial melting of the upper mantle. Variations in the degree of partial melting caused a range in basalt types, although most are olivine-tholeiites. Some of the basalts have been contaminated by crustal material on their way to the surface.

Correlation between the various magmatic events is difficult. The principal methods employed are isotopic age dating, palaeomagnetism, geochemistry, and biostratigraphy for the associated sedimentary horizons. K-Ar ages are most commonly quoted, but similar, repeated ages from the same sample need to be obtained for the results to gain credibility, and both weathering and contamination of samples can lead to unacceptable ages being obtained. Palaeomagnetism shows whether magmas crystallised when the Earth's magnetic field was in the normal or reversed polarity state (Figure 47). Geochemical analysis of major, trace, and rare-earth elements can be used to distinguish source material and contaminants.

Several attempts have been made to link all the dating techniques into a single, definitive time scale. Those of Harland et al. (1982) and Berggren et al. (1985) are most commonly quoted, but time scales by Haq et al. (1988) and Harland et al. (1990) are more recent; the latter is used in this chapter (Figure 47). Inconsistencies occur between the different scales, usually of the order of 2 to 3 Ma for the early

Tertiary, corresponding to one or two biostratigraphical zones or magnetochrons.

Within the report area, the principal manifestations of the BTIP are five igneous centres, widespread flood basalts, and an extensive sill complex intruded into sediments of the Rockall Trough, Faeroe–Shetland Basin and Møre Basin (Figure 46).

IGNEOUS CENTRES

The five igneous centres of the report area are the partially emergent intrusive centre of St Kilda, the buried and partially eroded volcanoes of Erlend, West Erlend and Geikie, and the buried Brendan Seamount (Figure 46). Other igneous centres in the immediate vicinity are Hebrides Terrace, Anton Dohrn, Rosemary Bank, Rockall (Figure 1), Darwin and Sigmundur. The Faeroe Bank Centre and the Faeroe Channel Knoll are other possible centres (Roberts et al., 1983). All these features are clearly defined by positive anomalies on the Bouger gravity anomaly map (Figure 4). The Brendan Seamount, Anton Dohrn and Rosemary Bank are discussed first as they are Cretaceous in age.

Brendan Seamount

At the south-western end of the Møre Basin (Figure 46) lies the buried Brendan Seamount (Smythe et al., 1983). No wells have penetrated it, and assuming it has a subaerial or submarine extrusive origin, its age must predate the oldest sediments which surround and bury it. Identification of seismic reflectors in the immediate vicinity of the seamount is difficult due to the presence of numerous intrusive rocks, but Smythe et al. (1983) considered the oldest sediments to be at least Turonian in age, leading them to consider the age of the seamount as Early Cretaceous or older. Smythe et al. (1983) also modelled the seamount against the associated 70 mGal free-air gravity anomaly; the best fit was a truncated cone extending down to just over 10 km depth, and increasing in diameter from 20 km at the top, to 50 km at its base.

Anton Dohrn

The Anton Dohrn seamount is centrally situated in the Rockall Trough (Figures 1 and 46). It is steep sided, and has a relatively flat top which is covered by sediment up to 100 m thick. Dredged samples of basic lavas and tuffs recovered from the eastern flank of the seamount were too altered for isotopic age dating (Jones et al., 1974). However, chalk showing no sign of thermal alteration, and hence postdating the lavas, was discovered both in vesicles and as a matrix between angular basalt clasts. The chalk yielded an abundant upper Maastrichtian nannofossil assemblage typical of an open-ocean environment. As a considerable proportion of the seamount has been removed by erosion, it is likely to be pre-Maastrichtian in age (Jones et al., 1974). The top of the seamount was drilled by BGS borehole 90/15, which did not penetrate the sedimentary cover of limestone that yielded microfossils of early Paleocene to early Eocene age. This is consistent with a Late Cretaceous age for the origin of the seamount.

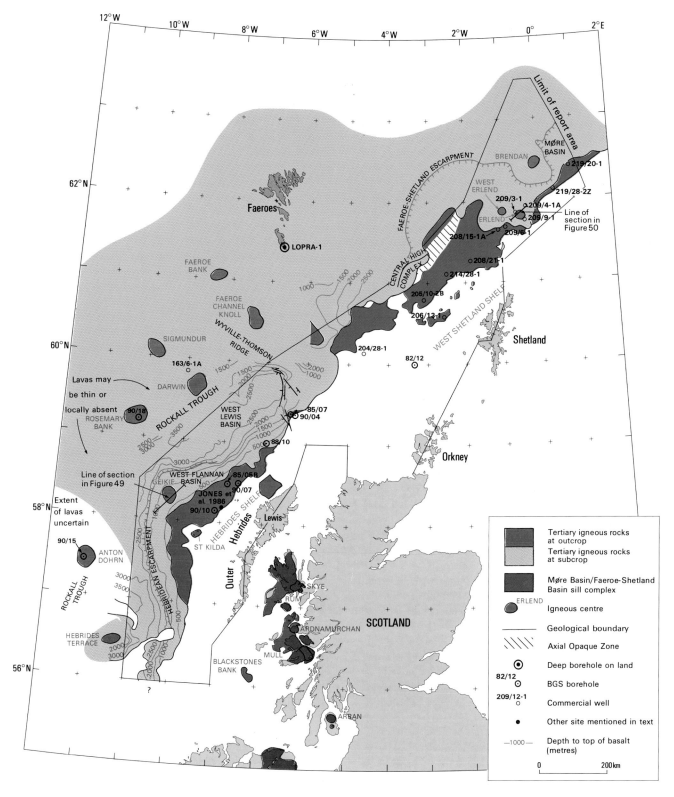

Figure 46 Distribution of Cretaceous and Tertiary igneous features in, and adjacent to, the report area.

Rosemary Bank

Rosemary Bank, which is centrally situated in the northern Rockall Trough (Figures 1 and 46), is a volcanic seamount now partially buried by younger sediments. The residual free-air positive gravity anomaly associated with the feature is 90 mGal; a pluton in the shape of a truncated cone extending to a depth of 22 km would account for this anomaly (Scrutton, 1971). On the top of the bank, volcanic rocks occur at the sea bed or are covered by a veneer of sediment.

Igneous rocks dredged from the south-western flank of Rosemary Bank by Dietrich and Jones (1980) comprise mild-

ly alkaline, porphyritic basalts in which the olivine phenocrysts are altered to chlorite-serpentine and haematite. They considered the original rocks to have been olivine-tholeiites with affinities to oceanic basalts. Highly alkaline tuffs and associated basalt blocks, with geochemical evidence for contamination by continental lithospheric material en route to the surface, were recovered from the top of the bank by Waagstein et al. (1989). BGS borehole 90/18, drilled on top of the bank, penetrated 17.7 m of fractured and agglomeratic lava and tuff which yielded ages which increase downhole from 24.2 ± 0.6 to 61.9 ± 1.1 Ma (Figure 48). This

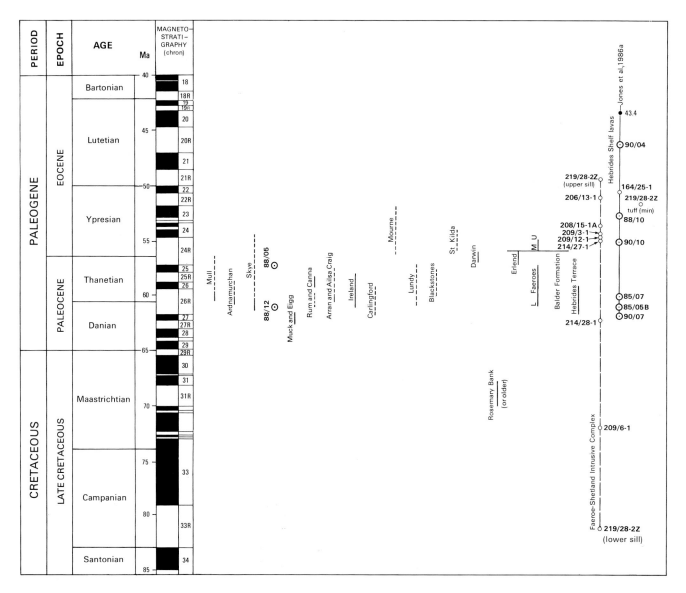

Figure 47 Comparison of age data for the British Tertiary Igneous Province. Timescale after Harland et al. (1990); shaded magnetic zones are normal, unshaded are reversed. Solid lines refer to extrusive rocks, whereas dashed lines show the age range of intrusive rocks. L, M and U refer to the Lower, Middle and Upper Faeroe Lava series.

range is probably the result of alteration to the original rocks, so that even the oldest age can be regarded as a minimum.

Immediately overlying the lavas in borehole 90/18 are approximately 1.5 m of recrystallised, bioclastic limestone which have yielded upper Maastrichtian nannofossils. Palaeomagnetic evidence indicates that the bulk of the seamount formed during a magnetic reversal (Miles and Roberts, 1981), and at lower latitudes than at present (Irving, 1964). Hence, the bulk of the bank may have formed between 70 to 68 Ma, the mid-Maastrichtian, or earlier. Some normally magnetised rocks either intrude or overlie the bank; this implies a phase of volcanic activity subsequent to the formation of the bulk of the seamount (Miles and Roberts, 1981). This phase may be responsible for the alteration of the dated lavas, and also for the recrystallisation of the overlying limestone.

Rockall

Much of the northern part of Rockall Bank is covered by basic lavas. A positive free-air gravity anomaly (Roberts and Jones, 1978), centred on a point 3 km south-east of Rockall Island (Figure 1), is associated with an arcuate pattern of

magnetic anomalies typical of ring dykes. These features are attributed to the presence of another igneous centre. Samples of aegirine-granite obtained from Rockall Island yielded isotopic age dates ranging from late Paleocene to early Eocene, whereas dredged samples of basaltic lavas and granites from Rockall Bank, and troctolitic microgabbro from Helen's Reef (3 km east-north-east of Rockall Island) indicate ages ranging from Late Cretaceous to early Eocene (Figure 48; Roberts et al., 1974). It seems likely that igneous activity here spanned the Cretaceous–Tertiary boundary.

Hebrides Terrace

The Hebrides Terrace Seamount is situated at the foot of the Hebrides Shelf on the eastern side of the Rockall

Figure 48 Cretaceous and Tertiary ages obtained from igneous centres in and around the report area. Chronostratigraphical ages derived from absolute ages using the timescale of Harland et al. (1990). For locations see Figure 46.

Location	Material	Method	Age (Ma)	Reference
ROCKALL BANK	Dredged boulders of basaltic lava	K-Ar whole rock	44. ± 1.8 Lutetian	Jones et al. (1972)
ROCKALL BANK	Dredged boulders of granite	K-Ar whole rock	55 ± 1.0	Pankhurst (1982) Recalculated from Jones et al. (1972)
ROCKALL ISLAND	Aegirine granite Aegirine granite	K-Ar whole rock Rb-Sr whole rock	55 ± 1 Ypresian 57 ± 7 ⎤ 54 ± 4 ⎬ Thanetian to 54 ± 4 ⎦ Ypresian	Harrison (1982) Hawkes et al. (1975)
ROCKALL BANK	Dredged boulders of basaltic lava	K-Ar whole rock	66 ± 2 Maastrichtian to Danian	Sanderson et al. (1975) Pankhurst (1982)
HELEN'S REEF; 3 KM ENE OF ROCKALL ISLAND	Dredged boulders of troctolitic microgabbro	K-Ar whole rock	83 ± 3 Santonian to Campanian	Roberts et al. (1974) Pankhurst (1982)
ANTON DOHRN SEAMOUNT; BGS BOREHOLE 90/15	Sea-bed core from sediments at top of seamount	Calcareous nannoplankton	Early Paleocene to early Eocene	Hitchen and Ritchie, in press
ANTON DOHRN SEAMOUNT	Dredged boulders of basic lava and tuff	Nannofossils	Pre-Maastrichtian	Jones et al. (1974)
ROSEMARY BANK SEAMOUNT	Dredged boulders of basalt	K-Ar whole rock	22.1 (minimum age)	Dietrich and Jones (1980)
	Magnetic data	Magnetic	Bulk of seamount is Late Cretaceous, but some activity extended into the early Tertiary	Miles and Roberts (1981)
ROSEMARY BANK SEAMOUNT; BGS BOREHOLE 90/18	Core of basalt	K-Ar whole rock	24.6 ± 0.6 ⎤ Chattian 24.2 ± 0.7 ⎦ 35.7 ± 1.1 ⎤ Priabonian 36.7 ± 1.1 ⎦ 42.0 ± 1.2 ⎤ Lutetian 45.2 ± 1.4 ⎦ 61.4 ± 1.0 ⎤ Danian 61.9 ± 1.1 ⎦	Hitchen and Ritchie, in press
BRENDAN SEAMOUNT	Seismic and well data	Dating of seismic reflectors	? Early Cretaceous	Smythe et al. (1983)
HEBRIDES TERRACE SEAMOUNT	Basic igneous rocks	Unspecified	67 to 60	Omran (1990)
ST KILDA	Rock samples	Rb-Sr	55 ± 1.0 Ypresian	Brook (1984)
DARWIN IGNEOUS CENTRE; WELL 163/6-1A	Cores of basaltic lava	K-Ar whole rock	53 ± 7 ⎤ 55 ± 3 ⎬ Thanetian to 58 ± 2 ⎪ Ypresian 57 ± 5 ⎦	Morton et al. (1988a)
	Cores of dacitic lava that underlies basalt	K-Ar whole rock	50.9 ± 1.0 ⎤ 56.2 ± 1.2 ⎬ Ypresian 54.6 ± 1.3 ⎦	Morton et al. (1988a)
	Junk-basket sample of dacitic lavas	K-Ar whole rock	70 ± 2 Maastrichtian	Morton et al. (1988a)
ERLEND IGNEOUS CENTRE; WELL 209/4-1A	Sidewall cores of rhyolite, dacite and pitchstone	K-Ar whole rock, and modelling of ages	58 ± 3 to 55 ± 4 Thanetian to Ypresian	Mitchell and Euwe (1988)
WELL 209/9-1	Sidewall core of rhyolite lava	Ar-Ar whole rock	64.8 ± 0.8 Maastrichtian– Danian boundary	Hitchen and Ritchie (1987)
WELL 209/9-1	Unspecified material from thin sedimentary interbeds within acidic lava pile	Microfossils	Campanian	Ridd (1983)

Trough (Figure 46). It protrudes more than 1000 m above the floor of the adjacent trough, but its top remains more than 1000 m below sea level. The seamount was probably formed during the early Paleocene (Omran, 1990), and its flat top, now covered by a veneer of sediments, is probably the result of subsequent marine planation. The maximum value of 140 mGal for the associated residual free-air gravity anomaly is the largest in the offshore BTIP (Abraham and Ritchie, 1991). The anomaly was first modelled (Buckley and Bailey, 1975) by simulating a dense cylinder extending down to the base of the crust at 23 km below sea level. Remodelling by Omran (1990) in the light of more recent crustal studies satisfied the anomaly by extending the cylinder to the Moho at only 17 km depth. The bulk of the seamount is reversely magnetised. Local magnetic anomalies observed over the summit may be caused by vertical dykes or feeder pipes extending to the summit (Buckley and Bailey, 1975). Dredging on the seamount recovered a predominance of olivine-rich basic igneous rocks (Omran, 1990).

St Kilda

The St Kilda igneous centre (Harding et al., 1984) is situated 65 km west-north-west of North Uist (Figure 46), and is the only igneous centre in the report area with subaerial expression. A positive gravity anomaly associated with the complex has a maximum Bouguer anomaly of over 120 mGal. The residual anomaly can be accounted for by a mafic pluton, shaped like an asymmetric, truncated cone, extending down from the surface to 21.5 km depth, with its diameter increasing from 16 km at the top to 34 km at its base (Himsworth, 1973).

The islands of St Kilda comprise a range of intrusive igneous rocks which were formed in the core of an early Tertiary volcano. No lavas or Tertiary sediments have been discovered on the islands. Palaeomagnetic data suggest that the whole complex was emplaced over a fairly short time interval during a single polarity reversal, and that Britain has drifted about 19° northwards since its intrusion (Morgan, 1984). As Rb-Sr age dating (Figure 48) yielded a figure of 55 ± 1 Ma (early Eocene) for the complex (Brook, 1984), it seems likely that intrusion occurred during the C24R magnetochron (Figure 47). Correlation with the chronostratigraphy is imprecise, but a latest Paleocene to earliest Eocene age is likely for the St Kilda centre.

The interrelationships between the various rock types exposed on the islands of St Kilda are complex (Harding et al., 1984). The oldest rocks consist of banded and layered gabbros, dolerites and breccias. Younger rocks typically contain more acidic lithologies such as granite and felsite. The last phase of igneous activity was the intrusion of a series of sheets and dykes which cut the major intrusions. Lavas and pyroclastic rocks, which are typical of other centres in the BTIP, were almost certainly present at one time in the vicinity of St Kilda, and may still exist offshore, but have been removed from the islands by erosion during subsequent uplift (Harding et al., 1984).

Geikie

The Geikie igneous centre lies approximately 80 km northwest of St Kilda. Its associated positive gravity anomaly (Figure 4) is broadly circular and was first identified by Himsworth (1973), but the centre was not named until much later (Evans et al., 1989; BGS Geikie Solid Geology sheet). The peak Bouguer gravity anomaly exceeds

180 mGal, and the residual anomaly is the second largest in the BTIP. The shape of the underlying pluton has been modelled by Evans et al. (1989) as two superimposed coaxial cylinders, the upper having a diameter of 13 km and extending from 0.7 km to 4 km below sea level. The lower cylinder has a diameter of 26 km, extending to 25 km depth (Figure 49).

Seismic data show that the whole area is covered by lavas (BGS Geikie Solid Geology sheet) which probably erupted from the Geikie volcano during the Paleocene. Their eroded surface generally dips north-westwards on the shelf, but in the vicinity of the igneous centre it is domed, and dipping horizons within the basalt radiate outwards. A 'rugged zone' on the basalt surface may represent either the location of the former volcanic vent or the top of the underlying pluton (Evans et al., 1989).

The Hebridean Escarpment (Smythe, 1989) is a buried, seaward-facing, basaltic scarp which can be traced for over 400 km along the eastern margin of the Rockall Trough. It reaches its maximum development near the Geikie igneous centre, where it exceeds 600 m in height and probably represents the hinge line, seaward of which the Rockall Trough subsided, notably during the Eocene. The line of the escarpment is deflected around the Geikie igneous centre, suggesting that the centre acted as a positive structural influence during the Eocene, possibly due to continued thermal buoyancy (Evans et al., 1989).

Darwin

The Darwin Complex, centre 'A' of Roberts et al. (1983), is situated outside the report area in the northern Rockall Trough (Figure 46). It consists of a buried and partially eroded volcano overlying a mafic pluton. The residual positive gravity anomaly associated with the feature can be modelled as a body approximating to two non-coaxial cylinders extending down to 15 km, and with 4000 to 4500 m of pre-Paleocene sediments between the base of the volcanic pile and the top of the pluton (Abraham and Ritchie, 1991). Seismic-reflection data have been used to identify five major lava sequences around the centre, each defined by a pro-

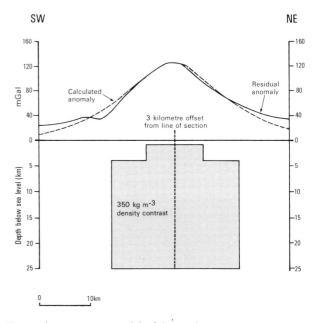

Figure 49 Gravity model of the Geikie igneous centre. For location see Figure 46. After Evans et al. (1989).

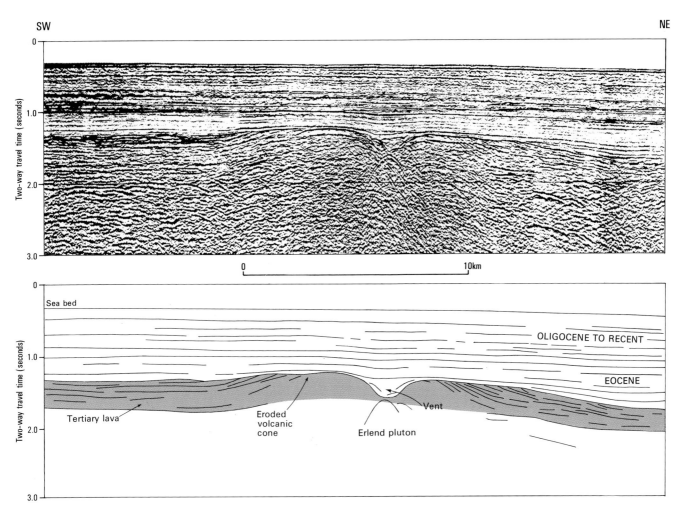

Figure 50 Seismic-reflection line, with interpretation, across the Erlend igneous centre. After Gatliff et al. (1984). For location see Figure 46.

nounced, arcuate scarp at its margin. The centre of the complex is marked by a vent 1600 m across and at least 100 m deep. The north-western flank of the complex has been drilled by well 163/6-1A (Figure 46), which proved 689 m of early Tertiary basalt (Figure 48) overlying 356 m of dacite in which the well terminated (Morton et al., 1988a). The dacite may have been derived from upper-crustal sediments melted by a shallow, basaltic reservoir; if so, they are of a broadly similar age to the late Paleocene to early Eocene basalts (Morton et al., 1988a).

Sigmundur

This igneous centre was first recognised as centre 'B' by Roberts et al. (1983), but was renamed Sigmundur by Andersen (1988). It lies in the north-west Rockall Trough (Figure 46) and comprises a buried and partially eroded volcano overlying a deeper intrusive centre. It is associated with a small, positive, free-air gravity anomaly which exceeds 40 mGal (Roberts et al., 1983), but no model estimating the size and shape of the pluton has been published. The top basalt surface exhibits scarps similar to those seen around Darwin; prograding bedding is seen within the basaltic lavas of the Sigmundur Seamount (Andersen, 1988), and seismic-reflection data show that lavas from the two centres coalesced. There is no direct evidence for the age of the seamount, although regional considerations, and the fact that Eocene sediments onlap its flanks, suggest that it is no younger than early Eocene.

Erlend and West Erlend

The existence of the Erlend Tertiary plutonic centre to the north of Shetland (Figure 46) was first suggested by Chalmers and Western (1979). Using gravity data, they modelled a thin lava above a single, cylindrical, dense, plutonic body with a diameter of 14 to 15 km extending to a depth of 25 to 30 km. Further gravity modelling and detailed seismic mapping by Gatliff et al. (1984) has demonstrated the existence of a second igneous centre, West Erlend, approximately 26 km to the west-north-west. Each centre consists of a buried, partially eroded shield volcano underlain by a basic pluton. The Erlend pluton was remodelled by Gatliff et al. (1984); a similar shape to that derived by Chalmers and Western (1979) was obtained, but with the base of the pluton at only 15 km depth.

On seismic-reflection profiles, the Erlend volcano exhibits dipping reflectors which represent the original depositional attitude of the lava flows. These are radially disposed around a central vent, which has a diameter of 2 km and a depth of 300 to 400 m (Figure 50). Well 209/9-1, on the south-eastern flank of the former volcano, proved tholeiitic basalts overlying an acidic suite consisting of rhyolite, dacite, obsidian and pitchstone (Figure 51). Dating of the latter unit is contradictory; Campanian microfossils from thin sedimentary horizons within the acidic suite have been reported by Ridd (1983). However, radiometric ages (Figure 48) of 64.8 ± 0.8 Ma (earliest Paleocene) were obtained from the base of this acidic suite by Hitchen and Ritchie (1987), and an age of 58 to 55 Ma (latest Paleocene to earliest Eocene) was reported by Mitchell and Euwe (1988). Well 209/3-1, drilled on the north-western flank of the vent (Figure 46), penetrated only basalt, although it can be divided into two series on the basis of seismic character and log response (Hitchen and Ritchie, 1987). This basalt has not been dated, but is probably of late Paleocene to early Eocene age, as the lower Eocene Balder Formation onlaps the eroded upper surface of the basalt on the southern and eastern flanks of the Erlend volcano.

The West Erlend volcano is more deeply eroded than Erlend, with no vent or radially dipping basalts seen on seismic data. Although there is a small volcanic plug on its flank, up to 1000 m of basalt may have been removed from the centre (Gatliff et al., 1984). The residual positive gravity anomaly is approximately half that of the Erlend centre. Two models have been proposed for the shape of the underlying pluton: the first with the base at 15 km and a diameter of 5 km, and the second with the base at 8 km and a diameter of 7 km (Gatliff et al., 1984).

BASALTIC LAVAS AND TUFFS

South of the Wyville–Thomson Ridge

Seismic mapping has shown that basaltic lavas underlie much of the northern Rockall Trough, and extend on to the Hebrides Shelf where they cover much of the West Flannan and West Lewis basins (Figure 46). Originally the lavas were probably more extensive than at present, especially on the shelf. An isolated occurrence, preserved as a faulted outlier just off Lewis (BGS Lewis Solid Geology sheet), indicates how much farther south-eastwards the lavas may once have extended. However, both Wood et al. (1987; 1988) and Ziegler (1988) suggested that the lavas have a more restricted occurrence in the northern Rockall Trough than shown on Figure 46, and may be locally absent. The lavas were probably derived from the igneous centres, the Wyville–Thomson Ridge, and numerous unidentified fissures, including any at the faulted eastern margin of the Rockall Trough. Adjacent to local sources the lavas may be thick; they have been proved to exceed 1000 m in well 163/6-1A near the Darwin igneous centre (Figure 46; Morton et al., 1988a; Abraham and Ritchie, 1991). On the shelf, lavas are likely to be relatively thin.

North of Lewis, BGS boreholes 85/07 (Stoker et al., 1988) and 90/04, drilled on the flank of the West Lewis Basin (Figure 46), recovered dark grey to black, fine-grained, amygdaloidal basalts closely comparable to normal (N-type) MORB (Mid-Ocean Ridge Basalt). Their proximity to the Wyville–Thomson Ridge suggests they might have been derived from that direction. Although drilled within 3 km of each other, significantly different ages have been obtained for the basalts (Figure 52). Borehole 85/07 yielded ages of 57.3 ± 5.2 and 62.3 ± 4.7 Ma (early to late Paleocene), whereas borehole 90/04 gave 46.4 ± 2.8 and 46.1 ± 2.7 Ma (early mid-Eocene). Borehole 88/10 recovered 4.7 m of fine to coarsely crystalline, amygdaloidal, dark grey to black basalt radiometrically dated 52.1 ± 0.5 Ma and 53.3 ± 0.5 Ma (Figure 52).

West of Lewis, BGS boreholes 85/05B (Stoker et al., 1988), 90/07 and 90/10, drilled on the flank of the West Flannan Basin (Figure 46), recovered basalts geochemically similar to, but more alkalic than, those in boreholes 85/07 and 90/04. The nearest major potential sources appear to be

Figure 51 The Erlend lavas in well 209/9-1. For location see Figure 46.

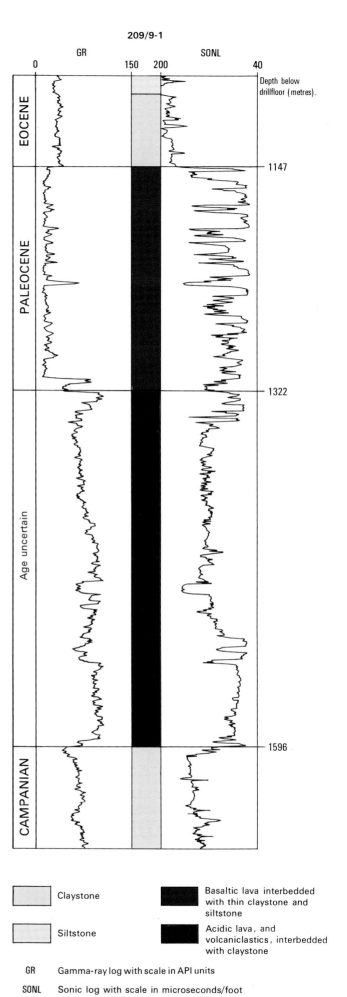

209/9-1

GR SONL

0   150   200   40

Depth below drillfloor (metres).

EOCENE

PALEOCENE

Age uncertain

CAMPANIAN

1147

1322

1596

Claystone	Basaltic lava interbedded with thin claystone and siltstone
Siltstone	Acidic lava, and volcaniclastics, interbedded with claystone

GR — Gamma-ray log with scale in API units

SONL — Sonic log with scale in microseconds/foot

Location	Material	Method	Age (Ma)	Reference
HEBRIDES SHELF	Dredged boulders of basalt lava	K-Ar whole rock	44.9 ± 1.0 42.9 ± 0.8 43.0 ± 0.7 42.9 ± 1.0 Lutetian	Jones et al. (1986a)
HEBRIDES SHELF; BGS BOREHOLE 90/04	Core of basalt lava	K-Ar whole rock	46.4 ± 2.8 46.1 ± 2.7 Lutetian	Hitchen and Ritchie, in press
HEBRIDES SHELF; BGS BOREHOLE 88/10	Core of basalt lava	K-Ar whole rock	52.1 ± 0.5 53.3 ± 0.5 Ypresian	Hitchen and Ritchie, in press
HEBRIDES SHELF; BGS BOREHOLE 90/10	Core of basalt lava	K-Ar whole rock	54.4 ± 0.7 55.8 ± 0.7 Ypresian	Hitchen and Ritchie, in press
FAEROE–SHETLAND ESCARPMENT	–	Seismostratigraphy	Paleocene to Eocene	Smythe et al. (1983)
HEBRIDES SHELF; BGS BOREHOLE 85/07	Core of basalt lava	K-Ar whole rock	57.3 ± 5.2 62.3 ± 4.7 Danian to Thanetian	Stoker et al. (1988)
HEBRIDES SHELF; BGS BOREHOLE 85/05B	Core of basalt lava	K-Ar whole rock	58.0 ± 6.2 63.1 ± 6.4 Danian to Thanetian	Stoker et al. (1988)
HEBRIDES SHELF; BGS BOREHOLE 90/07	Core of basalt lava	K-Ar whole rock	62.4 ± 1.3 60.7 ± 1.4 Danian to Thanetian	Hitchen and Ritchie, in press
WEST SHETLAND SHELF; BGS BOREHOLE 82/12	Core of tuff	Stratigraphy	Selandian	Morton et al. (1988b)

Figure 52 Cretaceous and Tertiary ages obtained from basalts and tuffs in and around the report area. Chronostratigraphical ages derived from absolute ages using the timescale of Harland et al. (1990). For locations see Figure 46.

the Geikie and St Kilda igneous centres, although they may have been derived from minor vents and fissures. Nearby (Figures 46 and 52), Jones et al. (1986a) dredged basaltic boulders which are chemically distinct from those of St Kilda, and which have a mean age of 43.4 ± 1.0 Ma (early mid-Eocene). The basalt from borehole 90/10 yielded early Eocene ages, whereas that from 85/05B was dated as early to late Paleocene. The basalt of borehole 90/07 gave ages of 60.7 ± 1.4 and 62.4 ± 1.3 Ma (early Paleocene).

Most lavas appear to be late Paleocene to early Eocene in age, but several sites in the area have yielded younger ages. Although these may represent a real geological event, it is perhaps more likely that they have been obtained as a result of in-situ alteration.

In the northern Rockall Trough, the distribution and extent of the lavas is not well defined, in particular the southern limit of the lavas is unknown. Roberts et al. (1984) considered that thin flows may extend across most of the trough, whereas Ziegler (1988) showed them to have a more restricted occurrence. The varied seismic character of the basaltic lavas was interpreted by Wood et al. (1987; 1988) as representing three facies: subaerial flows, hyaloclastite deposits de-

rived from the basalts, and tuffs. These facies were thought to record a near-source to distal transition. Buried lava scarps have been identified on seismic data; some are depositional in origin, the result of lavas freezing at contemporary shorelines, as at the Darwin centre where the basalts have been drilled in well 163/6-1A (Figure 46; see Darwin centre). However, the Hebridean Escarpment (Smythe 1989; Evans et al., 1989), which is over 600 m high at its maximum development, post-dates the lava, and probably overlies a major basement fault (BGS Peach Solid Geology sheet) which was active in the Eocene and Oligocene as the northern Rockall Trough subsided. As the lavas are now over 3 km below sea level, parts of the trough must have subsided by this amount since their extrusion during the late Paleocene to early Eocene, if they were subarially emplaced.

Wyville–Thomson Ridge

The Wyville–Thomson Ridge is a north-westerly orientated bathymetric high which separates the Faeroe–Shetland Channel from the northern Rockall Trough. The feature links the south of the Faeroe Bank to the Hebrides Shelf

(Figures 1 and 5), and its relatively flat top suggests at least some subaerial erosion. The ridge is associated with a positive Bouguer gravity anomaly (Figure 4), which at its south-eastern end reaches 60 mGal (Roberts et al., 1983). Seismic interpretation suggests that the ridge comprises mainly basaltic lavas, which in places occur at or near the sea bed, although the flanks are usually covered by younger sediments. No in-situ basalt samples have been recovered from the ridge, although basalts have been dredged from Faeroe Bank at its north-western end (Waagstein, 1988). The lavas are faulted, notably on the south-western side of the ridge (BGS Sula Sgeir Solid Geology sheet). In order to explain the observed gravity data, the ridge is either underlain by crust that is locally thickened due to igneous intrusion (Figure 21), or the crust is depressed beneath the lava pile (Roberts et al., 1983). A combination of these explanations is also possible.

The mode of origin of the ridge remains problematic, owing at least in part, to lack of data. Roberts et al. (1983) suggested that it is a massive Paleocene lava pile extruded directly on to middle Cretaceous oceanic crust. The lavas may be up to 12 000 m thick, and were erupted from fissures aligned north-west to south-east. The orientation of the fissures, and hence the ridge, may have been dictated by transfer faulting during the Paleocene. More recent data suggest that the northern Rockall Trough is underlain by stretched continental crust (Roberts et al., 1988), so that the lavas may have been extruded over Paleocene or older sediments resting on stretched and heavily intruded metamorphic basement. More recently an alternative explanation for the origin of the Wyville–Thomson Ridge has been proposed by Boldreel and Andersen (in press). They suggest that it is a compressional feature associated with a ramp anticline and reverse faults, formed as a result of tectonic forces that began during the latest part of the volcanic activity in the late Paleocene.

Prior to formation of the Wyville–Thomson Ridge, the Rockall Trough and Faeroe–Shetland Channel probably formed a continuous seaway. At the time of its formation, the ridge may have acted as a land bridge between the Faeroe Bank and the Hebrides Shelf (McKenna, 1983; Roberts et al., 1983), but was probably inundated by a marine transgression during latest Paleocene or earliest Eocene times (Stoker et al., 1988).

North of the Wyville–Thomson Ridge

In well 205/10-2B, on the south-eastern flank of the Faeroe–Shetland Basin, some 20 m of volcaniclastic sediments are interbedded with Albian claystone (Figure 46). This sequence is apparently isolated, and its significance is uncertain; of greater importance is that much of this region has early Tertiary basaltic lavas which cover the north-western side of the Faeroe–Shetland Basin and parts of the Møre Basin. In general, they become thinner south-eastwards and probably originated from the Faeroes, where over 5000 m of early Tertiary tholeiitic plateau basalts have been divided into Lower, Middle and Upper series (Berthelsen et al., 1984).

Dating of the three basalt series by isotopic, magnetostratigraphical and micropalaeontological methods has yielded variable results. The Middle and Upper series basalts are reversely (R) magnetised (as opposed to normal–N) throughout, as are the unexposed Lower Series basalts proved in the Lopra-1 borehole on the Faeroes (Figure 46). The 900 m of Lower Series exposed on the Faeroe Islands are magnetised N-R-N; Abrahamsen et al. (1984) correlated extrusion of all Faeroese lavas with magnetochrons C24R to C22R (Figure 47), although more recent estimates suggest that the Lower Series probably originated in C26R (Waagstein, 1988; Morton et al., 1988b). Most published correlations confirm a C24R age

for the Middle and Upper series (Smythe et al., 1983; Roberts et al., 1984; Waagstein, 1988; Morton et al., 1988b). Terrestrial microflora typical of the late Paleocene have been obtained from the thin sedimentary sequence between the Lower and Middle series basalts on the Faeroes (Lund, 1983), implying late Paleocene and early Eocene ages respectively for these series. This shows minor discordance with K-Ar ages of 54 ± 1 and 53 ± 2 Ma (early Eocene) obtained from the base and top of the exposed part of the Lower Series (Tarling and Gale, 1968; Tarling, 1970; Fitch et al., 1978), and it is likely that the isotopic ages are too young.

The Lower Series is over 3000 m thick on the Faeroes, and extends farthest into the report area. It consists of numerous stacked flows with some argillaceous or tuffaceous layers that increase in number and thickness upwards. The series formed subaerially, but parts of the Faeroe–Shetland Basin are now buried by over 2500 m of younger sediments, indicating more than 3.5 km of subsidence since their extrusion during the late Paleocene. The Lower Series becomes thinner south-eastwards, and its exact limit is difficult to determine using seismic-reflection data. In the Møre Basin, Smythe (1989) has shown that discrepancies of up to 50 km occur between various interpretations of their south-eastern limit. A thin tuff of equivalent age has been recovered on the West Shetland Shelf in BGS borehole 82/12 (Morton et al., 1988b). The lavas are of a similar age to, or slightly older than, those which emanated from the Erlend and West Erlend igneous centres.

Overlying the Lower Series on the Faeroe Islands are 10 m of argillaceous sediments, overlain by up to 100 m of tuffs and agglomerates. This succession has been correlated with a widespread tuffaceous siltstone interval that has been seismically correlated with the base of the Faeroe–Shetland Escarpment (Figure 46), which marks the limit of the Faeroese Middle Series basalts (Smythe, 1983; Smythe et al., 1983). However, the very local distribution and characteristic geochemistry of the tuff-agglomerate zone on the Faeroes (Waagstein and Hald, 1984) precludes a common source for these two volcaniclastic sequences (Waagstein, 1988).

Offshore, the widespread tuffaceous siltstone unit is of probable earliest Eocene age. It reaches a thickness of 163 m in well 208/15-1A (Mudge and Rashid, 1987) and 119 m in well 204/28-1 (Hitchen and Ritchie, 1987; Figure 46). It can be correlated with the Balder Formation of Deegan and Scull (1977), which can be traced over much of the northern and central North Sea. The unit produces a prominent, distinctive and synchronous seismic marker which can be traced across much of the offshore area to the north and west of Britain. The tuffaceous material is likely to have been derived from the Faeroes or east Greenland, and carried south-eastwards by the prevailing winds.

The Middle Series of basalts on the Faeroes consists of 1300 m of pahochoe-type flows, of which the uppermost 100 m is intensely weathered. Both the Lower and Middle series comprise aphyric, iron-rich and plagiophyric tholeiites. Lavas of the Middle Series are less extensive than those of the Lower Series, and occur in the report area only north of 62°N. Their south-eastern limit is usually marked by a sinuous, south-easterly facing scarp or slope, termed the Faeroe–Shetland Escarpment (BGS Flett Solid Geology sheet).

Segments of this escarpment were first mapped by Talwani and Eldholm (1972), who interpreted them as representing the boundary between continental and oceanic crust north of Shetland. However, this feature is now considered to be depositional in origin, and was caused by lavas of the Middle Series freezing at the contemporary shoreline (Smythe, 1983; Smythe et al., 1983). The south-eastward projecting lobe of

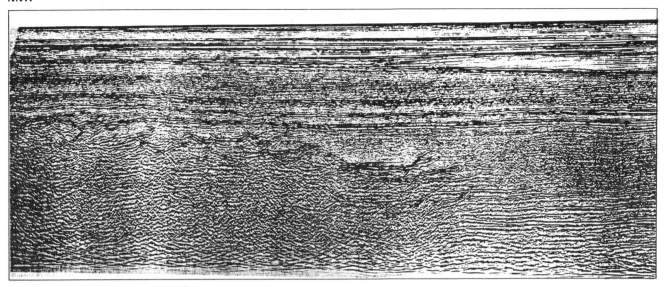

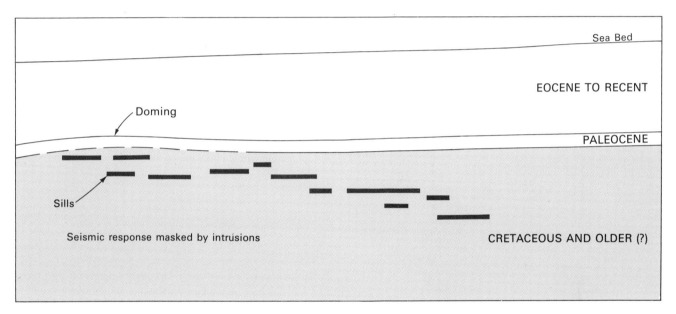

Figure 53   Seismic-reflection line, with interpretation, across the south-eastern edge of the Møre Basin/Faeroe–Shetland sill complex in the vicinity of well 219/20-1. After Gibb and Kanaris-Sotiriou (1988). For location of well see Figure 46. Scale unknown.

Middle Series lavas coincident with the location of the Brendan Seamount (Figure 46) is suggestive of a causal relationship between the two, but if the seamount is of Early Cretaceous age, it could not have sourced these early Eocene lavas (Smythe et al., 1983). The lobe can be explained by the seamount being maintained as a structural high from its origin until the early Eocene, possibly by compaction of the surrounding sediments. If the area over the seamount was a subaerial peninsula during the early Eocene, then the lobe could be formed as the Middle Series lavas flowed south-eastwards to the contemporary shoreline (Smythe et al., 1983).

The Upper Series on the Faeroes is 700 m thick, and is made up of flows typically 10 m thick. This series does not extend into the report area, but has geochemical similarities with sills drilled by well 219/20-1, and with the upper sill in well 219/28-2Z (Fitch et al., 1988; Gibb et al., 1986). This suggests that all these features were formed contemporaneously from the same source.

INTRUSIVE ROCKS

Møre Basin/Faeroe–Shetland Basin sill complex

This intrusive complex covers a large area extending south-westwards from the Møre Basin for over 400 km along the axis of the Faeroe–Shetland Basin (Figure 46). Isolated groups of sills also occur in the northern part of the West Shetland Basin and over the Rona Ridge (Hitchen and Ritchie, 1987). Within the Møre Basin, the complex was described as lavas by Hamar and Hjelle (1984), and as partially eroded volcanoes by Nelson and Lamy (1987), but the proposal that they are sills (Smythe, 1989) is corroborated by data from several wells. On seismic-reflection data, the sills appear as short, discontinuous, high-amplitude reflectors which may be either parallel or inclined to the bedding (Figure 53). Upper Cretaceous shales have acted as host sediment for most of the intrusions (Figure 54). The sills of the complex probably extend below the Tertiary basalts and into the Rockall Trough. Seismic data show that sills of presumed early Tertiary age

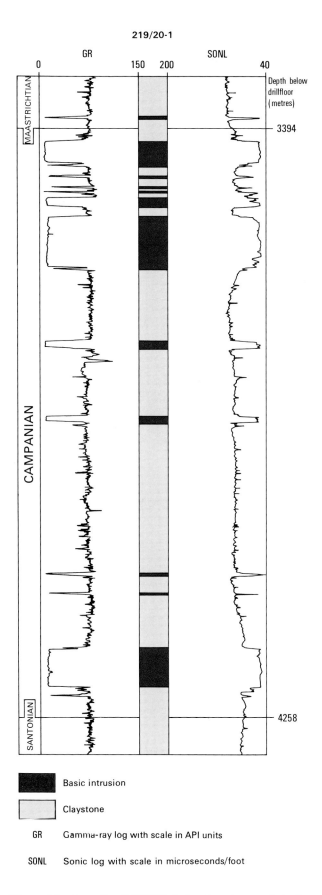

219/20-1

GR
0   150   200   SONL   40

MAASTRICHTIAN

Depth below
drillfloor
(metres)

3394

CAMPANIAN

SANTONIAN

4258

■ Basic intrusion

▨ Claystone

GR   Gamma-ray log with scale in API units

SONL   Sonic log with scale in microseconds/foot

Figure 54 Log of well 219/20-1 showing characteristically sharp geophysical-log responses from sills. Thermal metamorphism of the adjacent sediments is reflected in higher interval velocities above and below the large intrusions near the top and bottom of the Campanian section. For location see Figure 46.

occur across much of the Rockall Trough and its eastern margin, where they are intruded into Mesozoic sediments which may be over 2000 m thick (Wood et al., 1988).

Using mainly K-Ar dating techniques (Figure 55), most sills have yielded ages of 55 to 50 Ma (early Eocene), although the complex was probably emplaced over a period of only 1 to 2 Ma (Gibb and Kanaris-Sotiriou, 1988). However, ages ranging from about 80 Ma (Campanian) to 49 Ma (early mid-Eocene) have been recorded. The former age was obtained from the lower of two sills penetrated by well 219/28-2Z (Fitch et al., 1988), and probably belongs to a separate magmatic event as both the age and geochemistry are markedly different from the rest of the complex. An Eocene age for the complex was supported by Gibb and Kanaris-Sotiriou (1988), who suggested that the doming of the top-Paleocene seismic reflector over the complex was caused by distension of the sedimentary pile during sill emplacement (Figure 53).

Apart from the lower sill in well 219/28-2Z, most of the sills were probably intruded during a single magmatic event. The sills are typically internally differentiated, and display a wide range of grain size, mineralogy and texture. Pegmatitic dolerites are reported from well 219/20-1 (Gibb et al., 1986), whereas oceanic plagiogranites derived by fractional crystallisation of MORB-type magmas occur in well 208/21-1 (Kanaris-Sotiriou and Gibb, 1989). Overall, the sills comprise tholeiitic olivine-dolerites which have oceanic affinities on the basis of TiO_2-K_2O-P_2O_5 plots (Pearce et al., 1975). Geochemical and rare-earth element data suggest that the sills have transitional (T-type) MORB affinities (Gibb and Kanaris-Sotiriou, 1988). Hence the sills appear to have little in common with the Faeroese Lower and Middle series basalts, but are very similar to the Upper Series (Gibb et al., 1986), to which they may be related in genesis and age.

Axial Opaque Zone and Central High Complex

The Axial Opaque Zone was first recognised by Ridd (1981; 1983) as an area where the pre-Eocene succession is imaged seismically as nearly opaque. The zone is situated on the northwestern flank of the Faeroe–Shetland Basin (Figure 46), and is aligned north-east to south-west; it is partially covered by early Tertiary basalts of the Faeroese Lower Series (BGS Flett Solid Geology sheet). Ridd (1981; 1983) suggested that the Axial Opaque Zone may be a linear Paleocene igneous complex. At its south-western end it appears to be contiguous with the Central High Complex (Figure 46), a structural high associated both with a marked increase in magnetic intensity and with a positive Bouguer gravity anomaly (Hitchen and Ritchie, 1987). The Central High Complex was implied to be of igneous origin by Hitchen and Ritchie (1987), but was interpreted as a fault-bounded basement block by Mudge and Rashid (1987). It is similarly considered to be basement by Rumph et al. (in press), who named this feature the Corona Ridge; they regard it as the structural corollary of the Rona Ridge, which forms the south-eastern flank of the Faeroe–Shetland Basin. No wells have tested the origin and age of these features.

Location	Material	Method	Age (Ma)	Reference
MORE BASIN/FAEROE–SHETLAND SILL COMPLEX; WELL 219/28-2Z	Sidewall core of hornfels Sidewall core of tuff	Ar-Ar whole rock K-Ar whole rock	49.6 ± 2.3 51.7 ± 0.8 Ypresian to Lutetian	Fitch et al. (1988)
WELL 206/13-1	Core of dolerite sill	K-Ar whole rock	53.0 ± 0.5 48.7 ± 0.5 Ypresian to Lutetian	Hitchen and Ritchie, in press
WELLS 208/15-1A 208/21-1 219/20-1	Core	Geochemistry, seismostratigraphy	Eocene	Gibb and Kanaris-Sotiriou (1988)
WELL 208/15-1A	Core of sill	K-Ar whole rock	53.6 ± 1.0 52.9 ± 1.0 Ypresian	Hitchen and Ritchie, in press
WELL 209/3-1	Core of sill	K-Ar whole rock	54.8 ± 2 54.3 ± 2 Ypresian	Hitchen and Ritchie (1987)
WELL 209/12–1	Core of sill	K-Ar whole rock	54.8 ± 0.7 55.3 ± 0.7 Ypresian	Hitchen and Ritchie, in press
WELL 214/27–1	Core of hornfels	K-Ar whole rock	55 ± 0.6 Ypresian	Hitchen and Ritchie (1987)
ERLEND, BRENDAN DOME, MID-FAEROE RIDGE	Intrusive and extrusive rocks	Unspecified	Paleocene	Duindam and Van Hoorn (1987)
MORE BASIN/FAEROE–SHETLAND SILL COMPLEX; WELL 214/28-1	Core of olivine-basalt sill	K-Ar whole rock	c.61.2 c.62.9 Danian	Hitchen and Ritchie (1987)
WELL 208/15-1A	Dolerite sills	Unspecified	65 to 59 Danian to Thanetian	Mudge and Rashid (1987)
WELL 209/6-1	Unspecified material, olivine-tholeiite sills	Unspecified	70 to 73 Maastrichtian	Mudge and Rashid (1987)
WELL 209/6-1	Core of olivine-dolerite sill	K-Ar whole rock	72 ± 5.2 Campanian to Maastrichtian	Hitchen and Ritchie (1987)
FAEROE AND ERLEND PLATFORMS	Dense network of sills. Plutonic intrusive centres	Unspecified	'Towards the end of the Cretaceous'	Duindam and Van Hoorn (1987)
MORE BASIN/FAEROE–SHETLAND SILL COMPLEX; WELL 219/28-2Z	Core of alkali olivine-dolerite sill	K-Ar biotite K-Ar whole rock	79.1 ± 2.4 Campanian 81.0 ± 4.1 Santonian to Campanian	Fitch et al. (1988)

Figure 55 Cretaceous and Tertiary ages obtained from wells in the Møre Basin/Faeroe–Shetland sill complex. Chronostratigraphical ages derived from absolute ages using the timescale of Harland et al. (1990). For locations see Figure 46.

11 Tertiary sedimentary rocks

Tertiary strata extend westwards from the outer parts of the shelf into the adjacent deep-water basins, but are largely absent from the inner shelf (Figure 56). The landward limit is broadly coincident with, and probably related to, the zone marking the transition from 'normal-thickness' continental crust beneath the shelf, to highly attenuated crust beneath the Rockall Trough–Faeroe–Shetland Basin–Møre Basin rift zone (Figure 19). The Tertiary sediments generally form a seaward-thickening wedge in which the sediments are sub-horizontally bedded. In basinal areas, the Paleocene rests directly on the Cretaceous, but towards their eastern feather-edge, Tertiary strata overstep onto Mesozoic, Permo-Triassic or older rocks. The landward limit is erosional and partially controlled by faulting or flexure along the zone of crustal thinning, with the inner shelf having remained as a broad platform.

Igneous and sedimentary rocks of Paleogene age crop out extensively at or near sea bed on the outer part of the Hebrides Shelf and on the Wyville–Thomson Ridge, with more restricted outcrop north and west of Shetland (Figure 56). Paleogene strata also crop out at the Geikie Escarpment, which remains largely exposed due to its steepness and the presence of a northward-flowing contour current (Kenyon, 1987). Paleogene rocks are similarly exposed on seamounts and banks to the west of the report area. The Neogene succession generally unconformably overlies the Paleogene, and thickens westward on the outer shelf and upper slope, but has a variable thickness on the lower slope and in deep water (Figure 57). In the Faeroe–Shetland Channel, strong bottom currents have eroded and/or severely restricted the distribution of Neogene deposits, particularly at the south-western end of the channel, where Paleogene rocks crop out locally.

The base of the Tertiary is difficult to establish across much of the area, as the early Tertiary volcanic sequence effectively forms acoustic basement on seismic profiles. On the outer parts of the Hebrides and West Shetland shelves, the base of the Tertiary locally occurs at a depth shallower than 200 m below sea level. This deepens to the west, across the zone of rapid crustal thinning, and in areas not obscured by the volcanic rocks, the base lies at a depth of up to 3600 m below sea level in the Rockall Trough, and at over 6000 m in the Faeroe–Shetland Channel. The total Tertiary thickness can only be estimated across much of the area, with up to 2000 m in the Rockall Trough (within the report area), and in excess of 3500 m in the Faeroe–Shetland Channel (Figure 56).

Early Tertiary tectonics mainly reflected an extensional regime associated with the opening of the North Atlantic Ocean, and the onset of sea-floor spreading to the north-west of the Rockall Plateau and the Faeroe and Møre platforms. This was accompanied by the extrusion of extensive and voluminous flood basalts emanating from the Faeroe Platform, from the Wyville–Thomson Ridge, from igneous centres, and from fissures. Numerous sills were intruded, mainly into Cretaceous rocks, and a widespread early Eocene tuffaceous interval has been recorded from most wells. The acme of igneous activity was during the late Paleocene to early Eocene, after which the Tertiary was generally characterised by massive subsidence, possibly of up to 3 km in the Rockall Trough and the Faeroe–Shetland and Møre basins. The rate of subsidence greatly exceeded sedimentation, so that these structural basins are broadly coincident with the present-day deep-water features. Volcanogenic, shallow-water sedimentation in early Tertiary times was replaced by deep-water, current-controlled sedimentation in the mid- to late Tertiary, when the deep-water basins were fringed by a seaward-prograding, outer-shelf, clastic wedge.

SEISMIC STRATIGRAPHY

Investigation of the Tertiary to the north and north-west of Scotland is based on a seismostratigraphical approach, although there is limited biostratigraphical control (R Harland, M J Hughes and I P Wilkinson, written communications, 1977–1991) from BGS boreholes and commercial wells (Figure 56). On seismic-reflection profiles, several prominent reflectors have been identified within the Tertiary succession in and adjacent to the report area, although no regional seismostratigraphical framework has been established. With the exception of the early Tertiary volcanic episode, which formed the acoustic basement imaged over a large area, the most important intra-Tertiary environmental change to provide seismic expression was the development of an abyssal circulation pattern in the mid-Tertiary; this resulted in significant unconformities that essentially separate Neogene from Paleogene strata. Attempts at a unified seismic stratigraphy have failed to consider the effects of diachronous development and/or re-excavation of unconformity surfaces. Consequently, the misidentification of seismic reflectors remains a major problem.

One of the most prominent of these reflectors is termed R4; in the Hatton–Rockall Basin it has been dated at DSDP (Deep Sea Drilling Project) sites 116 and 117 (Figures 58 and 59) as late Eocene to early Oligocene, essentially top Eocene (Roberts, 1975a; Smythe, 1989). On the south-east margin of the Hatton–Rockall Basin, R4 forms an angular unconformity, but this loses expression basinwards where the overlying sequences appear conformable (Roberts et al., 1970; Roberts, 1975a).

Roberts (1975a) attempted to continue R4 into the Rockall Trough, but DSDP site 610 on the Feni Ridge (Figures 58 and 59) indicates that the reflector correlated by Roberts with R4 was misidentified; site 610 proved this horizon, the green reflector of Masson and Kidd (1986), to be of latest early Miocene age. This age is equivalent to reflector R2 of Miller and Tucholke (1983), a widespread unconformity recognised throughout the North Atlantic as marking the onset of coherent, deep-water, current-controlled sedimentation. It should be noted that this change in reflector dating applies only to the Rockall Trough, and not to the Rockall Plateau. The equivalent of R4 is presumed to lie deeper within the Feni Ridge succession, and has been correlated by Masson and Kidd (1986) with their brown reflector (Figure 59).

Misidentification of reflectors between widely spaced areas is further exemplified in the report area, where Jones et al. (1986b) erected a seismic stratigraphy for the outer part of the Hebrides Shelf and Slope (Figure 59). On the Hebrides Shelf, their reflector H2 was attributed a mid-Oligocene age, but correlated with R4. BGS borehole 88/07, 07A (Figures

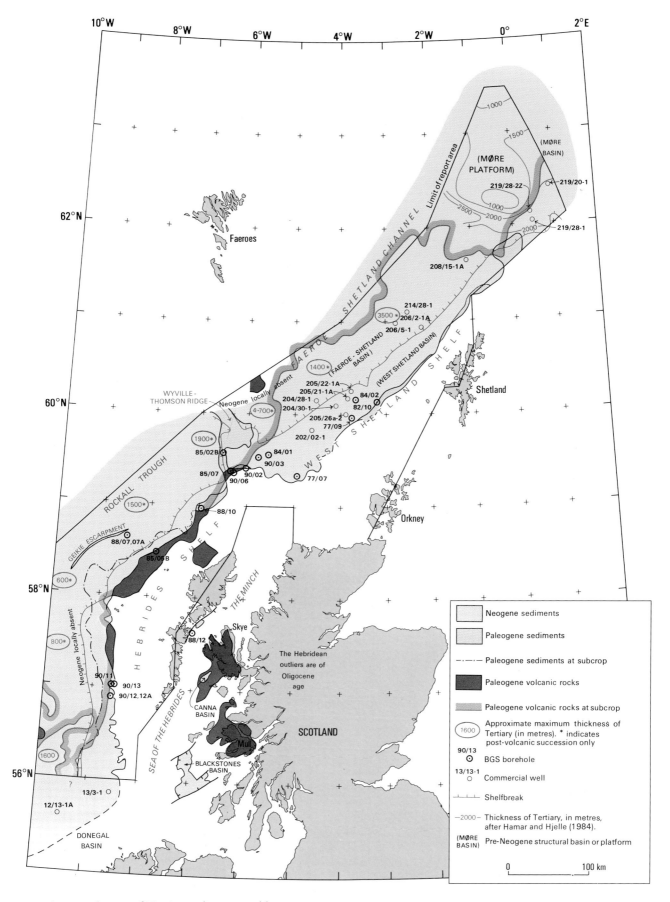

Figure 56 Distribution of Tertiary sediments and lavas.

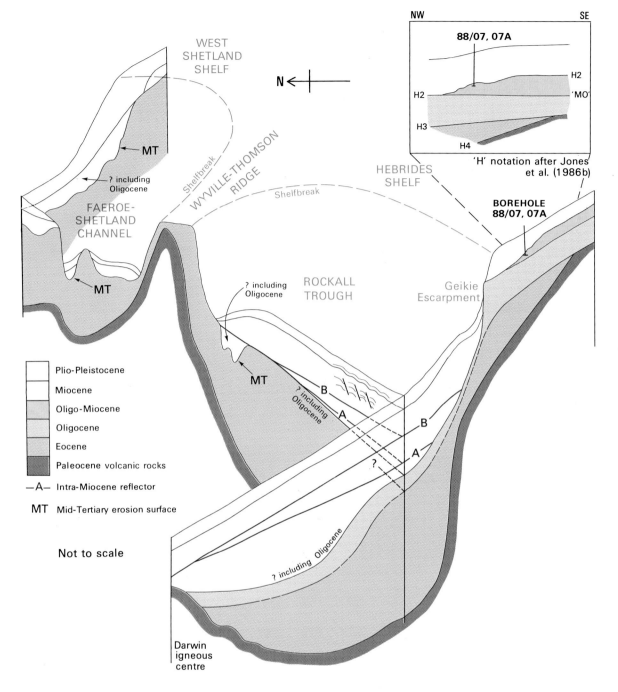

Figure 57 Schematic cross-sections (not to scale) illustrating the Tertiary seismic stratigraphy in, and adjacent to, the report area. For explanation of seismic-reflector notation, see Figure 59.

56 and 57) has subsequently indicated that this horizon is a composite unconformity surface, probably originating in the mid-Oligocene, but having been re-excavated during a late Miocene to early Pliocene erosional event. BGS high-resolution seismic data suggest that the undisturbed section of the mid-Oligocene surface (labelled MT in Figure 57) is preserved below that indicated as H2 by Jones et al. (1986b). The 'top Eocene' (R4) reflector in this area is considered to lie deeper within the Tertiary succession (BGS Geikie Solid Geology sheet).

The complexity of the Tertiary succession in the report area, and the problem of dating reflectors, is highlighted by the recognition of two distinct intra-Miocene horizons, A and B (Figures 57, 60 and 61). Reflector B, the younger, forms a marked angular unconformity over the Darwin igneous centre, where reflector A is truncated by reflector B,

but the two become increasingly parallel towards the basin margin. Adjacent to the Wyville–Thomson Ridge, reflector B downlaps on to reflector A, which forms a major unconformity at the basin margin, although some re-excavation during the reflector B interval seems probable.

Reflector B is a particularly significant horizon, as stable sediment-drift accumulation in this part of the Rockall Trough postdates its formation. Such characteristics also typify reflector R2 (Figure 59), but without borehole control, correlation between reflectors remains unproven.

On both flanks of the Wyville–Thomson Ridge and in the Faeroe–Shetland Channel, there is a major, highly irregular unconformity which separates Eocene from upper Oligocene to lower Pliocene strata (Figure 57). Although a broad mid-Tertiary age is assumed, the unconformity surface may have been eroded and modified several times between late Eocene

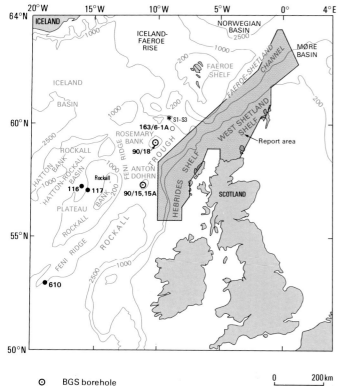

Figure 58 Locations of boreholes/wells which drilled Tertiary rocks to the west of the report area.

and late Oligocene times. In the north-eastern part of the channel, Mitchell et al. (in press) and Damuth and Olsen (in press) have assigned a latest Oligocene age to the unconformity. This erosion surface does not equate with any specific reflector in the RockallTrough.

PALEOGENE

Sedimentary and volcanic rocks of Paleogene age are found across most of the report area, and are absent only on the inner parts of the Hebrides and West Shetland shelves (Figure 56). The base of the Paleogene is not always easy to establish; on the Hebrides Shelf, the seismic response from beneath the basalts is degraded, whereas west of Shetland, the similarity between Upper Cretaceous and lower Paleocene sedimentary lithologies does not generally produce a prominent seismic reflector. West of the Hebrides, the basalts extend farther landward than the Paleogene sediments (Figure 56) and crop out at the sea bed. West of Shetland, the basalts are overlapped by younger Paleogene sediments, and the feather-edge of the component parts cannot be mapped beneath the Neogene.

During the Paleocene, renewed tectonic movement allowed deposition adjacent to major faults, but late Paleocene and early Eocene events were dominated by regional uplift and massive volcanism associated with North Atlantic rifting. Sediments deposited at this time are commonly typical of shallow-water, nearshore environments. Later during the Eocene, thermal subsidence throughout the area caused a return to marine conditions.

The initial development of the present bathymetric configuration began in mid- to late Eocene times, although water depths exceeding 500 m were probably not established before the early Miocene (Thiede and Eldholm, 1983). A vigorous, abyssal, water circulation developed in late Eocene to early Oligocene times (Miller and Tucholke, 1983; Stow and Holbrook, 1984; Berggren and Schnitker, 1983), and caused the formation of a widespread, irregular, erosion surface on the margin of the deep-water basins; this is prominent on seismic data, and there are deep channels cut into existing Paleogene sediments (Figures 56 and 59). This circulation pattern may have resulted from the establishment of a deep-water connection betweeen the Arctic and North Atlantic oceans (Berggren and Schnitker,1983; Ziegler, 1988), although Eldholm (1990) has suggested that this northern source of deep-water exchange is a Neogene and Quaternary phenomenon. Other sources of pre-Neogene bottom-current flow are little known, but southerly or westerly derived currents have been postulated by Scrutton and Stow (1984) at the southern end of the Rockall Trough. During the mid- to late Oligocene, current strengths waned, but deposition continued to be restricted. It was not until the mid-Miocene that currents stabilised (Stow and Holbrook, 1984) and the erosional hollows became filled.

Paleocene

The principal known area of Paleocene deposition in the report area is the Faeroe–Shetland Basin. Movement on the faults bounding the intrabasinal Mid Faeroe and Flett ridges allowed massive subsidence, and the development of a north-easterly orientated sub-basin, the Flett Sub-Basin (Figure 62), that was first proved by well 206/2-1A. Its depocentre is coincident with the axis of the Faeroe–Shetland Basin, but lies to the south-east of the main area of Cretaceous deposition, which was adjacent to the Faeroe Platform Margin Fault (Figures 17 and 42). The Flett Sub-Basin contains over 3000 m of marine shales and turbiditic sandstones (Figure 62), and at its deepest point is approximately 6000 m below sea level (Hitchen and Ritchie, 1987; Duindam and Van Hoorn, 1987). In places, notably over the Flett Ridge, seismic data reveal listric growth faults and associated rollover structures (Ridd, 1983). The sandstones were probably derived from the south-east, although some axial reworking may have occurred. Most of the Flett Sub-Basin infill has been dated as late Paleocene by Mudge and Rashid (1987), based on wells on the south-eastern margin of the basin, but lower and middle Paleocene sediments are also present.

Towards the end of Paleocene times, the north-west margin of the Faeroe–Shetland Basin was inundated by sub-aerially emplaced lavas of the Faeroes Lower Series, and to the north-east the Erlend and West Erlend volcanoes (Figure 46) were erupting.

At the south-west end of the Faeroe–Shetland Basin, interaction between Caledonoid structures and syndepositional transfer faults, such as the Judd Fault (Figure 17), caused rapid lateral variation in the thickness of Paleocene deposits (Hitchen and Ritchie, 1987). By the end of the Paleocene, transfer faulting had largely ceased. Late Paleocene to early Eocene lithologies are typically sandstones and shales, with several coal seams; widespread, shallow-marine, nearshore or deltaic conditions had become established across the whole basin.

In the West Shetland Basin, an early to mid-Paleocene tectonic pulse caused rejuvenation of local structural highs such as the Rona Ridge and West Shetland Platform (Figure 17), and renewed movement on the Shetland Spine Fault. The

NORTH-EAST ATLANTIC	ROCKALL PLATEAU Hatton-Rockall Basin	ROCKALL TROUGH Feni Ridge	HEBRIDES SHELF AND SLOPE Area of Geikie Escarpment	
Miller and Tucholke (1983) **DSDP sites**	Roberts (1975a) **DSDP 116, 117**	Masson and Kidd (1986) **DSDP 610**	Jones et al. (1986b)	**BGS 88/07, 07A** and adjacent sites
R1 (Late Miocene) _ _ _ _R1_ _ _ _ _ _ _ _ _ _ _Yellow (Latest late Miocene)				(H2) (Late Miocene to early Pliocene)
		Purple (Mid-middle Miocene)		
R2 (Late early Miocene) _ R2 _ _ _ _ _ _ _ _ _*Green (Latest early Miocene)				
R3 (Late Oligocene to early Miocene) _ _ R3				
			*H2 (Mid-Oligocene)	
R4 _ _ _ _ _ _ _ _ R4 (Late Eocene to earliest Oligocene) – _Brown			H3 (Intra-Eocene)	
	R5		H4 (Eroded Mesozoic to Upper Palaeozoic)	(H4) (Top basalt)

*The seismic horizons represented by the 'green' and 'H2' reflectors have been correlated
by Roberts (1975a) and Jones et al. (1986b), respectively, with R4 of the Rockall Plateau.
DSDP site 610 and BGS borehole 88/07, 07A have shown these seismic ties to be incorrect

Borehole control   Seismic interpretation

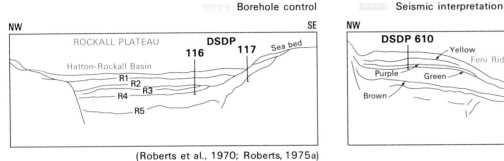

(Roberts et al., 1970; Roberts, 1975a)

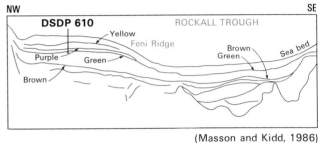

(Masson and Kidd, 1986)

Figure 59 Correlation chart of Tertiary seismic stratigraphy, detailing the seismic reflectors, and their assigned ages as identified by various authors. The schematic cross-sections (not to scale) illustrate the seismic stratigraphy. For locations of Rockall Trough and Plateau sites see Figure 58.

Scarvister Sub-Basin, which is nearly 90 km long, developed in the hanging wall of the fault. Here the Paleocene can be over 600 m thick (Figure 62), whereas it is thin or absent on the adjacent platform, and less than 200 m thick over the Rona Ridge (Hitchen and Ritchie, 1987). At the southwestern end of the basin, the infill includes a partially conglomeratic sandstone unit rich in locally derived bryozoan fragments. This unit, which rests on Danian marls, has a proven maximum thickness of 277 m in well 205/26a-2, and has been indentified in six other wells (Hitchen and Ritchie, 1987).

Elsewhere in and around the report area, details of Paleocene lithologies are less well known. In the Donegal Basin (Figure 56), well 12/13-1A proved that Paleocene cherty limestone overlies Maastrichtian limestone with minor unconformity. To the north, three BGS boreholes (90/11, 90/12,12A and 90/13), drilled just to the east of the basalt feather-edge, proved sandstones consisting largely of eroded volcanic debris, and dark grey mudstones; these have been dated as Paleocene to early Eocene. Palynological considerations suggest an open-marine depositional environment, but the sedimentary structures, the presence of abundant plant remains, and the carbonaceous nature of the sediments, are more indicative of a shallow-water, deltaic, or lagoonal setting.

Farther north, BGS shallow drilling has yielded information at several sites (Figure 56). In BGS borehole 90/02, a variety of interbedded lithologies has been dated as ?Paleocene, and the presence of discrete or fragmentary lignite beds, combined with an absence of in-situ marine fossils, suggests a freshwater or terrestrial palaeoenvironment. Borehole 85/07 proved 2 m of pale grey, fine-grained sand with lignite bands. This sequence overlies late Paleocene amygdaloidal basalt; no microfauna was recovered from the sediment, and woody material and pollen can only endorse a Tertiary age. Outside the report area in the Little Minch, borehole 88/12 drilled a conglomerate of Paleocene or younger age.

The north-eastern end of the Rockall Trough is marked by the Wyville–Thomson Ridge, thought to be a thick pile of lavas formed subaerially during the Paleocene. On its southwestern flank it is faulted (BGS Sula Sgeir Solid Geology sheet; Roberts et al., 1983), probably as a result of Eocene subsidence in the Rockall Trough. BGS borehole 85/02B, drilled on the south-western flank of the ridge, proved finegrained, tuffaceous sandstone consisting largely of reworked basaltic debris. The sandstone can be dated as latest Paleocene to earliest Eocene on the basis of the foraminifer *Nummulites rockallensis* Hinte & Wong, and records the age of the marine inundation of the Wyville–Thomson Ridge (Stoker et al., 1988).

BGS borehole 90/15,15A was drilled on the Anton Dohrn Seamount in the centre of the Rockall Trough (Figure 58). It

Figure 60 Cross-sections across the Wyville–Thomson Ridge and Rockall Trough, with examples of seismic profiles showing sediment waves, and both single- and double-mounded sediment drifts.

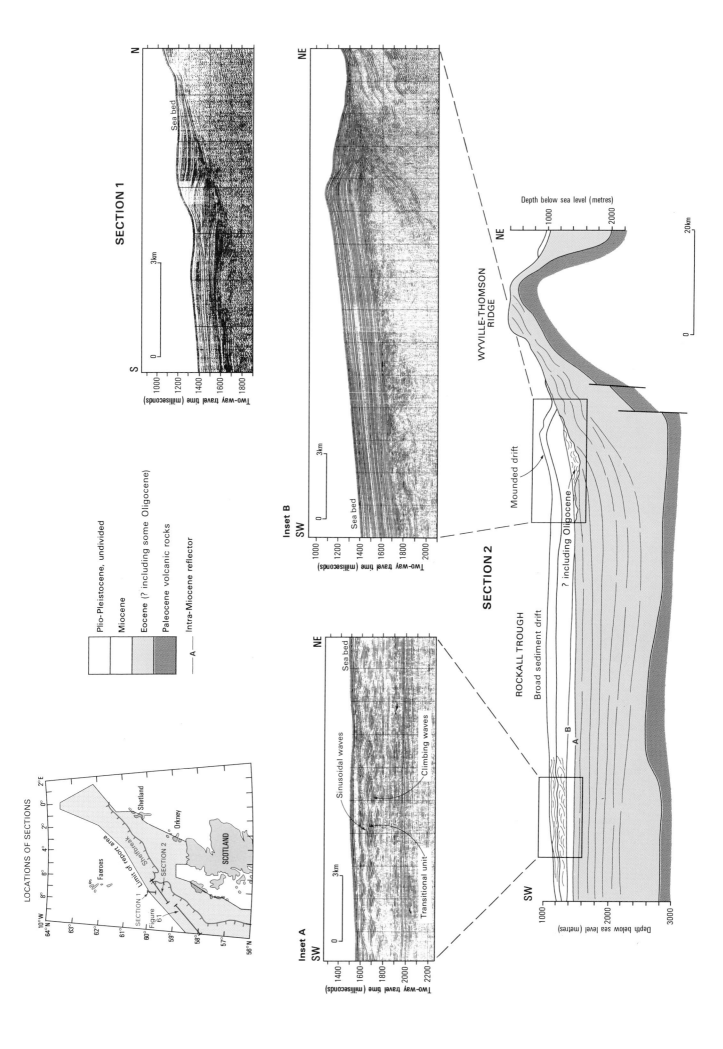

SECTION 1

LOCATIONS OF SECTIONS

Plio-Pleistocene, undivided

Miocene

Eocene (? including some Oligocene)

Paleocene volcanic rocks

A —— Intra-Miocene reflector

SECTION 2

Inset A

Inset B

Sea bed

Sinusoidal waves

Climbing waves

Transitional unit

WYVILLE-THOMSON RIDGE

ROCKALL TROUGH

Broad sediment drift

Mounded drift

? including Oligocene

Two-way travel time (milliseconds)

Depth below sea level (metres)

85

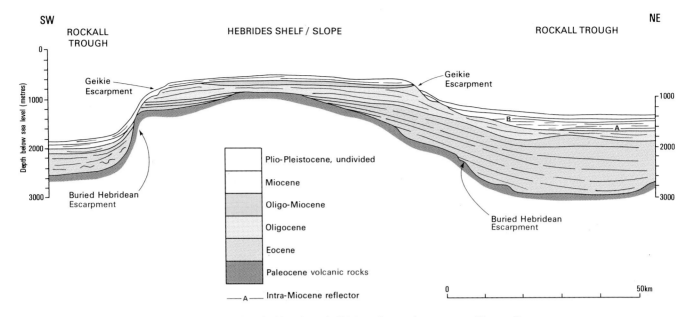

Figure 61 Cross-section across the Hebrides Shelf and Rockall Trough. For location see Figure 60.

proved 3.5 m of lower Paleocene to lower Eocene bioclastic limestone, with common hardground development, overlying coarse-grained gravel. The nature of the limestone suggests deposition in a shallow-water setting, and implies considerable subsidence of the seamount since its formation.

The Møre Basin (Hamar and Hjelle, 1984) was a site of major Tertiary deposition, for over 3000 m of Tertiary sediments are preserved at its centre, outside the report area (Figure 56). On the Møre Platform, Paleocene deposits are thin, typically 200 to 350 m, and lithologies consist mainly of lavas and shallow-water sediments (Nelson and Lamy, 1987). The platform probably acted as a structural high throughout much of the Tertiary.

Eocene

Rifting and volcanism waned through early Eocene times, so that during the mid- to late Eocene, the then-separated Rockall Trough and Faeroe–Shetland Channel became the main centres for deposition under the influence of passive, thermal subsidence.

At the northern end of the Rockall Trough, Jones and Ramsay (1982) recovered grey-green, indurated, calcareous tuffs from three closely spaced dredge sites (Figure 58). The tuffs were dated on the basis of calcareous nannofossil assemblages as Ypresian, and geochemical evidence suggests that the tuffs were derived from a volcanic centre in the Faeroese province.

On the shelf at the north-eastern corner of the Rockall Trough, BGS borehole 90/06 (Figure 56) proved interbedded, dark grey, marine sandstone and siltstone of ?mid-Eocene age. These crop out to the south-east of the feather-edge of westerly dipping basalts, and are likely to form a small outlier. A fine-grained, marine, ?Eocene sandstone was also proved by borehole 88/10 on the northern Hebrides Shelf.

At the eastern margin of the Rockall Trough, the Eocene thickens markedly seawards over the buried Hebridean Escarpment (Figures 61 and 63; Evans et al., 1989), indicating subsidence of the trough relative to the platform at this time. The platform may have been maintained as a structural high due to remnant thermal buoyancy of the Geikie and St Kilda igneous centres. The Geikie centre itself probably maintained a subaerial expression throughout most of the

Eocene, and may not have been completely inundated until the Miocene. In the Donegal Basin, well 12/13-1A (Figure 56) proved the post-Paleocene succession to consist of sandstone, siltstone and claystone with thin limestones, ranging up to ?late Eocene in age.

Wood et al. (1987; 1988) considered the distribution of Eocene sediments, at least in the north-east Rockall Trough, to be largely controlled by the topography of the underlying lavas. From seismic data they inferred that the sediments were deposited in a high-energy, shallow-water environment. Well 163/6-1A, drilled on the flank of the Darwin igneous centre (Figure 58), penetrated over 1150 m of upper Paleocene to Recent silt and clay before reaching the volcanic succession (Morton et al., 1988a); interpretation of shallow-seismic records suggest that most of these sediments are Eocene in age.

Middle to upper Eocene sediments of the Faeroe–Shetland Basin are generally fine-grained claystones and siltstones with occasional limestones and sandstones; these reflect the return to fully marine conditions after a regressive phase in the late Paleocene and early Eocene. However, in wells 205/22-1A and 206/5-1 (Figure 56) adjacent to the Rona Ridge, this interval is predominantly sandy.

Vigorous bottom-current circulation developed at the end of the Eocene, causing a widespread erosion surface which extended from the floor of the contemporary Faeroe–Shetland Channel into the mid-slope region (Figures 57 and 64). These erosive currents cut deep channels into the Eocene sediments; these channels may have been up to 250 m deep and 4 to 8 km wide, with channel-side gradients varying from 1° to 6°. Although the erosion surface is now largely buried, several of the channels are only partially infilled and remain as bathymetric features with relief in excess of 150 m. The present bathymetric configuration of the Faeroe–Shetland Channel probably began to develop during the mid-Eocene.

In the Møre Basin, subsidence during the Eocene allowed thick sequences to accumulate; wells 219/28-1 and

Figure 62 Isopachs and well logs for the Paleocene sediments of the Flett Sub-Basin. After Mudge and Rashid (1987) and Hitchen and Ritchie (1987).

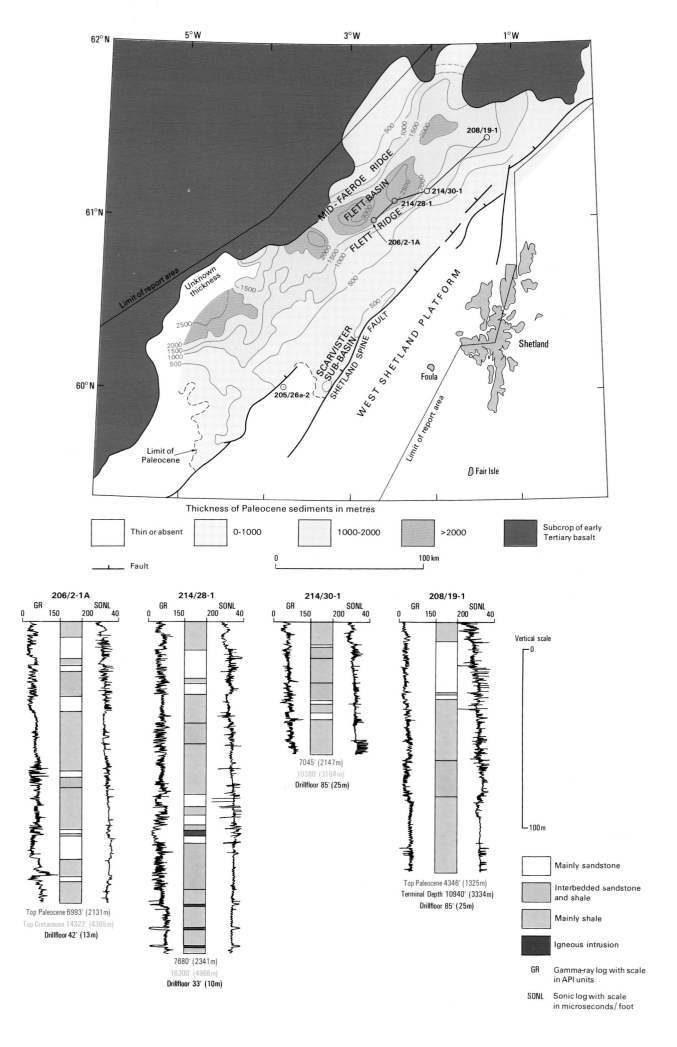

Thickness of Paleocene sediments in metres

Thin or absent	0-1000	1000-2000	>2000	Subcrop of early Tertiary basalt

Fault

0   100 km

206/2-1A

GR
0   150

SONL
200   40

Top Paleocene 6993' (2131m)
Top Cretaceous 14322' (4365m)
Drillfloor 42' (13m)

214/28-1

GR
0   150

SONL
200   40

7680' (2341m)
16300' (4968m)
Drillfloor 33' (10m)

214/30-1

GR
0   150

SONL
200   40

7045' (2147m)
10380' (3164m)
Drillfloor 85' (25m)

208/19-1

GR
0   150

SONL
200   40

Top Paleocene 4346' (1325m)
Terminal Depth 10940' (3334m)
Drillfloor 85' (25m)

Vertical scale
0

100m

	Mainly sandstone
	Interbedded sandstone and shale
	Mainly shale
	Igneous intrusion

GR   Gamma-ray log with scale in API units

SONL Sonic log with scale in microseconds/foot

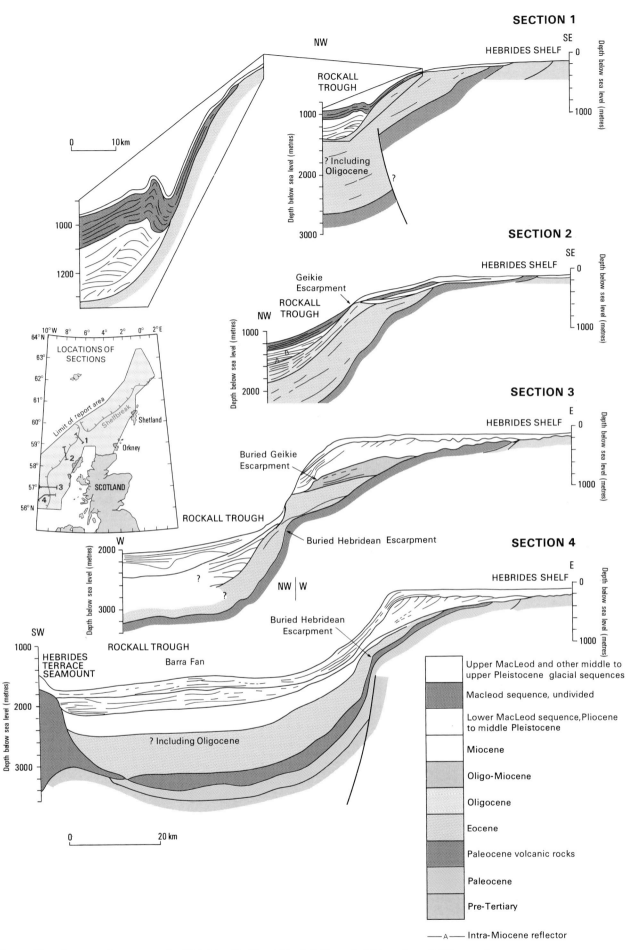

Figure 63 Cross-sections across the Hebrides Shelf and Rockall Trough. Taken from BGS map sheets, although Section 1 is modified after Earle et al. (1989).

219/28-2Z (Figure 56), drilled on the flank of the Margarita Spur, penetrated 867 m and 993 m respectively of lower to middle Eocene sediments above which the Oligocene lies unconformably. Slightly farther into the basin, well 219/20-1 proved a continuous, 1669 m-thick Paleogene succession that includes 925 m of Eocene which is dominantly shale with thin interbedded limestone stringers.

Oligocene

The Oligocene was a time of decreasing current strength and generally restricted deposition in the deeper-water regions (Miller and Tucholke, 1983; Stow and Holbrook, 1984). Most deposition appears to have occurred on the outer shelf, although small terrestrial basins (Fyfe et al., 1993) developed in The Minch and the Sea of the Hebrides (Figure 56). Little information exists on Oligocene lithologies in the report area.

On the eastern flank of the Rockall Trough, variable thicknesses of Oligocene sediments were deposited (Figures 57 and 63). In the north-eastern Rockall Trough, a channel cut on the south-western flank of the Wyville–Thomson Ridge exhibits an irregular, hummocky infill thought to represent the products of deposition from bed-load transport (Figure 60). In the northern Rockall Trough, Wood et al. (1987; 1988) inferred from seismic data that the Oligocene sediments are typical of a deeper-water environment; their subsidence curves indicate a marked increase in water depth during the early Oligocene.

At the edge of the Hebrides Shelf, a marked bathymetric scarp, termed the Geikie Escarpment (Figures 57, 61 and 63), has been eroded into a seaward-thickening wedge of sediments (Evans et al., 1989). This wedge was dated as early Oligocene on the basis of palaeontological analysis of a single sample of cream-coloured chalk retrieved from the scarp face (Jones et al., 1986b). The notch was probably cut at a time of eustatic low sea level (Jones et al., 1986b) by contour currents (Miller and Tucholke, 1983). Nearby, 11.2 m of upper Oligocene sandstone and calcareous siltstone, with scattered shell fragments, were recovered in BGS borehole 88/07,07A (Figures 56, 57 and see Figure 75), unconformably overlain by a veneer of middle to upper Miocene strata. This borehole penetrated a tongue of sediments previously estimated to be wholly Miocene (Evans et al., 1989), but now dated as Oligocene on the basis of palaeontological evidence (Stoker et al., 1992).

In the Faeroe–Shetland Channel, the Oligocene is thin, and most of the sequence overlying the mid-Tertiary erosion surface is considered to be late Oligocene to Pliocene, mainly Miocene, in age (Figure 64). Where channels into the underlying Eocene remain largely unfilled, this unit may not be present. Oligocene inversion (Earle et al., 1989) caused renewed erosion over the Rona Ridge and other local highs; in well 204/30-1 the Oligocene is absent, and in well 205/21-1A no Paleogene rocks are present (Figure 56).

NEOGENE

Neogene strata occur widely on the outer parts of the shelf, as well as in the Rockall Trough and Faeroe–Shetland Channel (Figure 56). Subdivision of these strata is tentative, and the distinction between upper Paleogene, Neogene and Quaternary strata is not commonly well constrained. Although Miocene and Pliocene sediments have been sampled both in wells and shallow boreholes on the shelf, accurate stratigraphical control is severely limited (Figure 65). In the deeper-water areas, the Miocene and Pliocene are tentatively recognised on the basis of regional seismostratigraphical evidence.

The major structural and palaeogeographic elements of the area have changed little since the Miocene. The British Isles have remained a positive area, although eustatic and glacioisostatic changes have caused transgressions and regressions, and fluctuations in oceanographic circulation have affected the deep-water basins. During the Miocene, the report area lay between 45° and 55°N, a northward drift of about 10° since the early Tertiary; this movement continued into the Pliocene, transporting the area into a cooler climatic belt (Smith and Briden, 1977).

The original extent of Neogene strata on the north-west shelf remains uncertain. Early Miocene uplift of the British Isles, a waning effect of the Alpine orogeny, probably exposed the Hebrides and West Shetland shelves to subaerial erosion as the sea retreated towards the present shelf edge (Anderton et al., 1979). However, the eustatic rise in sea level which began in the late Oligocene and continued into mid-Miocene times (Haq et al., 1987) gradually inundated the outer shelf, resulting in the deposition of middle to upper Miocene, marine, clastic sediments. Regional tilting, combined with a late Miocene to early Pliocene eustatic sea-level fall (Haq et al., 1987), contributed to shelf-wide erosion which may have removed Miocene strata from the inner shelf. An overall continued fall in sea level throughout late Pliocene to early Pleistocene time led to the development of a laterally extensive, prograding, lowstand wedge of deltaic and shallow-marine sediments along the outer shelf. The contemporary shelfbreak was located up to 50 km landward of the modern shelfbreak (see Figure 68).

Beyond the shelf edge, the pattern of Neogene sedimentation was closely linked with the subsidence of the Rockall Trough, Faeroe–Shetland Basin and Møre Basin. The water in these basins became deeper as the North-East Atlantic and Norwegian–Greenland Sea basins widened, although substantial deepening beyond 500 m water depth may only have occurred since the early Miocene (Thiede and Eldholm, 1983). According to Hamar and Hjelle (1984), the Møre Platform has subsided rapidly from above sea level to about 2500 m during the last 2 to 3 Ma. Depocentres moved to the shelf edge, and the outline of the deep-water basins became modified by a westerly prograding, clastic wedge.

Sediment thicknesses in the basins were controlled not by subsidence, but by sediment availability linked to the oceanographic development of the North-East Atlantic (Figure 66). The strongly circulating bottom-water flow which developed in the late Eocene to early Oligocene interval gradually decreased in strength, and stabilised during the mid-Miocene. Since then, the circulation pattern has not changed substantially, although it has been punctuated by the effects of further climatic and tectonic events (Miller and Tucholke, 1983; Thiede and Eldholm, 1983).

In the report area at present, a major bottom current is the southward-flowing Norwegian Sea Deep Water (Figure 66). To the south of the Rockall Trough, this current mixes with Labrador Sea Water and Antarctic Bottom Water to form North Atlantic Deep Water. The latter flows back northwards at a higher level into the Rockall Trough and along the western margin of the Rockall Plateau (Stow and Holbrook, 1984). The most important depositional products of the currents are sediment drifts and associated sediment-wave fields. The former are anomalous sediment accumulations which form positive features on seismic-reflection profiles (Figure 60). Although drift accumulation was initiated during the late Eocene to early Oligocene, significant build-up of the drifts has only occurred since the onset of modern flow conditions in the mid-Miocene. However, both the timing and sources of mid- to late Tertiary deep-water circulation remain uncertain (see Paleogene).

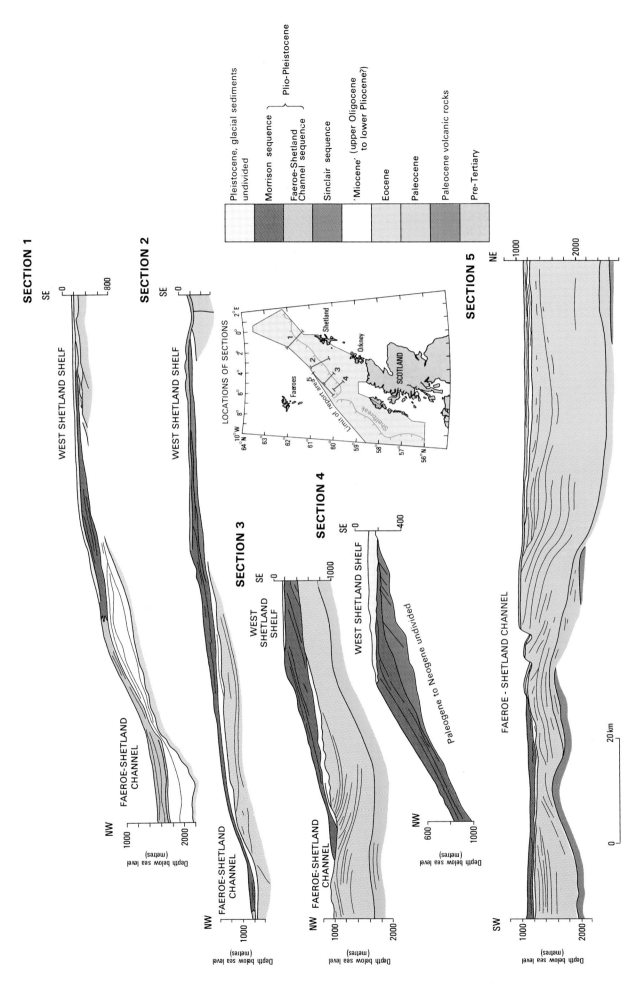

Figure 64 Cross-sections across the West Shetland Shelf and Faeroe–Shetland Channel. Note the change in vertical scale in Section 4.

90

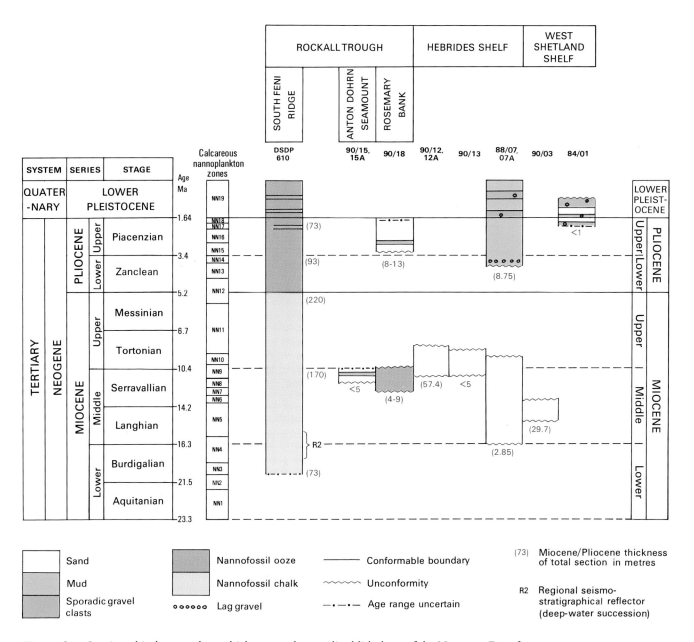

Figure 65 Stratigraphical-range chart, thickness, and generalised lithology of the Neogene. Data from DSDP site 610 taken from Kidd and Hill (1986). Timescale after Harland et al. (1990).

Sediments supplied from the shelf may have been fluvially transported to the shelf edge when sea level was low, leading to the build-out of large submarine fans such as the Barra Fan (Figure 63 and see Figure 68). South of the Barra Fan, the slope is cut by a minor canyon (Omran, 1990) down which sediment may have been transported directly to the Rockall Trough. To the west, the Rockall Bank probably contributed little detritus to the Rockall Trough, for it has been largely below sea level since the Miocene (Anderton et al., 1979). However, the Faeroe Shelf, and the Møre Platform prior to its subsidence in the late Pliocene and Pleistocene, may have acted as sediment sources for the Faeroe–Shetland Channel.

Miocene

SOUTH OF THE WYVILLE–THOMSON RIDGE

West of the Hebrides, Miocene sediments are preserved in two close but largely unconnected areas separated by the Geikie Escarpment, across which the sediments are not readi-

ly correlated on seismic profiles (Figures 57, 63 and 67). It is uncertain whether the Miocene was ever present on this steep scarp, for it may have been kept clear of sediment both by its steepness and contour-following bottom currents. Landward of the escarpment, the Miocene sediments form part of an eroded, seismically well-bedded, unconformity-bounded, Oligo-Miocene unit which locally exceeds 100 m in thickness. Borehole 88/07,07A penetrated the lower part of the unit, and proved 2.85 m of middle to upper Miocene strata overlying upper Oligocene deposits (Stoker et al., 1992; see Figure 75). The thickness of the Miocene section probably increases up-slope away from the escarpment, where the effect of erosion has been less severe.

The middle to upper Miocene in borehole 88/07,07A consists of bioturbated, glauconitic sandstone deposited in a warm, relatively shallow-water, shelf setting. To the south, rocks of similar age and facies were recovered in BGS boreholes 90/12,12A and 90/13, which penetrated 57.4 m and less than 5 m of Miocene strata respectively (Figures 65 and 67). Glauconitic sands of mid-Miocene age, reworked within a Quaternary channel, were cored in borehole 88/10 on the

91

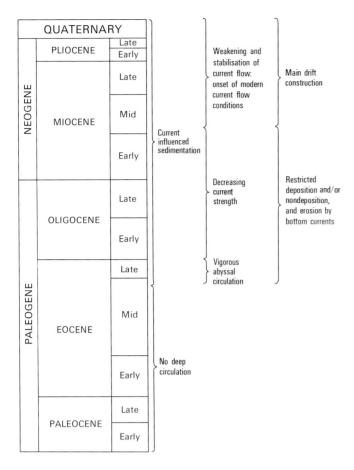

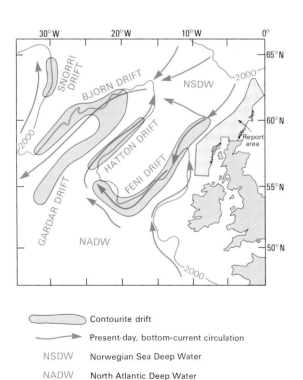

| Contourite drift |
| Present-day, bottom-current circulation |
| NSDW — Norwegian Sea Deep Water |
| NADW — North Atlantic Deep Water |
| —2000— — Bathymetric contour in metres |

Figure 66 The development of bottom-current circulation in the north-east Atlantic. Information taken from numerous sources quoted in the text. Timescale after Harland et al. (1990). The map shows the report area in relation to overall north-east Atlantic depositional and circulation patterns; modified from Stow and Holbrook (1984).

northern Hebrides Shelf, and imply a formerly more extensive distribution of these strata on the shelf. Miocene deposits continue to the south of the report area, where well 13/3-1 proved about 15 m of coarse-grained, bioclastic sediments of undifferentiated Miocene age.

In the Rockall Trough, the seismic character of the Miocene is unlike that of the contemporary shelf deposits, for their geometry and internal reflector configuration have been influenced by bottom-current circulation. In the north-east, Miocene strata overlie the mid-Tertiary erosion surface with angular unconformity and form positive, mounded accumulations of sediment (Figure 60). These vary from broad sediment drifts up to 50 km wide and 400 m thick in the bight adjacent to the Wyville–Thomson Ridge, to smaller, more discrete, single- and double-mounded drifts, 5 to 15 km wide and up to 200 m thick along the margin of the basin. The latter developed as sediment accumulated in relatively tranquil zones on one or both sides of a higher-speed core of bottom current that followed 'steep' slopes (McCave and Tucholke, 1986).

The sediment drifts retain a bathymetric expression adjacent to the Wyville–Thomson Ridge, albeit draped by Plio-Pleistocene deposits, but to the south they are progressively buried along the eastern basin margin by thicker Plio-Pleistocene fan sediments (Figures 60, 61 and 63). These drifts display consistent onlap on to the slope along the length of the margin, and indicate upslope migration and landward progradation of the Miocene sequence. Channel-like features, or 'moats', at the landward edge of the drifts, represent areas of attenuated sedimentation, probably resulting from intensified current flow adjacent to the slope (McCave and Tucholke, 1986).

Drift development in the north-eastern part of the trough was accompanied by the formation of deep-water sediment waves. Two separate developments have been identified, the larger of which extends over an area of about 550 km² (Figure 67) and forms a sediment package up to 200 m thick. On seismic profiles, these sediment waves were divided by Richards et al. (1987) into a basal climbing set, up to 105 m thick, passing upwards through a transitional unit into an upper unit characterised by sinusoidal waves, some of which have heights of 18 m and wavelengths of over 1 km. The latter locally have expression at the sea bed, but have a cover of debris-flow deposits in Figure 60. The relationships of these different wave forms is comparable to smaller-scale, sand-ripple drift systems evolving under conditions of decreasing energy. The sinusoidal or draped lamination implies that the waves are not actively moving at present, and are considered to be of Plio-Pleistocene age, although migration of sediment waves on the Feni Ridge sediment drift (Figure 58) in the southern Rockall Trough is thought to have persisted into the Pliocene (Kidd and Hill, 1986).

The unconformity at the base of the Miocene at the north-eastern margin of the Rockall Trough corresponds to Miocene reflector A (Figures 57, 60 and 61), probably with some re-excavation during the reflector B interval. When traced basinwards to the south-west, the base-Miocene unconformity loses expression, and reflectors A and B both appear to form conformable horizons within a thicker Miocene succession. These reflectors both display onlap on to the Hebrides Slope, but are more planar and subhorizontal away from the basin margin.

These two reflectors are significant in that stable sediment drift and wave formation began to develop above reflector A, and became most coherent above reflector B. The inferred Miocene strata below reflector A have a more-chaotic acoustic character, typical of the higher-energy bottom-circulation pattern associated with Oligocene sedimentation in the

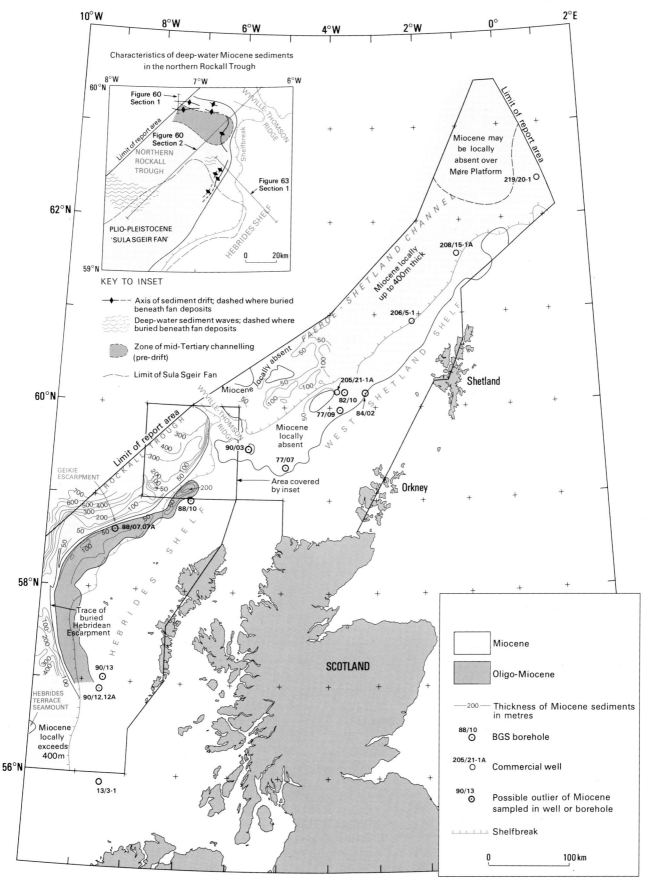

Figure 67 Distribution of Miocene sediments. Inset details some of the characteristics of the deep-water Miocene deposits in the north-east Rockall Trough.

North Atlantic (Miller and Tucholke, 1983). It has been suggested that the Miocene may locally exceed 700 m in thickness in the northern part of the trough (Figure 67; BGS Geikie Solid Geology sheet), with a sub-reflector A thickness of 400 to 500 m, although the possibility that this includes Oligocene strata cannot be discounted. In the southern Rockall Trough, DSDP site 610 (Figures 58 and 59) penetrated 463 m of a near-complete sequence of Miocene sediments on the Feni Ridge; this is comparable with the interpreted thickness of post-reflector A Miocene strata in the north-eastern part of the trough.

The only lithological information on the deep-water Miocene succession in the Rockall Trough is provided by DSDP site 610, which recovered pelagic nannofossil chalk, the bulk of which was deposited during the phase of stable sediment-drift accretion above reflector R2 (Figure 59). The broadly equivalent drifts in the report area may be lithologically similar, although their greater proximity to the British Isles, and their relatively shallower water depths, may have resulted in a greater terrigenous component.

Miocene strata have been recovered at two other locations in the Rockall Trough; from the relatively shallow tops of the Anton Dohrn and Rosemary Bank seamounts (Figure 58). On Anton Dohrn, BGS borehole 90/15,15A proved less than 5 m of bioclastic sands and muds of mid-Miocene (Serravallian) age, whereas less than 10 m of middle to upper Miocene (Serravallian to Tortonian) nannofossil ooze were penetrated in borehole 90/18 on Rosemary Bank.

NORTH OF THE WYVILLE–THOMSON RIDGE

West and north of Shetland, the Miocene extends from the outer part of the West Shetland Shelf into the Faeroe–Shetland Channel, where it unconformably overlies the mid-Tertiary erosion surface (Figures 64 and 67). On the shelf, the Miocene occurs as a sheet-like unit which is locally eroded, resulting in a poorly defined landward limit. On shallow-seismic profiles, the sequence appears well-bedded on the south-western part of the shelf, where borehole 77/07 proved a 30 m-thick succession of nonmarine sand, lignite and clay overlain by 65 m of marine, bioclastic, glauconitic greensand. The nonmarine sequence underlying the greensand was inconclusively dated as Neogene, and thus it would appear that marine conditions were locally absent during the early Miocene before a marine incursion later in the Miocene (Evans et al., 1981).

Similar greensands were also penetrated on the shelf in BGS boreholes 77/09, 82/10, 84/02 and 90/03, and well 205/21-1A (Figure 67). Micropalaeontological data suggest that these sediments are predominantly mid- to late Miocene in age, but with a possible age range of late Oligocene to early Pliocene. Farther north-east on the upper slope, well 206/5-1 penetrated 8 m of middle to upper Miocene sandstone, and well 208/15-1A drilled 80 m of interbedded greensand and claystone of undifferentiated Miocene age.

On the slope west of Shetland (Figure 67), seismic profiles reveal both layered and chaotic reflection configurations. The former commonly display drift-like mounded accumulations with evidence of up-slope migration, and occur mainly in the mid-to-lower slope. Drift thicknesses locally exceed 400 m, although thinning to less than 50 m is evident along the base of the slope, presumably an effect of bottom-current flow (Figure 64). The chaotic seismic texture is largely restricted to the south-western part of the slope, where the sequence is generally less than 100 m thick and is typically associated with irregular, lensoid units which may represent slope-front debris-flow deposits.

In the Faeroe–Shetland Channel, the thickness of the Miocene increases north-eastwards along the axis of the channel from less than 50 m to about 400 m (Figure 64). This may be a function of the shallowing and reduced width of the channel to the south-west, resulting in attenuation of the sediment sequence and leading to the persistence of bathymetric deeps formed in the late Paleogene. Miocene strata in these deeps, and in the equivalent infilled depressions associated with the mid-Tertiary erosion surface, locally display onlap and downlap on seismic profiles; this suggests deposition from bottom currents flowing along the deeps. It remains uncertain whether Miocene sediments were ever deposited on their steeper sides.

In the central and north-eastern parts of the Faeroe–Shetland Channel, the internal seismic reflection configuration is more commonly well layered and laterally continuous, although localised pinch-out through downlap or onlap occurs over topographic highs. In contrast to the Rockall Trough, the absence of sediment drifts on the floor of the channel may be a further indication that the channel experienced overall greater current velocities, which produced a sheet-form channel sequence. The nature of the Miocene in the Faeroe–Shetland Channel remains untested.

North of Shetland, a Neogene slope sequence prograded across the Møre Basin. Well 219/20-1 (Figure 67) penetrated a 605 m-thick succession of lower to upper Miocene siltstone and claystone with sporadic, thin limestones. In contrast, the Miocene overlying the Møre Platform is inferred to be thin to absent (Hamar and Hjelle, 1984), implying that the platform remained an emergent high.

Pliocene

SOUTH OF THE WYVILLE–THOMSON RIDGE

West of the Hebrides, Pliocene sediments are preserved as part of the Lower MacLeod sequence (see Chapter 12), which extends from the outer part of the Hebrides Shelf into the Rockall Trough. On the outer shelf and upper slope, the sequence was deposited during a lowstand of sea level, and forms a prograding sediment wedge which locally exceeds 600 m in thickness (Figure 63). Borehole data suggest that the bulk of the sequence consists of lower to middle Pleistocene strata, but with thin Pliocene sediments at its base, and no well-defined internal boundary. Consequently, the landward limit of the Pliocene depicted on Figure 68 remains tentative.

Borehole 85/05B, located near the landward edge of the Lower MacLeod sequence (Figure 68), recovered 2.4 m of Pliocene silt and very fine-grained sand characterised by the foraminifer *Cibicides grossa* Ten Dam & Reinhold. These sediments rest unconformably on Paleocene basalt.

To the north-west, borehole 88/07,07A (Figure 68 and see Figure 75) penetrated a condensed section of lower to upper Pliocene sediments preserved at the base of the Lower MacLeod sequence on the upper slope (Stoker et al., 1992). On seismic-reflection profiles, this section forms part of an acoustically well-layered, Pliocene to middle Pleistocene unit which locally onlaps and downlaps onto an irregular, eroded, Miocene surface. The basal 0.25 m of the Pliocene section consists of a glauconite-rich, gravelly, lag deposit of early Pliocene age; this contains a large number of reworked clasts of lithified Miocene sand. The lag deposit is overlain by 8.5 m of sand and muddy sand of late Pliocene age; these are glauconitic in their lower part, and become increasingly muddy towards the top where they pass transitionally into lower Pleistocene deposits. The sediments were deposited in a

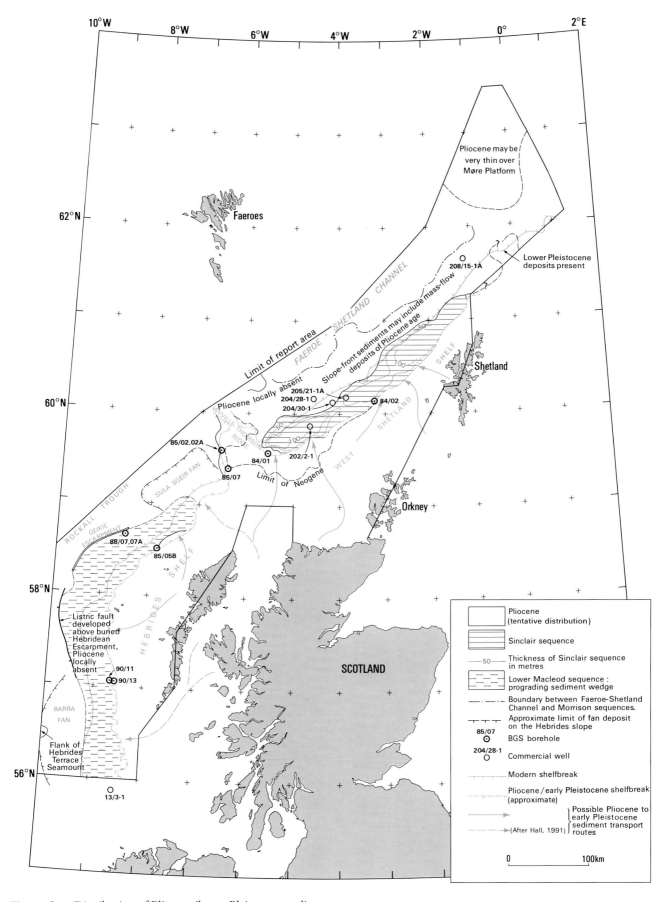

Figure 68 Distribution of Pliocene/lower Pleistocene sediments.

95

relatively warm, outer-neritic environment subjected to an oceanic influence. However, isolated gravel clasts in the upper Pliocene are interpreted as glacial dropstones, and broadly correlate with the first major pulse of ice-rafted debris in the mid-latitude, North Atlantic region (Shackleton et al., 1984).

On the northern part of the Hebrides Shelf adjacent to the Wyville–Thomson Ridge (Figure 68), reworked Pliocene foraminifera are incorporated into glacial deposits cored in BGS boreholes 85/02,02A and 85/07. On the southern part of the Hebrides Shelf, boreholes 90/11 and 90/13 recovered massive greensands of undifferentiated Pliocene to early Pleistocene age. Similarly undifferentiated Plio-Pleistocene clays with sands and lignites are recorded in well 13/3-1, immediately south of the report area.

Pliocene sediments may be locally absent on the middle to lower slope adjacent to the Geikie Escarpment and on the buried Hebridean Escarpment (Figures 63 and 68). Between 58°N and 59°N, it is uncertain whether Pliocene sediments were ever deposited on the steep slope of the Geikie Escarpment, which may have been kept clear of sediment by along-slope currents. On the slope to the south, a listric fault may have developed above the buried Hebridean Escarpment; the southernmost part of this fault plane is at outcrop, and the Lower MacLeod sequence has been offset downslope. Consequently, a thick accumulation of hummocky, lensoid, mass-flow deposits up to 400 m thick occurs at the foot of the slope and forms part of the Barra Fan. However, the thickness of the Pliocene is unknown. Adjacent to the Wyville–Thomson Ridge, a similar accumulation of mass-flow deposits may include Pliocene strata, although this deposit, termed the Sula Sgeir Fan, is best defined by its Quaternary component.

In the Rockall Trough, beyond the limit of the mass-flow deposits, acoustically well-layered Plio-Pleistocene sediments are interpreted to largely drape the underlying current-moulded Miocene strata (Figure 60), although the Miocene–Pliocene boundary picked on seismic profiles remains tentative. Evidence from the Gardar Drift, in the Iceland Basin (Figures 58 and 66), suggests that sediment drift and wave migration continued into the Pliocene, with an overlying draped package that is essentially of Pleistocene age. This pattern was not recorded on the Feni Ridge in the Rockall Trough (Kidd and Hill, 1986), where DSDP site 610 (Figures 58 and 59) proved 166 m of lower to upper Pliocene nannofossil ooze and calcareous mud passing up into lower Pleistocene sediments. A thinner Pliocene sequence is likely in the report area, where the entire Plio-Pleistocene section is generally less than 100 m thick.

The nature of the Pliocene deposits in the northern Rockall Trough remains untested, with the exception of the shallow top of Rosemary Bank (Figure 58). Here, BGS bore-

hole 90/18 penetrated between 8 and 13 m of bioclastic, occasionally pebbly, muddy sand and sandy mud of late Pliocene age, overlying Miocene sediments.

NORTH OF THE WYVILLE–THOMSON RIDGE

West of Shetland, Pliocene deposits (Figure 64) probably form part of the Sinclair, Morrison and Faeroe–Shetland Channel sequences (see Chapter 12). The Sinclair sequence occurs on the outer part of the West Shetland Shelf, where it forms a prograding sediment wedge which locally exceeds 100 m in thickness (Figure 68). It is broadly correlatable with the lower part of the Lower MacLeod sequence on the Hebrides Shelf (see Figure 72), which similarly consists largely of lower Pleistocene deposits with only thin Pliocene at the base. BGS borehole 84/01 may have penetrated the southwestern feather-edge of the Sinclair sequence, for it proved less than 1 m of pebbly and shelly sand and clay of late Pliocene age. Farther north-east, borehole 84/02 and well 205/21-1A penetrated 2.7 m and 30 m respectively of shelly, glauconitic sands of late Miocene to Pliocene age.

On the West Shetland Slope, the Sinclair sequence appears to pass laterally downslope into the basal part of the Morrison sequence (Figure 64), which encompasses most of a slope apron characterised by mass-flow deposits. This sequence locally exceeds 300 m in thickness on the upper slope, but is less than 100 m thick at the base of the slope. Pliocene strata have been proved in wells 204/30-1 and 208/15-1A (Figure 68); the former penetrated 27 m of lignitic clay resting unconformably on Paleogene sediments, whereas the latter drilled 148 m of shelly, interbedded sand and clay overlying Miocene deposits. Shelly, glauconitic sands cored in wells 202/2-1 and 204/28-1 yielded undifferentiated Plio-Pleistocene ages.

In the Faeroe–Shetland Channel, the Morrison sequence passes laterally into the Faeroe–Shetland Channel sequence, which is generally less than 60 m thick in the south-west, but locally exceeds 200 m to the north-east. On seismic profiles, the Faeroe–Shetland Channel sequence is acoustically well layered and generally lies conformably upon the Miocene, although towards the south-west the sequence overlaps onto the Paleogene. Plio-Pleistocene strata are very thin or absent in the area of incised deeps in the south-western part of the channel (Figure 64).

The nature and thickness of the Pliocene component of the Faeroe–Shetland Channel sequence is unknown. The relatively thin Plio-Pleistocene sediment cover in the channel implies that bottom currents at that time played, and probably continue to play, an active role in controlling sedimentation in this deep-water area. At the north-eastern end of the channel, thin Pliocene deposits are interpreted to overlie the subsided Møre Platform (Hamar and Hjelle, 1984).

12   Quaternary

The Quaternary Period began at 1.64 Ma (Harland et al., 1990), and is divided into two epochs, the Pleistocene and the Holocene, of which the latter represents only the last 10 000 years (Figure 69). The Quaternary has been a time of numerous cycles of climatic change, most dramatically demonstrated by the rhythmic growth and decay of extensive mid-latitude ice sheets during the last 0.75 Ma, although significant pulses of ice-rafting have influenced deep-water, marine sedimentation off the British Isles since the late Pliocene, at about 2.5 Ma (Shackleton et al., 1984; Boulton et al., 1991).

Quaternary strata are widespread across the report area, with the thickest accumulations preserved on the upper to mid-slope (Figure 70). The sedimentary succession contoured in Figure 70 includes some probable Pliocene deposits which remain undivided from Pleistocene strata on the outer shelf and slope, and in the deep-water basins (see Neogene section). The overall geometry of the succession displays a marked shelf to basin asymmetry; a thin to locally absent and extensively eroded sediment cover on the inner shelf thickens to over 800 m on the outer shelf to mid-slope, with a relatively condensed sequence, generally less than 100 m thick, on the floors of the deep-water basins. This asymmetry reflects a seaward progradation of the shelf by up to 50 km during the Plio-Pleistocene, although the shelfbreak has locally been eroded in the post-Anglian interval (Figure 6). The Quaternary cover is substantially thicker on the outer part of the southern Hebrides and West Shetland shelves than it is on the northern Hebrides Shelf (Figure 70). This may reflect regional variation in the rate of tectonic subsidence on the outer shelf, and changing rates and loci of sediment deposition.

During the late Pliocene and early Pleistocene, a lowered eustatic sea level (Haq et al., 1987) may have controlled the development of a laterally extensive, prograding, lowstand wedge of deltaic and shallow-marine sediments along the outer shelf. Sediment was probably derived mainly from the Scottish Highlands and Islands through intense weathering and erosion under warm, humid, temperate, climatic conditions (Hall, 1991). These sediments may have been fluvially transported to the shelf edge; transport routes included those running through the Hebridean region (Hall, 1991), which probably contributed to the build-out of the Barra and Sula Sgeir fans (Figure 68).

The climate deteriorated in a fluctuating manner during the early Pleistocene (Boulton et al., 1991), when glacial activity remained distal in character, as represented by ice-rafted debris. These climatic conditions persisted into the mid-Pleistocene, until about 0.44 Ma, when major ice-sheet activity first affected the area. This widespread glaciation, correlated with the Anglian glacial stage, may have reached the edge of the Hebrides Shelf. Much of the Hebrides and West Shetland shelves were subsequently glaciated, on at least two further occasions, during the Devensian.

The glaciated shelves display evidence of extensive erosion and deposition. The base of the glacial succession is commonly characterised by a subhorizontal, locally irregular erosion surface which cuts across all pre-existing strata. The overlying glacial succession comprises single and, more typically, multiple, stacked, unconformity-bounded, sheetform sequences predominantly composed of diamictons deposited by a variety of subglacial and proglacial processes. Relict glacial depositional landforms of different ages are locally preserved; these reflect both temporal and spatial variation in ice limits (Stoker and Holmes, 1991).

At their maximum extent, the ice sheets extended, at least locally, out to the shelf edge, and delivered ice-marginal sediments directly to the slope (Stoker, 1990). The Barra and Sula Sgeir fans (Figure 70) continued to be major slope-front depocentres accumulating reworked shelf detritus by mass-flow processes. Debris flows and turbidites occasionally travelled the entire width of the slope, dumping substantial amounts of shelf-derived glacial material on to the floor of the Rockall Trough and the Faeroe–Shetland Channel (Stoker et al., 1991). However, in these deep-water areas, the influence of glacial activity is mostly marked by ice-rafted deposits. The basin-plain sediments are all likely to have been subjected to some degree of bottom-current reworking; the most vigorous bottom circulation corresponded to changes in climate, such as the transition from a glacial to an interglacial regime (Ruddiman and Bowles, 1976; Stoker et al., 1989; Akhurst, 1991). Interglacial deposits, though uncommon on the shelves, are present in the deep-water basins, where a more-complete sedimentary record of climatic change is preserved.

Climatic fluctuation has traditionally formed the basis for defining the stages of the British and north-west European Quaternary successions (Mitchell et al., 1973). Substantial lower Pleistocene deposits are preserved in the North Sea Basin, where the north-west European stages have been used (Cameron et al., 1987). In contrast, the bulk of the Quaternary stratigraphical information in the report area relates to deposits of mid- and late Pleistocene age, so that British stages are applied.

Seismic-reflection profiling has allowed subdivision of the offshore succession, as well as regional correlation between seismostratigraphical units (Figures 71 and 72). These are mostly referred to informally as 'sequences', although several 'formations' extend into the report area from adjacent areas. In the southern part of the report area, a 'subsequence' terminology previously developed for the shelf succession (BGS Peach and St Kilda Quaternary Geology sheets) has been reappraised and upgraded to sequence level. In areas where the Quaternary is thin, the succession remains undifferentiated, resulting in some artificial sequence boundaries (Figure 71). Boreholes and shallow cores have penetrated many of the sediments, and recovered microfossils suitable for stratigraphical correlation, and environmental interpretation. BGS borehole 88/07,07A, located on the upper part of the Hebrides Slope, recovered the most significant Quaternary section, from which the magneto- and biostratigraphy provide some chronological control for the stratigraphical framework (Figures 69 and 72). This is supplemented by amino-acid, radiocarbon, oxygen-isotope and volcanic-ash data from other boreholes and shallow cores. In the following sections, the Quaternary is tentatively divided into pre-Anglian (pre-glacial), Anglian to middle Devensian, late Devensian, and Holocene successions. The general relationships of the Quaternary sequences are shown in Figures 72, 73 and 74.

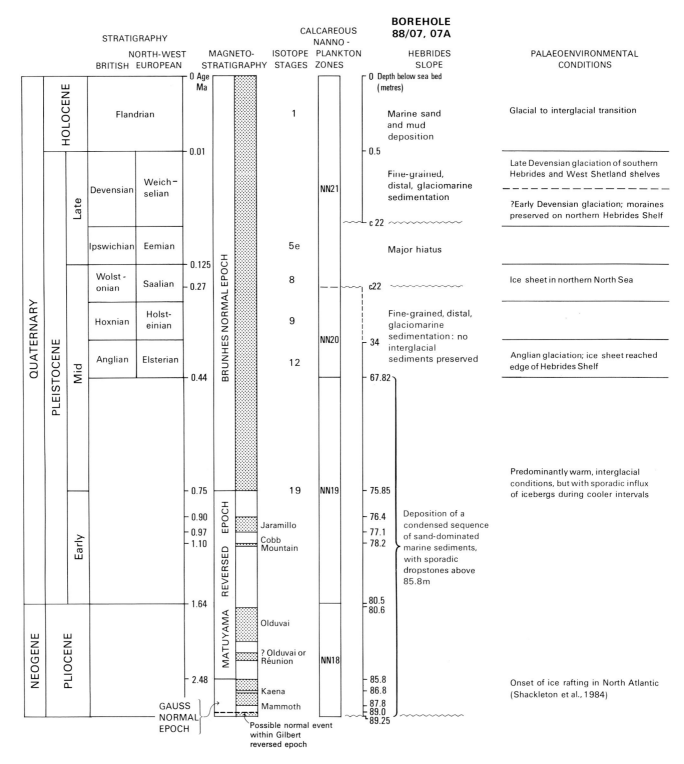

Figure 69   Quaternary correlation chart referenced to BGS borehole 88/07,07A. Normal polarity stippled
After Stoker et al. (1992). Magnetostratigraphical timescale after Harland et al. (1990).

PRE-ANGLIAN

Pre-Anglian deposits are largely nonglacial, and are restricted to the outer shelves, slopes, and deep-water basins (Figure 71). There was progradation of the outer shelf by up to 40 km during their deposition, and their landward extent partly results from marine erosion (Sutherland, 1987) and/or later glaciation of the shelf.

The Hebrides Shelf/Rockall Trough region

In this region, pre-Anglian sediments form part of the MacLeod sequence; a prograding, slope-front to basin-plain deposit that locally exceeds 800 m in thickness on the upper to mid-slope, but thins basinwards to less than 100 m. In the south, the MacLeod sequence has been split into Lower and Upper MacLeod sequences (BGS Peach and St Kilda Quaternary Geology sheets), with the pre-Anglian sediments assigned to the Lower MacLeod sequence (Figure 72). To the north, the Lower MacLeod sequence probably includes strata previously termed MacLeod subsequence A (BGS Sula Sgeir Quaternary Geology sheet).

LOWER MACLEOD SEQUENCE

The Lower MacLeod sequence extends from the outer part of the Hebrides Shelf into the Rockall Trough (Figure 73). It is

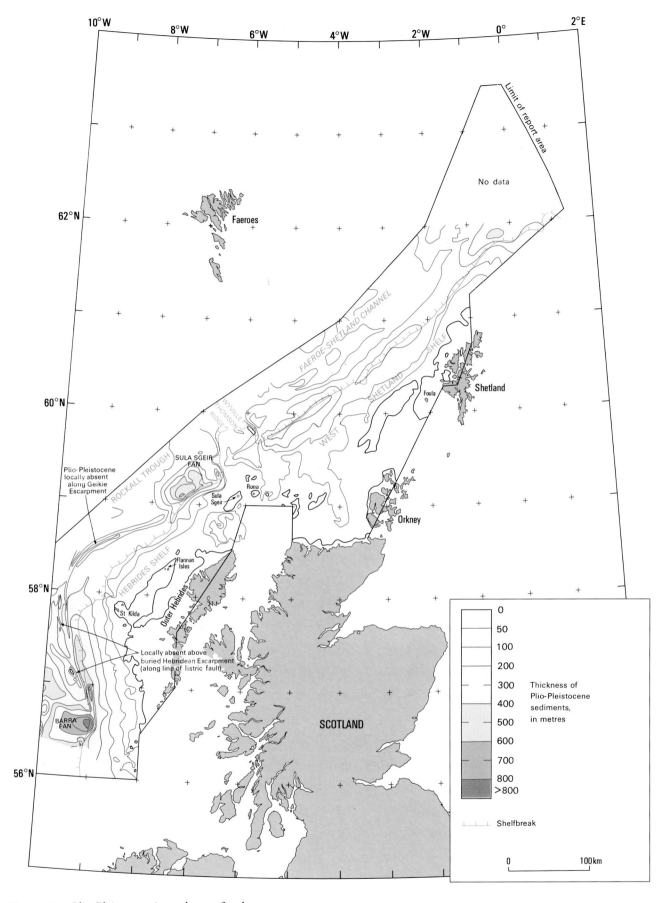

Figure 70 Plio-Pleistocene isopach map for the report area.

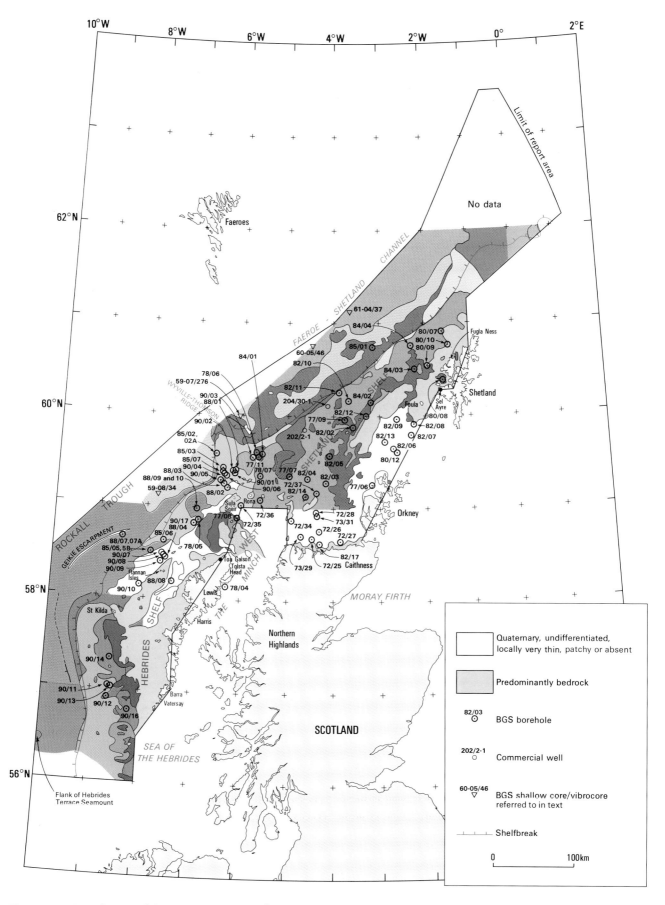

Figure 71 Distribution of Quaternary sequences/formations at or near the sea bed. For seismostratigraphical key see Figure 72.

thickest beneath the outer shelf and upper slope at the Barra and Sula Sgeir fans, where it reaches thicknesses of about 600 m and 300 m respectively. It thins to generally less than 100 m on the slope landward of the Geikie Escarpment. In the Rockall Trough, it is generally less than 100 m thick beyond the fan areas. The base of the sequence is a major unconformity across the outer shelf and upper slope, but this loses expression on the lower slope and in the Rockall Trough, although onlap occurs on to the flanks of both the Hebrides Terrace Seamount and the Wyville–Thomson Ridge (Figure 71). Widespread erosion on the shelf preceded the deposition of the overlying glacial sequences.

The Lower MacLeod sequence is typically wedge-shaped in section on the outer shelf, becoming more uniformly sheet-like on the slope and basin plain (Figure 73). On seismic profiles, the sequence displays low-angle, seaward-prograding reflectors on the outer shelf, which change westwards under the upper slope into a parallel configuration. The slope-front has been locally disturbed by slumping, particularly near the Geikie Escarpment and the buried Hebridean Escarpment, where the Lower MacLeod sequence is locally absent. Consequently, a thick accumulation of hummocky, lensoid, mass-flow deposits, up to 300 m thick, is locally preserved at the base of the slope. Similar deposits may occur on the Sula Sgeir Fan. In the Rockall Trough, beyond the limit of the mass-flow deposits, the Lower MacLeod sequence may occur at relatively shallow depths below sea bed (Figure 73), where it is essentially well layered, and mostly drapes the underlying drift- and wave-moulded Miocene strata. However, as a result of bottom-current activity, some degree of asymmetric drift development persisted, particularly adjacent to the Wyville–Thomson Ridge.

On the southern Hebrides Shelf, BGS boreholes 90/11 and 90/13 (Figure 71) penetrated the landward edge of the sequence, and proved up to 43.2 m of shelly, bioturbated greensands partly interbedded with dark grey, shelly, slightly pebbly, sandy clays of undifferentiated Pliocene to early Pleistocene age. To the north, borehole 85/05,05B cored 18 m of sandy diamicton interbedded with very fine-grained, silty sands of early Pleistocene age, overlying thin Pliocene silts and sands.

On the upper part of the Hebrides Slope, borehole 88/07,07A proved 12.68 m of acoustically well-layered, lower to middle Pleistocene sediments which may locally downlap and onlap (Figure 75) on to an irregular, eroded, Miocene surface (Stoker et al., 1992). Magneto- and biostratigraphical data suggest that deposition of these strata spanned the interval between 1.64 and 0.44 Ma; they are thus part of a condensed lower to middle Pleistocene section (Figure 69). These lower to middle Pleistocene sediments consist predominantly of muddy, marine sands deposited in an upper slope setting which was subjected to variable climatic and oceanographic conditions. Gravel clasts disseminated throughout the sediments, interpreted as glacial dropstones, are consistent with the sporadic input of ice-rafted debris.

The nature of the deeper-water sediments in this region is unknown. However, laterally equivalent deposits have been proved at DSDP site 610 on the Feni Ridge in the southern Rockall Trough (Figures 58 and 59), where 62 m of interbedded nannofossil ooze, marl and calcareous mud with dropstones have been recovered (Ruddiman et al., 1986; Kidd and Hill, 1986).

The West Shetland Shelf/Faeroe–Shetland Channel region

Pre-Anglian sediments here form the Sinclair, Morrison and Faeroe–Shetland Channel sequences, and the Shackleton and Mariner formations (Figure 72). In the south, the Morrison sequence has been informally divided into two units (BGS Judd and Rona Quaternary Geology sheets), of which unit 1 is regarded as being of pre-Anglian age. The Shackleton and Mariner formations are more fully developed in the northern North Sea (Johnson et al., 1993); the latter comprises two members, with pre-Anglian strata forming the lower.

SINCLAIR SEQUENCE

The Sinclair sequence forms a seaward-prograding wedge on the outer part of the West Shetland Shelf; it locally exceeds 100 m in thickness, but pinches out on the upper slope (Figure 68). It rests with angular unconformity on Tertiary and older strata (Figure 74). BGS boreholes 82/10, 82/11, 84/02 and 84/04 (Figure 71) recovered pebbly, shelly, glauconitic sands and thin interbedded muds of deltaic and shallow-marine origin (Cockcroft, 1987). Up to 65 m of sandy deltaic deposits were also recovered in well 202/2-1. Micropalaeontological data suggest that cold climatic conditions prevailed during their deposition, although some evidence of climatic fluctuation is preserved near the base of the sequence. The Sinclair sequence has been dated as Pliocene to early Pleistocene from dinoflagellate-cyst evidence (BGS Foula Quaternary Geology sheet).

MORRISON SEQUENCE (UNIT 1)

In the south, this unit forms an outer-shelf to upper-slope, prograding sediment wedge up to 200 m thick. It thins downslope, where it may be locally absent (Figure 74), but extends across the floor of the Faeroe–Shetland Channel at its narrow south-western end. Except where it overlies the Sinclair sequence, the base of the sequence is marked by an angular unconformity over Tertiary strata.

On seismic profiles, the seaward-prograding reflector configuration comprises transparent and structureless, to chaotic packages, bounded by high-amplitude, laterally continuous reflectors. There is significant variation in reflector continuity, for some seismic packages onlap the shelf whereas others are truncated (Figure 74). These changes may be due to the interplay between tectonic subsidence and sea-level change (BGS Judd and Rona Quaternary sheets); the truncated packages reflect intervals of regression and shelf bypass, whereas the onlapping packages were probably deposited during relatively higher sea levels. In well 204/30-1 at the south-western end of the shelf (Figure 71), 20 m of mud overlain by at least 140 m of diamicton may represent prodeltaic sedimentation followed by extensive mass-flow deposition as the shelf prograded. Although the Morrison sequence in the north remains undivided, its seismic character suggests that the bulk of the sequence here also is likely to consist of mass-flow deposits.

FAEROE–SHETLAND CHANNEL SEQUENCE

The Faeroe–Shetland Channel sequence forms a sheet-drape up to 80 m thick on the floor of the channel; it was deposited throughout the Quaternary Period. A basal unconformity at the south-western end of the channel loses expression in the deeper, north-eastern part of the basin. North of 61°N the sequence extends on to the slope, where it unconformably overlies Neogene deposits, and is up to 250 m thick (Figure 74).

The basin-floor deposits are acoustically well layered, with laterally continuous reflectors. Evidence of basal downlap and onlap, lateral accretion, thinning over palaeotopographic highs, and internal convergence of reflectors, all suggest that bottom-current activity greatly influenced the development of this part of the sequence (Akhurst, 1991). On the mid-

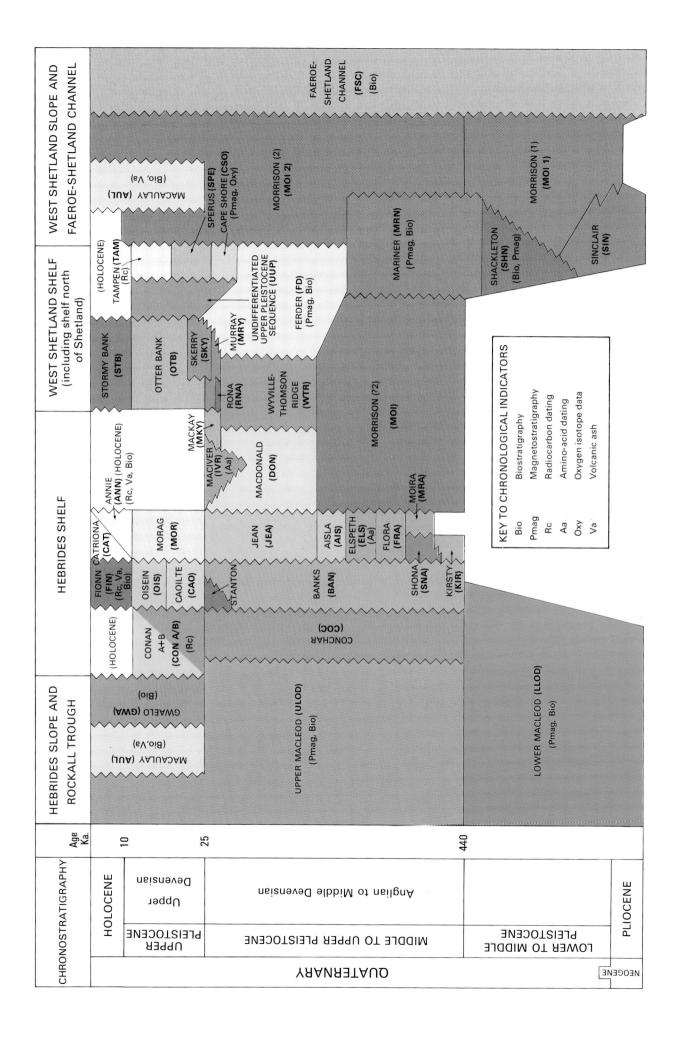

102

slope north of Shetland, seismic-reflection patterns display an onlapping, mounded character typical of bottom-current deposition (see Neogene section). These deposits have subsequently been disturbed through sediment instability associated with localised failures such as the Miller Slide (BGS Miller Quaternary Geology sheet).

SHACKLETON AND MARINER FORMATIONS

These formations occur at depth on the shelf and slope to the north of Shetland (Figure 74). They are more extensively developed in the northern North Sea (Johnson et al., 1982). The Shackleton Formation consists of shelly and pebbly, marine sands of early Pleistocene age; the overlying Mariner Formation includes a lower member which consists of pre-Anglian, marine, sandy, silty clays.

ANGLIAN TO MIDDLE DEVENSIAN

Anglian to middle Devensian deposits occur widely. Onshore localities on Lewis, St Kilda and Shetland (Figure 71) are mostly glacial in origin, but include remnants of interglacial peat beds. The offshore succession incorporates many sequences or formations (Figure 72), the oldest of which represent the earliest evidence of direct glacial activity on the shelf to the north and west of Scotland.

The Hebrides Shelf/Rockall Trough region

On the Outer Hebrides, evidence of pre-late Devensian events is preserved on the north of Lewis (Figure 71). Along its north-western coast, a pre-late Devensian raised beach is locally underlain by till and bedded sand and gravel, which rest on a marine-planated rock platform (Sutherland, 1984a; Peacock, 1991). At Toa Galson, a peat bed dated as more than 47 150 years BP postdates the deposition of the till, but predates the formation of the raised beach (Sutherland and Walker, 1984). According to Peacock (1984), the glacial phase involved ice from the Scottish mainland crossing the northern end of Lewis, and probably the more southerly islands of the Outer Hebrides. However, the age of this glaciation is unknown. Pollen analysis suggests that the overlying peat may be an interglacial deposit, and Sutherland and Walker (1984) have compared it with a similar deposit at Sel Ayre in Shetland (see below), that has been tentatively dated as Ipswichian (Birks and Peglar, 1979).

At Tolsta Head in north-east Lewis (Figure 71), an interstadial, organic deposit which accumulated under deteriorating climatic conditions has been dated as 27 333 ± 240 years BP (Von Weymarn and Edwards, 1973). Additionally, beach gravels similar to those at Toa Galson have been identified underneath till on both Barra and Vatersay, at the southern end of the Outer Hebrides (Peacock, 1984; Selby, 1989).

West of the Outer Hebrides on St Kilda (Figure 71), there is evidence for at least two phases of pre-late Devensian glaciation, and an interval of milder climate (Sutherland et al., 1984). The Ruaival drift forms the oldest in-situ glacial deposit on the island; it is interpreted as an early or pre-

Devensian till associated with a valley glaciation. Exotic erratics, particularly red sandstone fragments, have been recovered from a variety of deposits including the Ruaival drift, and are cited by Sutherland et al. (1984) as evidence for an earlier, more extensive glaciation associated with Scottish mainland ice. The Abhainn Ruaival organic sand is a fluvial deposit laid down under deteriorating interstadial or end-interglacial climatic conditions; a minimum age of 24 710 +1470/-1240 years BP indicates that it predates the late Devensian.

To the north-east, the Flannan Isles, Sula Sgeir and Rona (Figure 71) have been considered to have been overrun by Scottish ice at some time during the Quaternary (Geikie, 1894), an interpretation supported by the occurrence of foreign erratics (Stewart, 1932; 1933). Rona is locally covered by a thin till, generally less than 0.5 m thick (Gailey, 1959). In the light of the evidence for the restricted extent of late Devensian ice (see Figure 78), these deposits are likely to predate the last Scottish ice sheet. West of Sula Sgeir, a submerged rock platform at about -125 m has been attributed to marine erosion prior to the late Devensian glacial maximum (Sutherland, 1987).

Offshore, thick and extensive Anglian to middle Devensian deposits are recognised on the Hebrides Shelf and Slope (Figure 71). These reflect the westward expansion of ice sheets on to the Hebrides Shelf on at least two occasions: during the Anglian, and the early Devensian (Figure 69). On the southern part of the shelf, extensive erosion and subglacial channelling at the base of the Banks and Conchar sequences are attributed to Anglian glaciation, when an ice margin was located at or near the contemporary shelf edge (Figure 76).

On the upper Hebrides Slope, Anglian glaciomarine sediments of the Upper MacLeod sequence form the thickest part of the Quaternary section proved in BGS borehole 88/07,07A (Figures 69 and 75). The upper part of this sequence is mainly of early to mid-Devensian age, and is laterally equivalent to a submarine end-morainal system, associated with the MacDonald sequence (Stoker and Holmes, 1991), that is preserved at the edge of the northern Hebrides Shelf (Figures 75 and 76). These deposits may be associated with the expansion of early Devensian ice in northern Scotland (Bowen, 1991). Landward of this moraine, two glacially overdeepened basins, the North Lewis and Sula Sgeir basins, are filled by a number of sequences which may record the deglaciation of the early Devensian ice sheet, as well as preserving remnants of the older glaciation.

In both glaciations, ice sheets may have extended on to part of the Wyville–Thomson Ridge, where isolated, mounded accumulations are preserved (Stoker, 1988; Stoker and Holmes, 1991). However, the main ice-marginal depocentre was located at the junction of the ridge and the shelf, where an ice-contact fan, 50 to 150 m thick, up to 10 km wide and at least 25 km long (Figures 73 and 76), lies along strike from the shelf-edge end moraine and prograges on to the ridge (Stoker and Holmes, 1991). This deposit includes the Morrison, MacDonald and Mackay sequences, and may have been the site of glacial sediment accumulation on more than one occasion.

West of Lewis, the deposits are thin and largely undifferentiated, but morailal topography of probable Anglian and early Devensian age is preserved, and BGS boreholes such as 88/04 and 90/09 have proved diamictons. In the following description, the shelf sequences are described from south to north.

BANKS AND CONCHAR SEQUENCES

These are two laterally equivalent sequences preserved in the south, extending from the shelf on to the upper slope. Both are interpreted as composite glacial units containing ice-

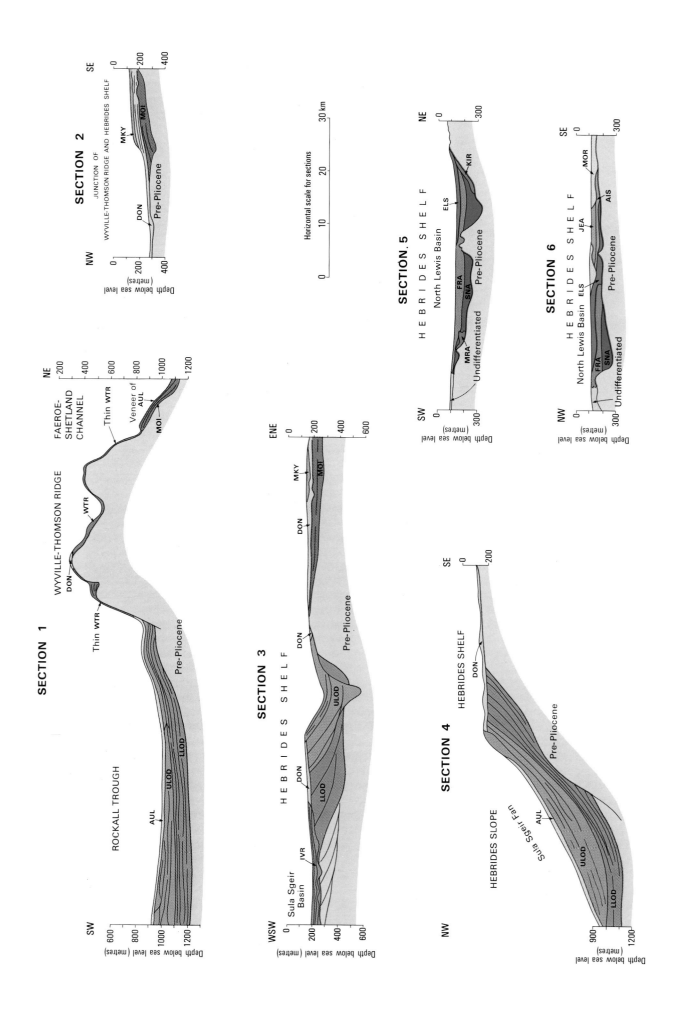

104

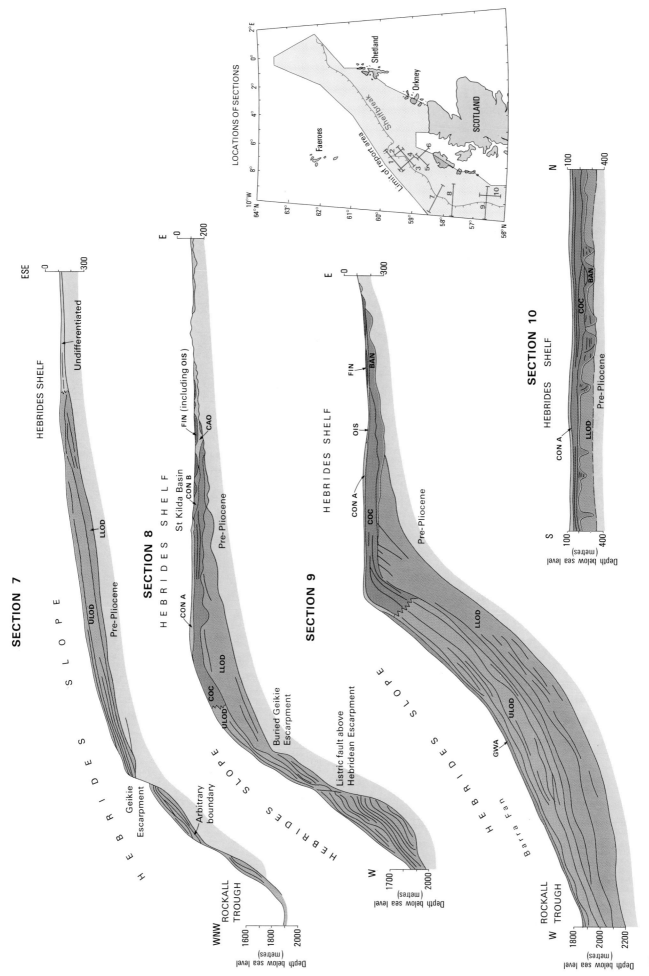

Figure 73 Sections illustrating the stratigraphy in the Hebrides Shelf/Rockall Trough region. For stratigraphical key see Figure 72.

contact, ice-proximal and glaciomarine deposits which over-lie a basal unconformity surface formed by subglacial and/or ice-marginal, meltwater erosion (BGS Peach Quaternary Geology sheet). Regional stratigraphical considerations (Figure 72) suggest that the sequences were laid down during at least two shelf glaciations, including the Anglian and the early Devensian. The basal unconformity is considered to be an erosional remnant of the Anglian glaciation; the first indication of direct glacial activity on the Hebrides Shelf.

The Banks sequence occurs on the eastern part of the shelf, where it is up to 110 m thick. It has a variable acoustic character with hummocky, mounded reflectors locally on-lapped by ponded, acoustically well-layered deposits; in the west, these packages occur in stacked association. The base of the sequence is a highly irregular erosion surface associated with a series of east–west-trending subglacial channels up to 6 km wide and 100 m deep (Figure 73). The sediments infilling the channels vary from acoustically chaotic to well layered, and show several phases of cut and fill (BGS Peach Quaternary Geology sheet).

Lithologically, the Banks sequence varies from very soft silts and clays to stiff, pebbly clays, sands and gravels. BGS borehole 90/12 (Figure 71) cored 20 m of dark grey, stiff to hard, bioturbated, shelly, sandy and gravelly mud occasionally interbedded with muddy sand, overlying a 1.2 m-thick shelly diamicton at the base. To the south-east, borehole 90/16 gave poor recovery from a 64 m-thick section that suggests an interbedded sequence of dark grey, soft to firm, shelly, glaciomarine clay with dropstones and very dark grey, firm to stiff, diamicton. The Banks sequence is broadly equivalent to the Skerryvore, Malin and Canna formations farther east (Davies et al., 1984; Fyfe et al., 1993).

To the west, the Banks sequence is partly overlain by, and partly interbedded with, the Conchar sequence, which extends on to the upper slope (Figure 73). The thickness of the Conchar sequence is very variable, but ranges up to about 100 m. On the shelf, it has an eroded, subplanar to irregular base, locally forming basins up to 4.5 km wide and 110 m deep. On the upper slope, the base is more uniformly planar. The top of the sequence occasionally forms mounded relief at the sea bed, and relict iceberg scour marks are locally preserved beneath the overlying Conan sequence.

The Conchar sequence displays a variable acoustic character; it is predominantly chaotic, but with sporadic, subhorizontal to westward-dipping, low-angle reflectors. Locally, seismic packages similar to those in the Banks sequence are present. Deposits infilling depressions display a seismically chaotic basal and marginal fill, and a well-layered, concordant upper fill (BGS Peach Quaternary Geology sheet). In the area of the Barra Fan, reflectors traced upslope from the Upper MacLeod sequence display evidence of both shelf onlap and truncation, perhaps reflecting some interplay between sea-level change and tectonic subsidence.

In BGS borehole 90/12, the Conchar sequence consists of a 12 m-thick, massive, basal diamicton overlain by 75 m of shelly, organic-rich, glaciomarine dropstone muds up to 90 m thick with occasional thin beds of bioclastic sand. Dropstone muds have also been recovered in boreholes 90/11, 90/13 and 90/14, and in numerous shallow cores, particularly from the upper slope.

STANTON FORMATION

The Stanton Formation unconformably overlies the Banks sequence in the extreme south-east of the report area, where it forms a basin-fill deposit, up to 100 m thick, of early to mid-Devensian age. This unit is more extensively developed farther east (Davies et al., 1984; Fyfe et al., 1993).

KIRSTY, MOIRA AND SHONA SEQUENCES

These form the oldest units in the North Lewis Basin (Figure 73; BGS Lewis Quaternary Geology sheet), where the Kirsty sequence is restricted to the north, and is less than 20 m thick. The Moira sequence occurs on the southern margin of the basin where it forms an elongate, moraine-like deposit over 30 km long, up to 6 km wide and 50 m thick, extending north-westwards from Lewis. It consists of several irregular and impersistent wedges of acoustically structureless sediment. On its north-east margin, the sequence grades rapidly into the acoustically well-layered deposits of the Shona sequence, although to the north-west, the latter becomes more structureless and transparent. The Shona sequence partially buries an irregular basin-floor topography, and locally overlaps the Kirsty and Moira sequences; it is thickest, up to 120 m, in the northern part of the basin. No lithological information exists for these sequences, which are probably pre-Devensian in age.

FLORA, ELSPETH, AISLA AND JEAN SEQUENCES

These sequences form the bulk of the infill to the North Lewis Basin, and are individually up to 100 m thick (Figure 73). Their stratigraphical disposition (Figure 72) indicates a progressive infilling of the basin from west to east. They all display a sheetform geometry with relatively planar bases, although the Flora and Elspeth sequences locally overlie irregular bedrock. The internal acoustic character of the sequences is similar, being predominantly structureless and transparent but with some discontinuous reflections in the two lower sequences. Lithological data from the Elspeth, Aisla and Jean sequences (BGS Lewis Quaternary Geology sheet) suggest a predominantly glaciomarine basin infill. In BGS borehole 77/08 (Figure 71), a 20 m-thick succession of reddish brown, sandy and pebbly mud of the Elspeth sequence is overlain by 50 m of dark to very dark grey, soft to stiff, pebbly and slightly sandy mud of the Jean sequence. The sediments contain an arctic microfauna indicative of glaciomarine sedimentation in water depths of 20 to 50 m, with seasonal or permanent sea ice. Similar deposits have been sampled from the Aisla sequence in The Minch (Fyfe et al., 1993).

In the Elspeth sequence, amino-acid racemisation results on the foraminiferal species *Elphidium excavatum* forma *clavata* (Cushman), yielded a ratio of 0.175, which in relation to data from Knudsen and Sejrup (1988), may suggest a pre-Devensian age. The overlying Aisla and Jean sequences have been assigned a pre-late Devensian age on the basis of having suffered erosion attributed to the last glaciation (Fyfe et al., 1993).

MACDONALD SEQUENCE

The MacDonald sequence occurs at or near to sea bed on the northern Hebrides Shelf where it extends to the shelfbreak, and partly on to the Wyville Thomson Ridge (Figure 71). It continues on to the southern part of the West Shetland Shelf, but is progressively eroded and buried beneath younger glacial sequences. West of Lewis, the distribution of the MacDonald sequence is probably more extensive than indicated in Figure 71. The sequence overlies a planar to irregular erosion surface which forms a distinctive angular unconformity on the northern Hebrides Shelf (Figure 73). Regional stratigraphical considerations (Figure 72) suggest

Figure 74 Sections illustrating the stratigraphy in the West Shetland Shelf/Faeroe–Shetland Channel region. For stratigraphical key see Figure 72.

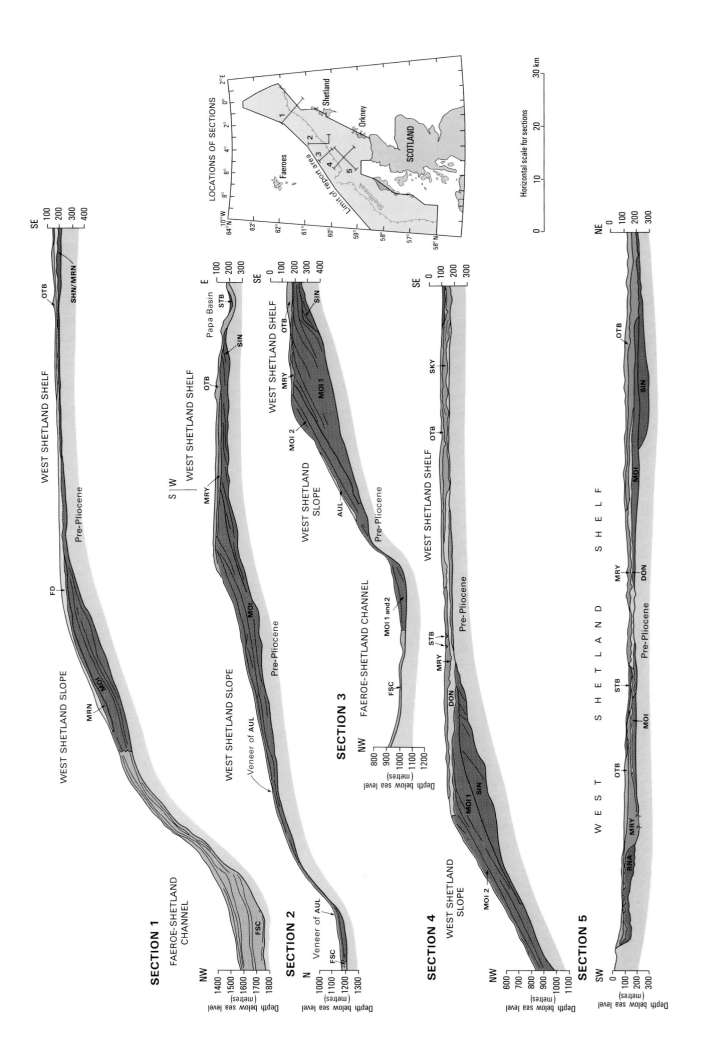

SECTION 1

FAEROE-SHETLAND
CHANNEL

WEST SHETLAND SLOPE

WEST SHETLAND SHELF

MRN

MOI

FD

Pre-Pliocene

OTB

SHN/MRN

NW

SE

100
200
300
400

1400
1500
1600
1700
1800

Depth below sea level
(metres)

FSC

SECTION 2

N

Veneer of AUL

FSC

WEST SHETLAND SLOPE

Veneer of AUL

MOI

Pre-Pliocene

MRY

WEST SHETLAND SHELF

Papa Basin

SIN

STB

S | W

WEST SHETLAND SHELF

E

100
200
300

1000
1100
1200
1300

Depth below sea level
(metres)

SECTION 3

FAEROE-SHETLAND CHANNEL

FSC

MOI 1 and 2

Pre-Pliocene

WEST SHETLAND SLOPE

MOI 2

AUL

MOI 1

MRY

OTB

SIN

WEST SHETLAND SHELF

NW

SE

0
100
200
300
400

800
900
1000
1100
1200

Depth below sea level
(metres)

SECTION 4

WEST SHETLAND SLOPE

MOI 2

MOI 1

SIN

DON

MRY

STB

FSC

Pre-Pliocene

OTB

SKY

WEST SHETLAND SHELF

NW

SE

0
100
200
300

600
700
800
900
1000
1100

Depth below sea level
(metres)

SECTION 5

W E S T   S H E T L A N D   S H E L F

RNA

MRY

OTB

MOI

STB

Pre-Pliocene

DON

MRY

MOI

SIN

OTB

SW

NE

0
100
200
300

0
100
200
300

Depth below sea level
(metres)

LOCATIONS OF SECTIONS

Faeroes

Shetland

Orkney

SCOTLAND

Limit of report area

Shelfbreak

1
2
3
4
5

2°E
0°
2°
4°
6°
8°
10°W

64°N
63°
62°
61°
60°
59°
58°
57°
56°N

Horizontal scale for sections

0   10   20   30 km

107

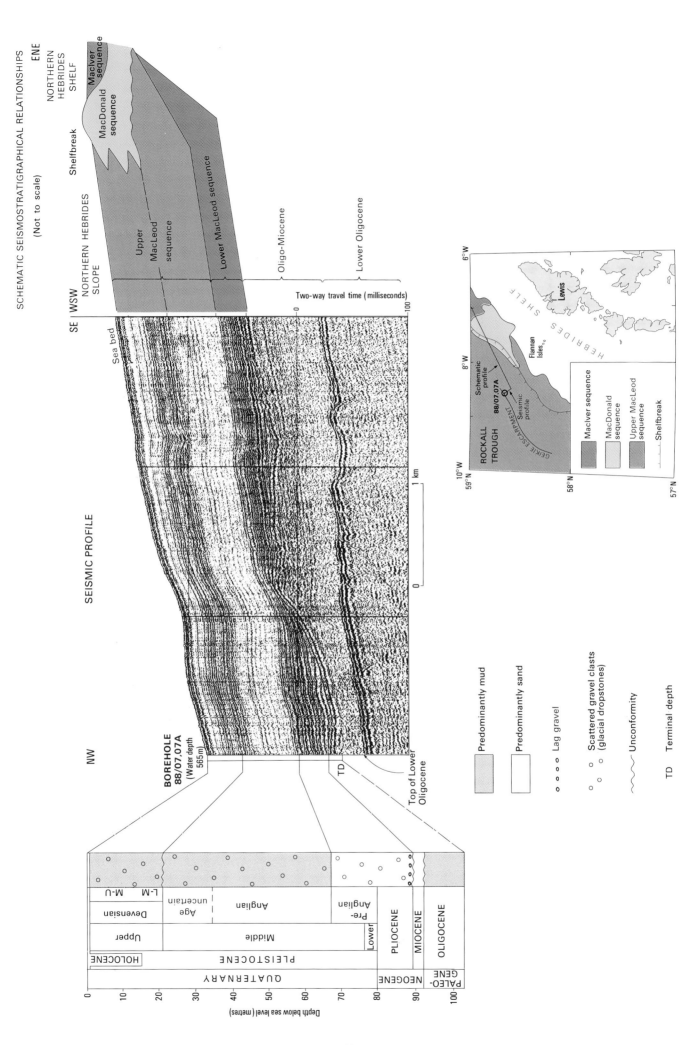

108

Figure 75 Age and lithology of the sediments in BGS borehole 88/07,07A; and their correlation with the seismic stratigraphy of the northern Hebrides Shelf and Slope.

that the MacDonald sequence is probably of early Devensian age.

Over a large part of the shelf, the MacDonald sequence is generally less than 10 m thick and has a sheet-like geometry, locally draping the floor of erosional hollows and basins, including the Sula Sgeir Basin. Its form is locally modified by discrete mounded accumulations which form prominent, iceberg-scoured ridges at the sea bed; these are interpreted as submarine end moraines (Stoker, 1990; Stewart and Stoker, 1990; Stoker and Holmes, 1991). The most significant ridge occurs at the shelf edge; it is 20 to 30 m high, up to 4.5 km wide, and can be traced laterally for 70 km (Figures 76 and 77). This implies widespread glaciation of the northern Hebrides Shelf at this time, but the southern and northern limits of this ice sheet remain undefined. To the north-east, the sequence forms part of an ice-contact fan which progrades on to the Wyville–Thomson Ridge, where isolated mounded accumulations are preserved.

On seismic profiles, a predominantly structureless to chaotic acoustic character is recognised both in the sheet-like and mounded deposits, although low-amplitude reflectors of the slope-front Upper MacLeod sequence interdigitate with the MacDonald sequence at the shelf edge (Stewart and Stoker, 1990; Stoker, 1990). On the West Shetland Shelf, acoustically layered deposits infill depressions at the base of the sequence (BGS Rona Quaternary Geology sheet).

At the junction of the Hebrides Shelf and the Wyville–Thomson Ridge, BGS boreholes 85/02,02A and 85/07 (Figure 71) proved up to 23 m of proximal, glaciomarine deposits (Stoker, 1988). The sediments consist of massive to crudely stratified, matrix- to clast-supported diamictons, dropstone muds and thin, inversely graded, mass-flow sands. Foraminifera and dinoflagellate cysts suggest deposition occurred in close proximity to ice, in water depths of 20 to 50 m. Similar diamictons up to 40 m thick, with some interbedded sands and gravels, were penetrated in numerous other boreholes, including 88/01.

WYVILLE–THOMSON RIDGE SEQUENCE

This sequence occurs on the crest and flanks of the Wyville–Thomson Ridge, below 300 m water depth, where it is generally less than 20 m thick but locally exceeds 100 m in discrete basins (Figure 73). It rests unconformably on an irregular bedrock surface of Paleogene sedimentary and volcanic rocks, and has been extensively scoured by icebergs.

On seismic profiles, its acoustic character ranges from structureless, chaotic, and sheet-like on the shallower parts of the ridge, to complex channel- or basin-fill patterns in the depressions. Onlapping, mounded-onlapping, and draped reflection configurations, as well as intraformational unconformities, characterise the complex-fill deposits, which also contain chaotic, wedge-shaped, mass-flow accumulations. Shallow cores have recovered interbedded, massive to stratified diamictons, muddy sands and gravels, and some sandy muds; these were probably deposited in a glaciomarine environment. A pre-late Devensian age is inferred for the sequence (Figure 72).

MACIVER SEQUENCE

This acoustically well-layered sequence infills a number of small basins on the northern Hebrides Shelf, notably the Sula Sgeir Basin where up to 80 m of sediment are preserved

(Figures 71, 73 and 76), generally draped over the MacDonald sequence on to which it pinches out at the basin margin (Figure 77). However, interdigitating and gradational contacts between these two units occur on the southern edge of the basin. Internal reflection continuity is interrupted in places by buried iceberg/sea-ice scour marks, which occur at levels down to 40 m below sea bed. The top of the sequence is eroded at the sea bed.

BGS borehole 78/05 (Figure 71) cored 40.7 m of very soft to soft, sandy and partly pebbly, glaciomarine mud from the sequence. Shallow-water glaciomarine deposits were also recovered in boreholes 88/09 and 88/10, which proved soft to firm, silty clays with monosulphidic knots, streaks and lenses and scattered sand and gravel. Amino-acid racemisation analysis of the foraminifera *E. excavatum* forma *clavata* from these boreholes yielded ratios ranging from 0.072 to 0.114, which in relation to data from Knudsen and Sejrup (1988) may suggest an age span of Wolstonian to early Devensian. Regional stratigraphical evidence (Figure 75) favours an early Devensian age.

MACKAY SEQUENCE

The Mackay sequence is part of an ice-contact fan preserved at the junction of the Hebrides Shelf and the Wyville–Thomson Ridge, where it forms an acoustically structureless to chaotic, sheet-like deposit up to 20 m thick (Figure 73). The base of the unit varies from planar to irregular and erosive, with depressions about 5 to 10 m deep and 200 to 300 m wide cut into the underlying MacDonald sequence. Vibrocores have recovered dark grey, stiff to hard clays and rounded to well-rounded, lithic and shelly gravels. The sequence is tentatively assigned a pre-late Devensian age.

UPPER MACLEOD SEQUENCE

The Upper MacLeod sequence is a predominantly slope-front deposit (Figure 73) that extends from the outer part of the Hebrides Shelf into the Rockall Trough. It is thickest beneath the mid- to lower slope in the area of the Barra and Sula Sgeir fans, where the sediments are up to 460 and 200 m thick respectively, but thins both along slope and downslope. In the intervening area, the sequence is best developed landward of the Geikie Escarpment, where it is up to 150 m thick on the outer shelf and upper slope. It is locally absent across the escarpment due to slumping and the effects of along-slope currents that may have restricted sediment accumulation on the steeper parts of the slope. In the Rockall Trough, beyond the area of the fan deposits, the thickness of the Upper MacLeod sequence is largely unknown. At the northern end of the trough, the Sula Sgeir Fan effectively pinches out, and the laterally equivalent basin-plain sediments are about 30 m thick.

The geometry of the Upper MacLeod sequence is wedge-shaped on the slope over the Barra and Sula Sgeir fans, but is more uniformly sheet-like away from the fans, both in slope and basin-plain settings. The base of the sequence is generally parallel with the top of the Lower MacLeod deposits, although reflectors in the underlying sequence are locally truncated on the slope. A marked unconformity occurs at the base of the Sula Sgeir Fan, where the Upper MacLeod sequence downlaps and pinches out on to the underlying strata.

On the northern Hebrides Shelf, a discrete channel was cut on the outer shelf and upper slope prior to the deposition of the Upper MacLeod sequence (Figures 73 and 76). This channel ranges from 1 to 8 km wide and is up to 200 m deep, narrowing downslope and ultimately disappearing on the mid-slope. The channel fill, which occurs at the base of

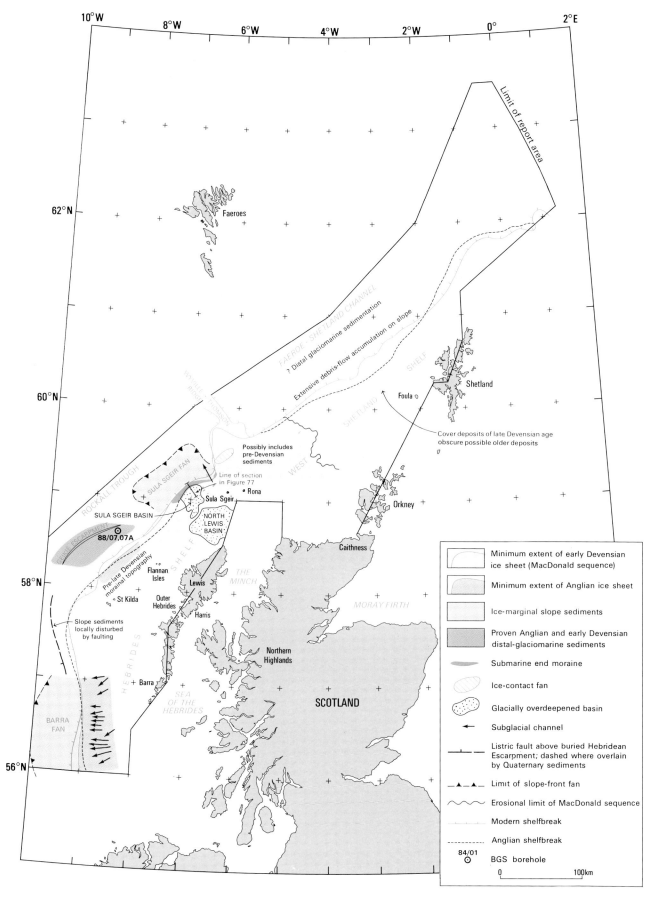

Figure 76 Schematic palaeogeographic reconstruction showing the minimum extent of Anglian and early Devensian glaciations.

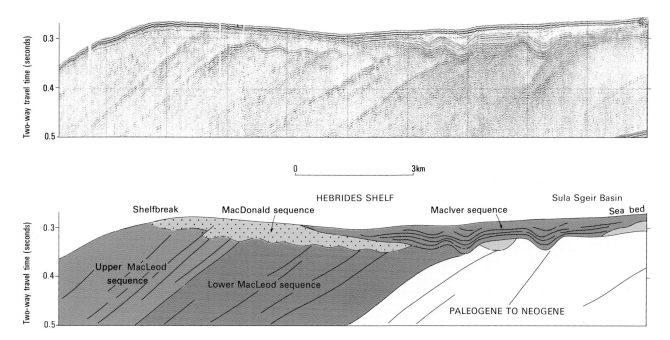

Figure 77 Shelf-edge end moraine (stippled), developed where the MacDonald sequence interdigitates with the glacigenic slope apron of the Upper MacLeod sequence; partly overlain by the MacIver sequence. For location see Figure 76.

the sequence on the Sula Sgeir Fan, displays a variable acoustic character, with onlapping reflectors interbedded with chaotic-fill deposits. A fluvial origin modified by later glacial activity is inferred.

The slope-front fan deposits display a prograding reflection configuration which consists of laterally continuous slope-wide reflectors separating acoustically structureless and chaotic packages tens of metres thick. The latter form the bulk of the fan deposits, and represent an amalgamated succession of mass-flow sediments, probably derived largely through direct ice-marginal input on to the slope (Stoker, 1990). In the Rockall Trough, the sequence is acoustically well layered, with laterally persistent reflectors mostly draping the Lower MacLeod sequence. However, bottom-current activity may have led to asymmetric drift development, particularly adjacent to the Wyville–Thomson Ridge.

Landward of the Geikie Escarpment, a well-layered acoustic texture gradually deteriorates upslope, and the sequence becomes seismically chaotic on the outer shelf (BGS Geikie Quaternary Geology sheet). The upper part of the Upper McLeod sequence correlates with the 'moraginal' MacDonald sequence; the change in acoustic character is complemented by a change in the nature of the sediments. On the outer shelf, BGS borehole 85/06 (Figure 71) cored 20 m of stiff to hard, shelly, gravelly diamicton; similar deposits have been recovered in shallow cores to the north (Stoker, 1990). However, on the upper slope close to the Geikie Escarpment, borehole 88/07,07A proved 67.82 m of soft to firm, bioturbated muds with dropstones (Stoker et al., 1992). These changes are interpreted to reflect increasing distance from the contemporary ice margin, which reached the shelfbreak in this area on at least two occasions. Calcareous nannoplankton suggest that the sediments between 67.82 m and about 34 m in borehole 88/07,07A are of Anglian age, about 0.44 to 0.38 Ma (Figure 75). The age of the sediments from about 34 to 22 m depth is unknown, although the nannofossils imply that deposition occurred at some time within the inter-

val between 0.38 and 0.27 Ma (Stoker et al., 1992). The deposits may represent the latest Anglian and/or belong to a younger glacial stage such as the Wolstonian. No interglacial sediments were encountered at this borehole site.

The bulk of the overlying deposits are of early to mid-Devensian age, and are separated from the older strata by a major hiatus (Stoker et al., 1992). On the Sula Sgeir Fan, the Upper MacLeod sequence had been regarded as the deposit of a single major glacial phase associated with the early Devensian MacDonald sequence (Stoker, 1990); the data from borehole 88/07,07A now suggest that the deposits of an older glaciation may additionally be preserved in this fan.

The nature of the deeper-water sediments in the Rockall Trough is unknown. To the south-west on the Feni Ridge (Figure 58) between 54° and 56°N, a series of piston cores recovered up to 10 m of predominantly Ipswichian to Devensian calcareous oozes and marls interbedded with terrigenous silty clays with dropstones (van Weering and de Rijk, 1991). Oxygen-isotope analysis suggests that middle Devensian strata occur within about 4 m of the sea bed.

The West Shetland Shelf/Faeroe–Shetland Channel region

Onshore evidence for Anglian to middle Devensian deposits is restricted to Shetland at Fugla Ness and Sel Ayre (Figure 71). Although the shelly tills of Caithness and Orkney have been suggested to be pre-late Devensian in age (Sutherland, 1984a), more recent evidence implies a late Devensian origin (Hall and Whittington, 1989; Sutherland, 1991).

At Fugla Ness, an interglacial peat bed separates a lowermost till from two upper tills (Chapelhowe, 1965). On the basis of pollen and macrofaunal analysis, the peat has been dated as Hoxnian (Birks and Ransom, 1969). Although the uppermost till is probably of late Devensian age, it is uncertain whether the underlying tills are the same age, with the peat as an erratic, or if they are the products of separate glaciations (Sutherland, 1991). The former interpretation implies only two intervals of glaciation at this site, both post-dating the peat; the latter suggests three phases of glaciation, the earliest of which may be of Anglian age. To the south, a further peat bed underlying late Devensian till occurs at Sel Ayre; a radiocarbon age of 36 800 +1950/ -1560 (mid-Devensian) was obtained from the peat (Mykura and Phemister, 1976), although its pollen content suggested an Ipswichian age to Birks and Peglar (1979).

The westward transport of erratics is interpreted by Flinn (1977b, 1978) to indicate that Scandinavian ice crossed the southern Shetland Islands at least as far as Foula. However, whilst the early glaciation(s) of Shetland may have been influenced by Scandinavian ice, it remains uncertain whether this involved direct inundation by Scandinavian ice, or westward deflection of Scottish ice (Sutherland, 1991).

Offshore, a much thicker and more extensive series of Anglian to middle Devensian deposits is recognised on the shelf to the west and north of Shetland. Direct evidence for ice limits has been largely obliterated by the effects of late Devensian ice, but the extensive accumulation of glacigenic debris flows on the West Shetland Slope implies widespread, earlier, shelf glaciation. Included in the shelf deposits is the early Devensian MacDonald sequence that extends northwards from the Hebrides Shelf on to the southern part of the West Shetland Shelf (Figure 76).

In the following description, the predominantly shelf units are presented first, followed by the slope and deep-water units. In the south, where the Morrison sequence has been informally subdivided, unit 2 is tentatively regarded as including sediments of Anglian to mid-Devensian age. Deposition of the Faeroe–Shetland Channel sequence is inferred to have spanned the entire Quaternary Period, and only the relevant part of the section is described here.

MARINER AND FERDER FORMATIONS

The Mariner Formation occurs on the outer shelf and upper slope to the north and west of Shetland (Figure 74). Glacio-marine sandy gravels and diamictons of Anglian to Wolstonian age form the upper member of this formation, which was extensively eroded prior to deposition of the overlying Ferder Formation. In the northern North Sea, where both formations are more widely developed, this erosion has been attributed to Wolstonian glaciation (Johnson et al., 1993).

North and west of Shetland, the Ferder Formation extends from the outer shelf to the mid-slope, and forms a seismically layered, sheetform deposit up to 60 m thick (Figure 74). Its base varies from planar to irregular, with channel-like features cut into the underlying sediments. In the northern North Sea, it comprises sediments of Wolstonian, Ipswichian, and early Devensian age (Johnson et al., 1993). The deposits include stiff to hard, glacial and glaciomarine gravelly sandy muds. Similar deposits have been recovered from the West Shetland Shelf, where BGS borehole 84/04 (Figure 71) cored about 20 m of proximal glaciomarine diamicton (Cockcroft, 1987). Interglacial marine sands, silts and clays proved in the North Sea have not been found in the report area.

RONA AND MURRAY SEQUENCES

These closely related sequences occur on the south-western part of the West Shetland Shelf, where they unconformably overlie bedrock and older glacial deposits (Figure 74). The Rona sequence is an acoustically well-layered deposit up to 100 m thick, extensively incised by northerly trending channels which mark the base of the Murray sequence. BGS bore-holes 72/36 and 78/07 (Figure 71) proved glaciomarine, finely layered, carbonaceous clays, silts and sands, with drop-stones.

The Murray sequence extends from the inner shelf to the shelfbreak, and is generally less than 40 m thick. On seismic profiles, acoustically structureless to chaotic packages in the north-east, which occasionally form northerly trending ridges, interdigitate with seismically well-layered deposits to the south-west. A westward transition from ice-proximal to ice-distal environments has been inferred with the support of borehole evidence (BGS Rona Quaternary Geology sheet). In the north-east, BGS borehole 82/10 (Figure 71) proved 25 m of ice-proximal diamicton (Cockcroft, 1987), whereas bore-hole 72/36 to the south-west penetrated 10 m of glaciomarine sand and clay. A pre-late Devensian age for both sequences is predicted from regional considerations (Figure 72).

CAPE SHORE AND SPERUS FORMATIONS, AND UNDIFFERENTIATED UPPER PLEISTOCENE SEQUENCE

North of Shetland, the Undifferentiated Upper Pleistocene sequence forms a seismically well-layered to transparent, un-sampled, slope deposit up to 50 m thick. To the east in the northern North Sea, laterally equivalent units include the mid-Devensian Cape Shore Formation and the mid- to late Devensian (pre-glacial maximum) Sperus Formation (Johnson et al., 1993). The Cape Shore Formation consists mainly of acoustically layered, glaciomarine sands and muds up to 100 m thick. The overlying Sperus Formation displays a similar acoustic character and comprises up to 40 m of firm to very stiff, sandy, glaciomarine muds.

SKERRY SEQUENCE

The Skerry sequence occurs to the north-west of Orkney, extending across the shelf as a tongue of sediment up to 60 m thick. To the north, it pinches out on to the MacDonald sequence, whereas to the east it interdigitates with the lower part of the Otter Bank sequence. The sequence displays an acoustically well-layered character which both onlaps and drapes the underlying sediments; there is some evidence of internal erosion.

BGS boreholes 82/03 and 82/04 (Figure 71) proved up to 33 m of shelly glaciomarine muds and clays with dropstones (BGS Rona Quaternary Geology sheet). Micropalaeon-tological data indicate evidence of an ameliorative interval during the deposition of the sequence, but a deteriorating climate is recorded towards the top of the unit in borehole 82/04. A mid- to late Devensian age (pre-glacial maximum) is suggested for the sequence (Figure 72).

MORRISON SEQUENCE (UNIT 2)

This unit is well defined in the southern part of the region, where it forms an outer shelf to slope, prograding sediment wedge up to 100 m thick (Figure 74). It probably extends on to the northern Hebrides Shelf, where it is the basal Quaternary unit. At the south-western end of the Faeroe–Shetland Channel, it constitutes a major component of the basin-plain succession. The base of the sequence is erosive on the shelf and also locally on the slope. On the upper slope, the unit has been disturbed and eroded by icebergs.

BGS boreholes 85/03 and 85/07, in the south (Figure 71), penetrated acoustically transparent and structureless to chaotic deposits, and recovered ice-proximal, sandy diamictons (Stoker, 1988). On the slope and basin plain, seismic profiles reveal packets of lensoid deposits bounded by moderate- to high-amplitude, laterally continuous reflectors. The former consist of debris-flow diamictons which are resedimented glacigenic material derived from the West Shetland Shelf, whereas the acoustically layered deposits probably comprise current-reworked, distal-glaciomarine sediments (Akhurst, 1991; Stoker et al., 1991).

In the central and north-eastern parts of the region, the Morrison sequence remains undivided. Reworked glacigenic deposits have been sampled from the upper part of the sequence, where borehole 85/01 (Figure 71) penetrated mainly debris-flow diamicton (BGS Foula Quaternary Geology sheet). Similar deposits have been recovered in numerous shallow cores across the length of the slope. In the absence of chronological control, the extent of the Anglian to middle Devensian section is unknown.

FAEROE–SHETLAND CHANNEL SEQUENCE

Vibrocores 60-05/46 and 61-04/37 (Figure 71) were taken at the axis of the Faeroe–Shetland Channel; they recovered interbedded, bioturbated, contouritic muds, sandy muds, muddy sands and sands with scattered pebbles. The sediments are of Ipswichian to Devensian age (Akhurst, 1991). In core 61-04/37, the top of the Ipswichian occurs at 4.9 m below the sea bed, and this section is at least 1 m thick; the overlying Devensian section is not differentiated. In core 60-05/46, middle Devensian sediments are at least 4.04 m thick and extend up to 1.3 m below the sea bed.

Micropalaeontological data indicate that fluctuating stadial and interstadial conditions prevailed during the Devensian (Stoker et al., 1989). According to Akhurst (1991), the changes in palaeoclimate correspond to fluctuations of bottom-current activity, resulting in intermittent phases of erosion and reworking of the basin-plain deposits to form muddy and sandy contourites. Despite the effects of bottom currents, the original glaciomarine character of the sediment is discernible.

UPPER DEVENSIAN

Upper Devensian deposits occur widely across the report area, where they record the maximum extent of the last major ice sheet in Scotland and the adjacent shelves. The mainland ice sheet developed over the Highlands of Scotland and spread outwards; to the west it incorporated smaller ice sheets which had formed in the upland areas of Skye, Mull and Arran (Sutherland, 1984a). The Outer Hebrides and Shetland probably also supported local ice sheets, although Outer Hebridean and mainland ice may have coalesced at the glacial maximum, at about 18 000 years BP (Selby, 1989; Boulton et al., 1991). Late Devensian ice extended on to the western shelves, and may locally have reached the shelf edge, although evidence of this glaciation is conspicuously absent from the northern Hebrides Shelf (Figure 78). The offshore succession incorporates several sequences/formations which record the advance and retreat of the ice. Several of these record the late-glacial climatic oscillations which comprise the Windermere Interstadial (13 000 to 11 000 years BP), and the Loch Lomond Stadial from 11 000 to 10 000 years BP (Gray and Lowe, 1977).

The Hebrides Shelf/Rockall Trough region

With the exception of the extreme north of Lewis, the Outer Hebrides were glaciated during the late Devensian glacial maximum, and the bulk of their glacial deposits are of this age (Peacock, 1991). These sediments largely consist of lodgement till which is patchily distributed and generally less than 10 m thick. In northern Lewis, ice-contact diamictons and shelly tills, up to 25 m thick, are associated in places

with waterlain silts, sands and gravels from which shell fragments have yielded radiocarbon ages of between 40 000 and 23 000 years BP (Sutherland and Walker, 1984). Following the retreat of the main late Devensian ice sheet, a vigorous valley glaciation, resembling the Loch Lomond Readvance of the Scottish mainland, occurred in south-west Lewis, north Harris and locally farther south (Peacock, 1991). The valley glaciers deposited bouldery till, sand and silt.

West of the Outer Hebrides during the glacial maximum, St Kilda was subjected to valley glaciation, accompanied by intensive periglacial activity (Sutherland et al., 1984). The resulting till comprises two distinct facies; a lower, lodgement or melt-out facies, and an upper, supraglacial facies. Beyond the glaciated area, bedrock is directly overlain by periglacial slope deposits. During the Loch Lomond Stadial, only periglacial processes were active. Submerged marine-erosion surfaces around St Kilda, at -120 m and between -80 and -40 m, are thought to have been produced during low sea levels coincident with late Devensian and 'Loch Lomond' glaciations (Sutherland, 1984b).

On the Hebrides Shelf, late Devensian glacial deposits are mostly preserved south and west of St Kilda. According to Selby (1989), this largely reflects the expansion of the Outer Hebrides ice sheet on to the shelf, although the evidence suggests that it did not inundate St Kilda (Sutherland et al., 1984) or reach the shelf edge (Figure 78). The western limit of the ice sheet is defined by a large morainal bank complex associated with the Conan sequence (Selby, 1989). Landward of this bank, the glacially overdeepened St Kilda Basin includes a number of sequences which record the deglaciation of the southern Hebrides Shelf.

The limit of the ice sheet to the north is unclear (Figure 78); it has been shown that it did not cover the extreme north of Lewis (von Weymarn, 1979; Peacock, 1984; Sutherland and Walker, 1984), but its extent to the west, where it is inferred to have covered the Flannan Isles (Selby, 1989), remains conjectural as the Quaternary succession is largely undifferentiated. A thin, basal diamicton of unknown age, overlain by late-glacial sands of the Catriona sequence, was recovered in BGS borehole 88/08, in the Flannan Trough. There is no evidence to suggest that the northern part of the shelf and the Wyville–Thomson Ridge were glaciated during the late Devensian, and the shelf may have been partly exposed.

Glaciomarine sequences preserved in the eastern part of the North Lewis Basin and The Minch suggest the existence of a marine connection from the north, although their deposition was preceded by widespread erosion attributed to the northward advance of the late Devensian ice sheet across The Minch (Fyfe et al., 1993). This implies that the maximum ice limit was located north of The Minch, close to the islands of Sula Sgeir and Rona (Figure 78). However, the predominance of glaciomarine deposits implies rapid recession of the ice sheet in this particular area which, as a persistent topographic low since the late Tertiary, may have acted as a conduit for ice expansion. This topographic low would have been particularly susceptible to any rise in sea level, so that the glaciomarine embayment depicted in Figure 78 probably developed shortly after the glacial maximum. The ice limit shown in The Minch possibly marks a major stillstand during the retreat of late Devensian ice.

CAOILTE AND CONAN SEQUENCES

These laterally equivalent sequences were deposited during the late Devensian glacial maximum, following widespread glacial erosion of the shelf (Selby, 1989; BGS St Kilda Quaternary Geology sheet). The St Kilda Basin (Figure 78)

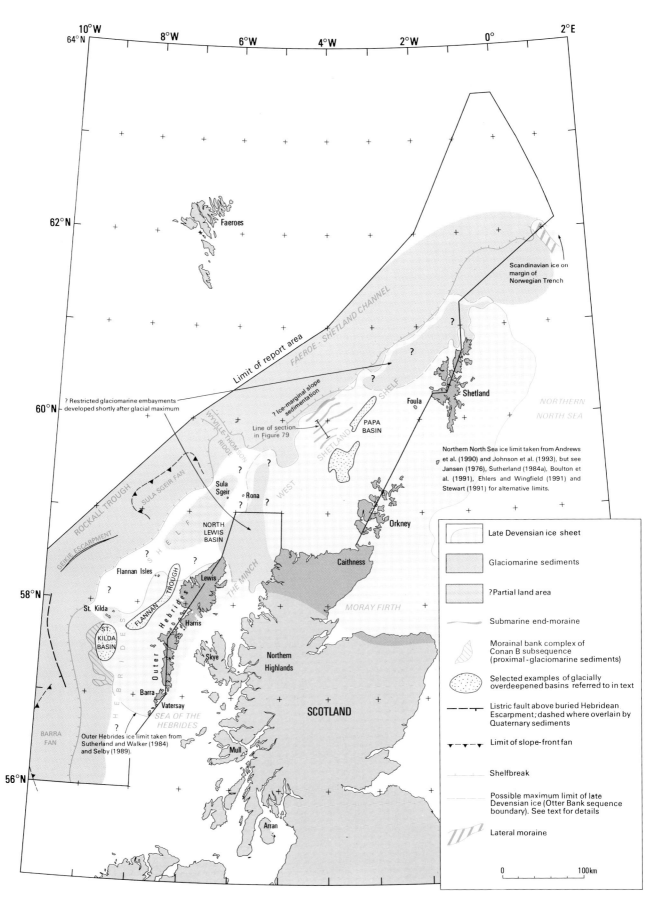

Figure 78 Schematic palaeogeographic reconstruction showing the inferred extent of the late Devensian ice sheet at, or shortly after, the glacial maximum.

was formed at this time, as part of a regional unconformity surface preserved at the base of these units (Figure 73).

The Caoilte sequence forms the basal fill of the St Kilda Basin, and also occurs at or near to sea bed in other bedrock depressions to the east. In the basin, it forms a discontinuous, locally mounded, sheet-like deposit up to 30 m thick, with a complex internal structure of impersistent reflectors and lensoid, well-layered units. Shallow cores have recovered stiff, muddy diamictons interpreted as lodgement till, although the lensoid deposits may be glaciofluvial sands and gravels forming esker-like features (Selby, 1989).

Westwards, the subglacial Caoilte sequence passes laterally into contemporaneous glaciomarine deposits of the Conan sequence, which has been divided into two laterally equivalent subsequences; A and B. The Conan B subsequence is restricted to the western margin of the St Kilda Basin, and consists of an interconnected series of seismically chaotic banks that are 2.5 km wide and 10 m high, from which borehole 90/14 (Figure 71) cored soft to firm, slightly shelly, pebbly mud with sandy horizons. Similar sediments have been recovered in adjacent shallow cores, and an abraded fragment of *Arctica islandica* (Linné) gave an infinite radiocarbon age of more than 43 000 years BP (Selby, 1989). This implies that some bioclastic material has been reworked. The Conan B subsequence is interpreted as an ice-marginal, morainal-bank deposit, and possibly marks the site of the grounding line when the Outer Hebrides ice sheet began to float and deposit sediment in a marine environment (Selby, 1989; BGS St Kilda Quaternary Geology sheet).

The Conan A subsequence is a sheet-like deposit up to 60 m thick, which is locally moulded into ridges parallel to the shelfbreak. It displays a chaotic acoustic character with some discontinuous, low-amplitude reflectors, and discrete layers of hyperbolic reflections. BGS borehole 90/11 penetrated about 20 m of the unit, and recovered soft to firm, pebbly, distal-glaciomarine mud. Similar but stiffer deposits with bioclastic debris have been proved in shallow cores, from which a specimen of *Yoldiella lenticula* (Möller) yielded a radiocarbon age of 22 480 ± 300 years BP (Selby, 1989).

OISEIN AND FIONN SEQUENCES

The Oisein and Fionn sequences form the middle and upper fill, respectively, of the St Kilda Basin, as well as occupying other small troughs and depressions on the shelf. The Oisein sequence is up to 25 m thick, and in the St Kilda Basin occurs as a drape over the Caoilte sequence (Figure 73). It consists of acoustically well-layered, distal-glaciomarine muds which were laid down as a relatively restricted basinal deposit during the initial stages of retreat of the late Devensian ice sheet (Selby, 1989). According to Peacock et al. (1992), this occurred after 15 250 years BP. Reflector truncations at the top of the unit imply some degree of erosion prior to the deposition of the overlying Fionn sequence.

The Fionn sequence is up to 40 m thick, and consists of acoustically well-layered, sandy, glaciomarine muds displaying an onlapping reflection configuration, although there is some evidence of erosion and basin-margin progradation. The sediments were probably deposited when the Outer Hebrides ice sheet had retreated from the St Kilda Basin on to the inner shelf (Selby, 1989). Fragments of *Buccinium terranovae* Beck and *Macoma calcarea* (Gmelin) have yielded radiocarbon ages of 11 680 ± 240 years BP and 11 210 ± 90 years BP respectively (Selby, 1989). The sediments also contain volcanic glass shards comparable with the Vedde Ash of western Norway, dated at about 10 600 years BP (Mangerud et al., 1984). This volcanic ash may have been transported into the St Kilda Basin by pack-ice (Peacock et al., 1992).

Dinoflagellate-cyst data imply an age range extending into the early Holocene (BGS Peach Quaternary Geology sheet).

MORAG, ANNIE AND CATRIONA SEQUENCES

The Morag and Annie sequences are best developed in The Minch (Figure 71), where they consist predominantly of acoustically well-layered, muddy, glaciomarine deposits up to 90 m thick infilling late Devensian erosional basins and hollows (Fyfe et al., 1993). BGS borehole 78/04, east of Lewis (Figure 71), proved a late Devensian to Holocene age for the Annie sequence (Graham et al., 1990).

The Catriona sequence may be partly contemporaneous with the Annie sequence (Fyfe et al., 1993). West of Lewis, this acoustically well-layered unit is most extensively preserved as a progradational build-out on the western margin of the Flannan Trough (Figure 78), where BGS borehole 88/08 (Figure 71) proved about 10 m of fine- to very fine-grained, muddy, shallow-water, glaciomarine sand.

GWAELO, MACAULAY AND UPPER MACLEOD SEQUENCES

The Gwaelo and MacAulay sequences occur on the Barra and Sula Sgeir fans respectively, and form acoustically well-layered to structureless drapes over the debris-flow deposits of the Upper MacLeod sequence (Figures 71 and 73). They locally exceed 30 m in thickness on the mid-slope, but thin into the Rockall Trough where bottom-current activity may have restricted sediment accumulation. On the upper slope, the sequences pinch out at about 300 m water depth, and have been locally disrupted by iceberg scouring; the Gwaelo sequence has also been affected by slumping.

Shallow cores have recovered up to 6 m of soft to very soft, bioturbated muds and sandy muds with dropstones, overlain by a Holocene veneer. Dinoflagellate-cyst data have confirmed the late-glacial climatic oscillation (Stoker et al., 1989; BGS Sula Sgeir and Peach Quaternary Geology sheets), and volcanic glass shards comparable with the Vedde Ash of western Norway (Mangerud et al., 1984) have been identified (Stoker et al., 1989). The possibility cannot be discounted that older Devensian sediments, associated with the retreat of the early Devensian ice sheet from the northern Hebrides Shelf, are preserved in the lower part of the MacAulay sequence.

On the intervening slope and basinward of the fans, sediments equivalent to the Gwaelo and MacAulay sequences cannot be seismically defined. Upper Devensian strata in these areas remain undifferentiated within the Upper MacLeod sequence. On the Feni Ridge (Figure 58), the upper Devensian is about 2 m thick (van Weering and de Rijk, 1991).

The West Shetland Shelf/Faeroe–Shetland Channel region

In Caithness and Orkney, two till units are widely mapped, the upper of which is usually referred to as the shelly till (Sutherland, 1984a). This locally reaches 20 m in thickness, and contains fragmented marine shells, and clasts of Mesozoic sediments derived from the Moray Firth. There is no evidence to indicate a break in deposition between the two till units, and they are generally regarded as the products of a single glaciation. In Caithness, this has generally been ascribed to the late Devensian (Jardine and Peacock, 1973), an assertion supported by recent radiocarbon and amino-acid data. This implies that the most northerly limit of the last Scottish ice sheet (Figure 78) was located at least as far north as the Orkney–Shetland Channel (Hall and Whittington, 1989; Sutherland, 1991). Following the retreat of the ice sheet, small valley glaciers developed in north-west Scotland and northern Hoy, and deposited end moraines. These are probably related to the Loch Lomond Readvance (Sissons, 1977; Sutherland, 1991).

Shetland is partly covered by a thin till of presumed late Devensian age; this is generally attributed to the development of a local ice cap, with ice flowing outwards from an ice-shed located along the long axis of the island (Mykura, 1976; Sutherland, 1991). On Foula, tills contain boulders derived from the eastern side of Shetland. Although the transport of these erratics may be due to an earlier glaciation (Flinn 1977b; 1978), the till is probably of late Devensian age and associated with the westward growth of the Shetland ice cap (Mykura, 1976). A minimum age for its termination on Shetland is provided by radiocarbon dates from organic sediments overlying the till, the oldest date being 12 090 ± 900 years BP (Hoppe, 1974). The final remnants of the ice sheet may have consisted of corrie glaciers and ice patches, suggesting that the Loch Lomond Readvance was of very limited extent on these islands (Mykura, 1976; Sutherland, 1991).

On the West Shetland Shelf, deposits of probable late Devensian age occur extensively on the middle and outer shelf. In the south, these include a series of submarine end moraines (Figures 78 and 79) associated with the Otter Bank sequence (Stoker and Holmes, 1991), which may reflect the local westward expansion of the late Devensian ice sheet close to the shelf edge. Glacially overdeepened basins such as the Papa Basin (Figure 78) occur landward of the moraines. On the north side of Shetland, Flinn (1983) has suggested that the ice sheet may not have extended beyond the coastlines of the northern islands, although glacial tongues may have terminated farther north in a marine environment (Long and Skinner, 1985; Johnson et al., 1993).

Broader glaciomarine embayments may have developed to the west and south-west of Shetland. However, The Minch embayment to the south perhaps developed shortly after the glacial maximum (see above), and a similar situation may have existed north-west of Shetland. Thus, the possibility that the boundary of the Otter Bank sequence (Figure 78) represents an approximation to the maximum late Devensian ice limit cannot be discounted. This would imply a more widespread input of ice-marginal sediments on to the West Shetland Slope. In the northern North Sea, Shetland/ Scottish ice remained separated from Scandinavian ice, which terminated on the western margin of the Norwegian Trench (Johnson et al., 1993).

OTTER BANK SEQUENCE

The Otter Bank sequence occurs extensively on the outer part of the West Shetland Shelf, where it forms a mounded to sheet-like deposit up to 60 m thick (Figures 71 and 74). It has a planar to highly irregular and erosive base, and west of Foula it rests on the floor of the Papa Basin. Locally it appears to interdigitate with the Skerry sequence, and is considered to be of late Devensian age (Figure 72). The top of the sequence has been extensively scoured by icebergs.

On the southern part of the shelf, the sequence appears to pinch out landwards of the shelfbreak, but to the north-east it extends to the edge of the shelf, and passes laterally into the upper part of the Morrison sequence (Figure 74). On the inner shelf, the Quaternary succession remains undifferentiated (Figure 71), although it seems likely that the Otter Bank sequence extends towards mainland Scotland, Orkney and Shetland as a thin diamicton cover similar to that proved in boreholes 72/26 and 82/07.

The morphology of the outer shelf is locally influenced by the surface expression of the Otter Bank sequence, particular-ly where it is mounded (Stoker and Holmes, 1991). A number of prominent ridges occur on the sea bed; they are up to 60 m high, 8 km wide, and can be traced laterally for up to 60 km (Figures 78 and 79). The ridge complex is interpreted as a series of submarine end moraines (Stoker and Holmes, 1991). Each ridge probably marks a stillstand during the eastward retreat of the ice sheet, resulting in the local accumulation of glacigenic sediments. The ridges exhibit an acoustically structureless to chaotic texture, with hyperbolic reflections originating from cobbles and boulders on the ridge crests, and from sporadic, discontinuous, internal horizons. The north-western flank of each ridge interdigitates with acoustically well-layered, ponded deposits. Sedimentation occurred in a diachronous manner, with the oldest deposits occurring to the north-west. Each ridge was systematically buried or partially buried beneath successively younger, acoustically layered sediments on its south-eastern flank. In Figure 79, the most eastward ridge partly overlies the layered deposits; this may reflect occasional surging of the ice front. Around Rona, the bulk of the sequence is acoustically well layered (BGS Rona Quaternary Geology sheet).

Shallow cores from the tops of the ridges, together with boreholes such as 77/09 (Figure 71), have recovered interbedded, stiff to very stiff, glacial and glaciomarine diamictons, sands and gravels. Micropalaeontological data from the diamictons suggests that deposition occurred in water up to 50 m deep. Some variation in facies is recorded in boreholes 72/36, 84/02 and 84/04, which proved shelly, gravelly sands up to 30 m thick, which were probably deposited in a high-energy, shallow-water, glaciomarine-deltaic environment (Cockcroft, 1987). The inter-ridge, acoustically well-layered deposits have been sampled by shallow cores which proved sandy, glaciomarine muds.

STORMY BANK SEQUENCE

The Stormy Bank sequence consists of acoustically well-layered deposits, up to 20 m thick, that fill hollows and small basins cut into glacial deposits and bedrock (Figures 71 and 74). Internal erosion surfaces are present, and gas blanking and pockmarks occur on the deeper parts of the shelf. Locally, the base of the sequence appears to merge with the underlying Otter Bank sequence. Sandy, carbonaceous, partly gassy, soft to firm, glaciomarine, dropstone muds have been recovered in a number of boreholes, such as 77/07. These are locally capped by a veneer of fine-grained, shelly sand, and gravel. The sequence was probably deposited during the waning stages of the late Devensian glaciation, with some reworking at the top of the sequence in the early Holocene.

TAMPEN FORMATION

The Tampen Formation (Figures 71 and 72) forms a topographic ridge on the western margin of the Norwegian Trench (Johnson et al., 1993). The formation is up to 50 m thick, and consists of acoustically structureless, firm to very stiff, sandy muds with interbedded sand and gravel, and forms a lateral moraine created by northward-flowing Scandinavian ice largely constrained within the Norwegian Trench. Radiocarbon dates from shell material in the Norwegian sector yielded a maximum age of about 19 000 years BP (Rise et al., 1984).

MORRISON SEQUENCE (UNIT 2)

The possibility that the upper part of this unit is late Devensian in age cannot be discounted if, as is suggested by the evidence of the Otter Bank sequence, the late Devensian ice sheet locally reached the shelf edge. Glacigenic debris flows interbedded with distal-glaciomarine muds are known

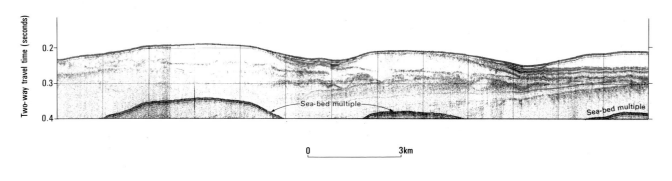

WEST SHETLAND SHELF

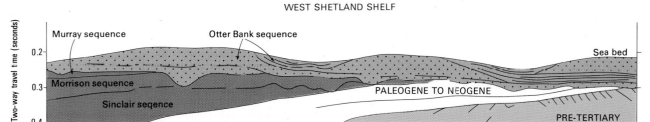

Figure 79 A series of morainal ridges (stippled) of the Otter Bank sequence, which become younger to the south-east, showing their relationship to ponded, acoustically well-layered deposits. For location see Figure 78

to occur near sea bed on the floor of the Faeroe–Shetland Channel (Stoker et al., 1991). Unfortunately, chronological data from the glacigenic sediments are lacking; thus the distribution and thickness of any late Devensian slope-front deposits remains unknown.

MacAulay sequence

The MacAulay sequence forms a seismically well-layered, slope-front to basin-plain veneer overlying the debris flows of the Morrison sequence (unit 2), and is generally less than 5 m thick in this region. The sequence pinches out on the upper slope at about 300 m water depth (Figure 74), where it has also been eroded and disrupted by iceberg scouring. At the south-western end of the Faeroe–Shetland Channel, the sequence displays drape and onlapping characteristics, the latter being an effect of bottom-current reworking. On the slope, borehole 85/01 (Figure 71) proved 3.3 m of very soft, glaciomarine muds with scattered shells and dropstones capped by a 0.2 m-thick veneer of Holocene sediment (BGS Foula Quaternary Geology sheet). Similar deposits recovered in shallow core 59-07/276, at the south-western end of the Faeroe–Shetland Channel, record the effects of late-glacial climatic oscillation (Stoker et al., 1989).

Faeroe–Shetland Channel sequence

From the top of this sequence, vibrocore 60-05/46 (Figure 71) recovered about 1 m of bioturbated, interbedded mud and sandy mud with scattered pebbles. It is of late Devensian age, and is overlain by 0.3 m of Holocene deposits (Akhurst, 1991). No record of the late-glacial climatic oscillation is recorded in this core, which implies erosion and reworking of the sediments by bottom currents.

HOLOCENE

Holocene sediments form a widespread veneer across the area, largely recording the effects of reworking during the early postglacial transgression of the shelves, together with enhanced bottom-current flow on the slopes and basin plains. Deglaciation produced a eustatic sea-level rise which continued until about 6000 years BP in northern Scotland, when isostatic uplift led to a regression resulting in a series of raised beaches (Anderton et al., 1979; Boulton et al., 1991). However, in areas away from the main centre of glacio-isostatic uplift in the Scottish Highlands, such as the Outer Hebrides, Orkney and Shetland, sea level may have risen continuously to its present level (Lambeck, 1991).

Since the rise in sea level, the shelves have been essentially starved of sediment (see Sea-bed sediments chapter). In the deeper-water areas, the change from glacial to interglacial conditions appears to have corresponded with extreme fluctuations in bottom-current velocity, resulting in erosion and resedimentation of the slope and basin-plain deposits (Stoker et al., 1989; Akhurst, 1991). Fully marine, interglacial circulation may have been established by about 9500 years BP (Peacock and Harkness, 1990). Little mass-flow activity is evidenced in the Holocene, but bottom currents have played an active role in controlling sedimentation. Although a number of the late Devensian sequences previously described extend into the Holocene (Figure 72), the postglacial cover is mostly undifferentiated.

The Hebrides Shelf/Rockall Trough region

In the Outer Hebrides, extensive blown sand, alluvium, and large areas of peat developed during the Holocene (Peacock, 1984). The general submergence of the islands is confirmed by the absence of raised beaches, and the presence of several submerged peats. Radiocarbon dates suggest that sea level on Lewis was at least 5 m below present at about 5700 years BP (Ritchie, 1966).

To the west, the late Devensian Village Bay Till of St Kilda (Figure 71) is overlain by slopewash and soil (Sutherland et al., 1984). Immediately offshore, a submerged rock platform of Loch Lomond Stadial age suggests a rise in sea level of about 40 m during the Holocene, accompanied by little marine erosion (Sutherland, 1984b). A similar scenario has been invoked for Sula Sgeir, to the north-east (Sutherland, 1987).

Most of the adjacent shelf is covered by a discontinuous, unconformable Holocene veneer of sand and gravel, generally less than 2 m thick (BGS St Kilda and Sula Sgeir Quaternary Geology sheets). However, early Holocene, boreo-temperate, marine muds and shelly, sandy muds up to 16 m thick, have been recovered from the Fionn and Annie sequences (BGS Peach Quaternary Geology sheet; Graham et al., 1990). Muddy sands may be present in the laterally equivalent Catriona sequence (BGS Sutherland Sea Bed Sediments and Quaternary Geology sheet).

On the Hebrides Slope and in the Rockall Trough, the MacAulay sequence preserves a Holocene veneer less than 0.5 m thick. In core 59-08/34 (Figure 71; Stoker et al., 1989) it consists of bioturbated, marine mud and sandy mud with occasional pebbles, coarsening upwards into contouritic muddy sand which forms the sea bed. Dinoflagellate cysts in these sediments indicate that they were deposited under temperate climatic conditions, accompanied by the establishment of modern oceanographic circulation. Similar deposits may occur in the Gwaelo sequence at the Barra Fan (Figures 71 and 78), although the sea-bed sand layer is discontinuous, and where the water depth is greater than 900 m the postglacial cover consists predominantly of hemipelagic mud (BGS St Kilda Sea Bed Sediments sheet). The variable thickness of the sand layer may suggest that it is being actively winnowed and eroded. The overall continuity of the Holocene from the upper slope to the basin floor implies little significant mass movement on the slope, at least since the end of the Devensian.

The West Shetland Shelf/Faeroe–Shetland Channel region

On Orkney and Shetland, blown sand, freshwater alluvium and peat developed in the Holocene (Mykura, 1976). Submerged peat beds and the absence of raised beaches confirm the gradual submergence of Orkney and Shetland in postglacial times. On Shetland, Hoppe (1965) recorded a se-

ries of dates from peats, the oldest of which suggest that sea level was at least 9 m below present by about 7000 years BP, reaching a level of -8.8 m after 5500 years BP. According to Flinn (in Harkness and Wilson, 1979), sea level around Shetland reached approximately its present level after 4000 years BP.

On the West Shetland Shelf, sand and gravel at the top of the Stormy Bank sequence (Figure 71) are probably a relict of erosion from the early Holocene transgression (BGS Rona Quaternary Geology sheet). Over most of the shelf, this resulted in a discontinuous veneer, generally less than 0.5 m thick, of poorly sorted, bioclastic sands, unconformably overlying older glacial deposits (BGS Judd and Miller Sea Bed Sediments sheets). On the slope, the uppermost part of the MacAulay sequence consists of about 0.5 m of predominantly argillaceous Holocene sediments, including a thin (0.1 m) muddy sand layer at sea bed.

In the Faeroe–Shetland Channel, Holocene sediments are locally preserved at the top of the MacAulay and Faeroe–Shetland Channel sequences. Shallow cores, such as 59-07/276 and 60-05/46 (Figure 71) have recovered up to 0.3 m of bioturbated pebbly muds which coarsen upwards into massive, bioturbated, pebbly, shelly and muddy sands at the sea bed (Stoker et al., 1989; Akhurst, 1991). Similarly graded muddy sands and fine gravels, up to 0.7 m thick, have been recovered in adjacent cores (Stoker et al., 1991; BGS Judd Sea Bed Sediments sheet).

The sea-bed sand layer is similar to that found in the Rockall Trough, and is interpreted as a contourite resulting from increased bottom-current activity. Locally, as at site 61-04/37 (Figure 71), winnowing and/or erosion by bottom currents has removed the Holocene section. In core 59-07/276, volcanic glass shards discovered mainly within the sea-bed layer (Stoker et al., 1989) are comparable with the Saksunarvatn Ash of the Faeroe Islands, which is dated at 9100 to 9000 years BP (Mangerud et al., 1986). This suggests that the bottom currents are reworking sediments of predominantly early Holocene age. However, in the north-eastern part of the channel, an extensive area of gravelly muds (see Figure 81; BGS Flett Sea Bed Sediments sheet), implies that deposition of laterally extensive sheet-like sediments is continuing (Akhurst, 1991).

13 Sea-bed sediments

The sea bed is essentially a relict surface which dates from the late Pleistocene, and its morphology has remained largely unaltered since the early Holocene rise in sea level. It is covered by a patchy veneer of unconsolidated sediments which consists of an admixture of terrigenous and biogenic carbonate material. These sea-bed sediments usually range from a few centimetres up to about 2 m thick, although on the inner shelf, thicker accumulations exceeding 20 m occur where large sand waves and sandbanks have formed.

The terrigenous component of the sediments is mainly derived from underlying or adjacent Pleistocene deposits and bedrock. This has been brought about by glacially related processes during late Pleistocene times, and by hydraulic processes during the early Holocene transgression. Since the rise in sea level, most of the report area has been starved of further terrigenous input, but the sediment, especially the sand fraction, has been reworked throughout the Holocene by bottom currents.

In contrast, the biogenic-carbonate component has been accumulating throughout the Holocene. During the early Holocene, carbonate production was limited to what are now the deeper parts of the shelves, but the rate of production there has probably declined since the rise in sea level (Farrow et al., 1984). The main centres of carbonate production are now located on the inner shelf; a pattern of production, accumulation and dispersal established over the past 6000 years (Farrow et al., 1984). The faunal composition of the biogenic component across the shelf is indicative of variations in the modern sedimentary environment (Wilson, 1982; Allen, 1983; Scoffin, 1988), and also provides information on changes during the Holocene (Wilson, 1988).

Belderson et al. (1970) described three categories of sea-bed sediments within the report area. The first consists of extensively occurring, transgressive, gravelly lag deposits dating from the early Holocene or earlier, that may remain uncovered at the sea bed. The next category consists of deposits which are in equilibrium with the modern sedimentary environment; these vary in geometry from large sheets to small patches, and range in grain size from gravel to sand and mud, some with a significant biogenic content. The final category consists of sediments, usually well-sorted sands, which are presently being transported across the sea bed; these exhibit a variety of bedforms related to the strength of the prevailing bottom currents and the availability of sediment.

HYDRAULIC CONDITIONS

Throughout the Holocene, both the composition and distribution of the sediments have been influenced by a combination of tidal, wave-induced, wind-driven, and oceanic currents. All four types of current occur on the shelf, whereas oceanic currents are predominant on the adjacent slopes and basin floors.

On the shelf, there is a good correlation between both the direction and strength of the surface tidal currents, and the orientation and distribution of sedimentary bedforms (Kenyon and Stride, 1970). The currents are strongest on the inner shelf, with speeds exceeding 1.0 m/s in the vicinity of the Outer Hebrides and between Orkney and Shetland (Figure 80). The net direction of sediment transport by the tidal currents can be related to differences in the strength and duration of the peak, ebb and flood streams (Johnson et al., 1982). These flow along-shelf and parallel to the coastlines, as illustrated by the flood tidal-stream data.

The shelf sediments are also influenced by oscillatory, wave-induced currents generated by strong winds which sweep across the North Atlantic. The maximum fifty-year wave height is estimated to range from about 30 m in the nearshore to over 32 m at the shelfbreak (Department of Energy, 1985). Orbital currents induced at the sea bed by such waves range from about 1 m/s on the outer shelf to over 4 m/s on the inner shelf (Figure 80). The strength of these currents make them important initiators of sediment movement, for strong winds acting on the sea surface are also capable of causing sediment transport by generating storm-surge currents; these can cause mass movement of sediment when acting in conjunction with tidal currents (Pantin, 1991).

The sediments on the upper part of the slope and on the adjacent outer shelf are influenced by a persistent, northerly or north-easterly flowing, oceanic current (Kenyon, 1986). This is caused by the northward circulation of relatively warm and saline Atlantic water into the Norwegian Sea. To the north of Shetland, part of the current diverges to the east and flows into the Norwegian Trench. Peak current speeds of up to 0.84 m/s have been recorded in the bottom 100 m of the water mass, and the current generally follows the trend of the bathymetric contours. The current probably extends down to water depths of between 400 and 600 m on the slope, and to about 800 m in the Norwegian Sea. To the north-east of the Wyville–Thomson Ridge (Figure 80), the current crosses the West Shetland Shelf, and part of it diverges to the south-east, where it flows between Orkney and Shetland into the North Sea.

There is also a deeper-water, southerly returning current which affects the sediments on the lower slope and basin floor. This is caused by the flow at depth of relatively cold and dense water from the Norwegian Sea into the Atlantic (Kenyon, 1986). The core of the water mass lies in depths below 800 m, and near-bottom current speeds of over 0.6 m/s have been recorded in water deeper than 1000 m (Figure 80). At the southern end of the Faeroe–Shetland Channel, most of the current is deflected north-westwards into the Faeroe Bank Channel by the Wyville–Thomson Ridge. Some of the water mass passes over the ridge to flow southwards along the Hebrides Slope and across the floor of the Rockall Trough.

The net movement of water due to nontidal currents, at least in the upper half of the water column, is estimated to be northwards and north-westwards, with part of the flow diverging to the east and south-east on the West Shetland Shelf (Lee and Ramster, 1981). This pattern of flow is very similar to that of the flood tidal stream (Figure 80). In the gap between Orkney and Shetland, where there are strong, opposing tidal currents of almost equal strength, the nontidal current which flows towards the North Sea may determine the overall direction of sand transport (Johnson et al., 1982).

SEDIMENT DISTRIBUTION

There is a great deal of variability in sediment grain size, both locally and on a regional basis. In general, sand- and gravel-

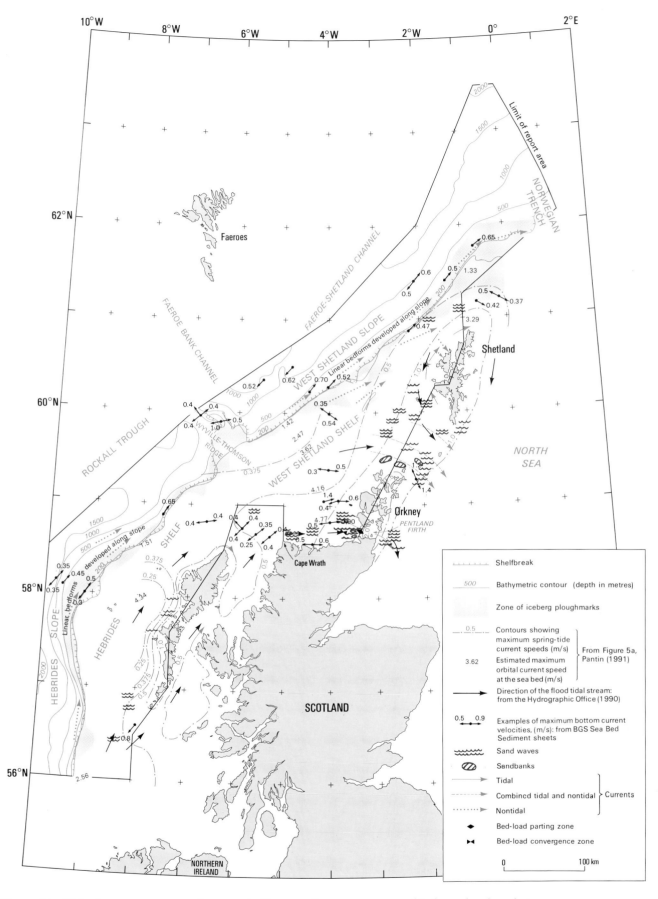

Figure 80 Tides, bottom currents, sedimentary bedforms, sediment transport and iceberg ploughmarks in the report area. Based on BGS data, Kenyon and Stride (1970), Eden et al. (1971), Flinn (1973), Bishop and Jones (1979), Johnson et al. (1982), Allen (1983), Farrow et al. (1984), Kenyon (1986), Perry (1987), Beg (1990), Hydrographic Office (1990), and Pantin (1991).

rich sediments are predominant on the shelf, whereas mud-rich sediments are found in the adjacent deep-water slopes and basin floors (Figure 81). The biogenic carbonate content of the sediments has a relatively simple distribution by comparison. Carbonate-rich sediments occur mainly in the vicinity of bedrock and gravel substrates on the inner and middle shelf; sediments on the outer shelf and seaward of the shelf-break have a low carbonate content (Figure 82).

Rock outcrop

Approximately 10 per cent of the sea bed on the shelf in the report area consists of largely uncovered bedrock (Figures 81 and 83). Most is rugged Precambrian basement, but Tertiary igneous rocks are found in the vicinity of St Kilda. Devonian sedimentary rocks crop out on the Orkney–Shetland Platform (Figure 3).

Rock outcrop also occurs locally in the deep-water areas beyond the shelfbreak. On the Hebrides Slope, Oligocene chalk has been sampled from the face of the Geikie Escarpment (Jones et al., 1986b), and igneous rocks probably crop out on the flanks of both the Wyville–Thomson Ridge and the Hebrides Terrace Seamount. In the Faeroe–Shetland Channel, Tertiary sediments form the steep sides of enclosed deeps.

Gravelly sediment

Sediments containing significant amounts of gravel are common, not only across the shelf but also on the adjacent slopes beyond the shelfbreak where they can occur down to water depths of between about 900 and 1000 m (Figure 81). The lithic portion of the gravel fraction ranges in size from granules up to boulders, and consists, depending upon location, of varying mixtures of metamorphic, igneous and sedimentary rocks. In many areas, especially on topographic highs, the lithic clasts form lag deposits which are either exposed at the sea bed or are overlain by a thin cover of finer-grained, mobile sediment. On the Hebrides Shelf to the west of Barra, lithic gravels and sandy gravels occur mainly on the summits and leeward sides of banks on the outer shelf, and on slopes leading towards the shoreline on the inner shelf (Ferentinos, 1976).

In the region of the shelfbreak south-west of Barra, lithic gravels have been observed from the manned submersible *Pisces* in water depths of between 215 and 318 m (Eden et al., 1971). Here, the gravel is made up of very well-compacted cobble beds, loose cobbles including low ridges up to 0.2 m in height, mixed sand and gravel with clusters of boulders, and spreads of well-graded pebbles. The clasts are mostly well rounded, and are partially encrusted with bryozoa and small corals (Figure 84). The cobble beds are inferred to have been transported to their present location by glacial processes, but their generally rounded appearance, together with evidence of sorting, suggests that they have also been subjected to wave action.

At greater depths, the gravel is more sandy, with irregular patches and stringers of granule to pebble-grade clasts, and isolated cobbles and boulders up to at least 1 m in diameter. Photographic evidence from the slope north-west of St Kilda, where the sediments consist mainly of bioturbated pebbly sands and muds, indicates that this pattern of distribution continues downslope to water depths of about 900 m (Figure 85). The gravel includes spreads of pebbles adjacent to fine-grained sediments, as well as isolated pebbles, cobbles and boulders.

The lithic gravels and bedrock outcrop on the shelf provide a favourable environment for a prolific and diverse cal-careous fauna. The faunal remains make a significant contribution to the gravel fraction in many regions, especially between Orkney and Shetland, which is a major high-latitude centre of carbonate production (Farrow et al., 1984; BGS Orkney Sea Bed Sediments sheet). Allen (1983) estimated that on the shelf as a whole, the most likely rate of production is 24 g/m^2/year, whereas in the vicinity of Orkney this figure rises fourfold.

The carbonate component of the gravel consists mainly of bivalve and echinoid fragments, serpulid tubes, barnacle plates and bryozoans. It is commonly a mixture of apparently older, stained and abraded fragments with younger material of fresher appearance. The composition of this carbonate fraction varies with location; near Shetland, barnacles and attached serpulids are dominant, whereas west of Orkney and west of the Outer Hebrides, bivalves predominate (Wilson, 1979). Patches of cold-water coral occur in the vicinity of the shelfbreak in water depths of between 220 and 250 m (Wilson, 1982).

Radiocarbon dating indicates that the carbonate material has been accumulating throughout the Holocene. Wilson (1979; 1982) reported that the mean age of bulk samples of shell gravel ranges from over 8000 years BP to less than 3000 years BP, the oldest dates being obtained from samples of shell lag gravels on the deeper parts of the shelf. Dating also supports the observation of mixing of older and younger material; age differences of between about 1000 and 2000 years have been obtained by dating individual shell fragments within samples (Wilson, 1982; Farrow et al., 1984).

Sandy sediment

Throughout the Holocene, sand-grade sediment has been reworked, sorted and transported by bottom currents. On the shelf, the sand is transported away from regions of high hydraulic energy, mainly the elevated parts of the sea bed, which are therefore characterised by gravelly deposits. The sand is redeposited on the surrounding, lower-lying sea floor where the current is weaker. On the slope, sand is being transported along-slope due to the prevailing, slope-parallel, bottom currents.

The redeposition of sand-grade sediment is readily apparent on the middle and inner shelf, where sand-rich sediments are relatively abundant and form homogeneous, sheet-like deposits which can be up to 2 m thick. In the St Kilda Basin (Figure 81), the sand is generally medium to fine grained, becoming very fine grained in the deepest part of the basin where water depths are greater than 150 m and there are significant quantities of mud-grade material. The sediments within the basin are mostly less than 0.5 m thick, and overlie a shelly lag gravel which has provided radiocarbon dates of 11 300 to 9560 years BP (Jones et al., 1986b). Farther south, Ferentinos (1976) inferred that the source of similar sandy sediment was the raised outer shelf to the west.

On the current-swept outer shelf, sand commonly occurs as mobile, thin, longitudinal patches and streaks overlying, or only partially covering, coarser-grained lag and Pleistocene deposits (BGS Peach and Sula Sgeir Sea Bed Sediments sheets). Sand also partially infills many iceberg ploughmarks or other local hollows and depressions. Beyond the shelf-break, sand generally forms a thin, superficial layer overlying soft, muddy sediments. At the northern end of the Hebrides Slope, fine-grained sand up to 30 cm thick extends downslope to water depths of over 1000 m (BGS Sula Sgeir Sea Bed Sediments sheet). Farther south, poorly sorted, pebbly sands up to 15 cm thick extend downslope to about 900 m depth (BGS St Kilda Sea Bed Sediments sheet).

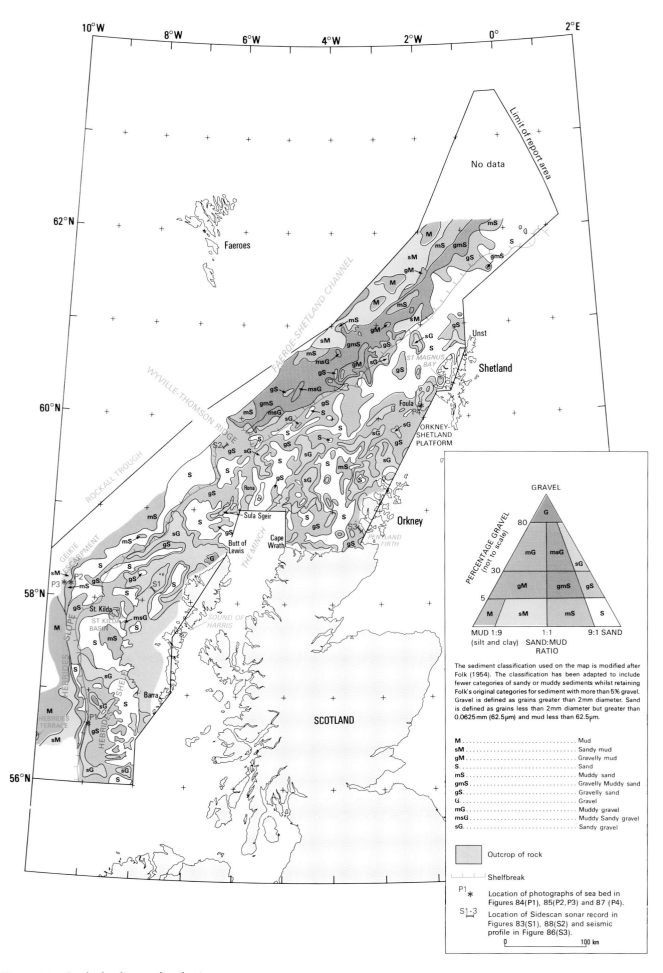

Figure 81 Sea-bed sediment distribution.

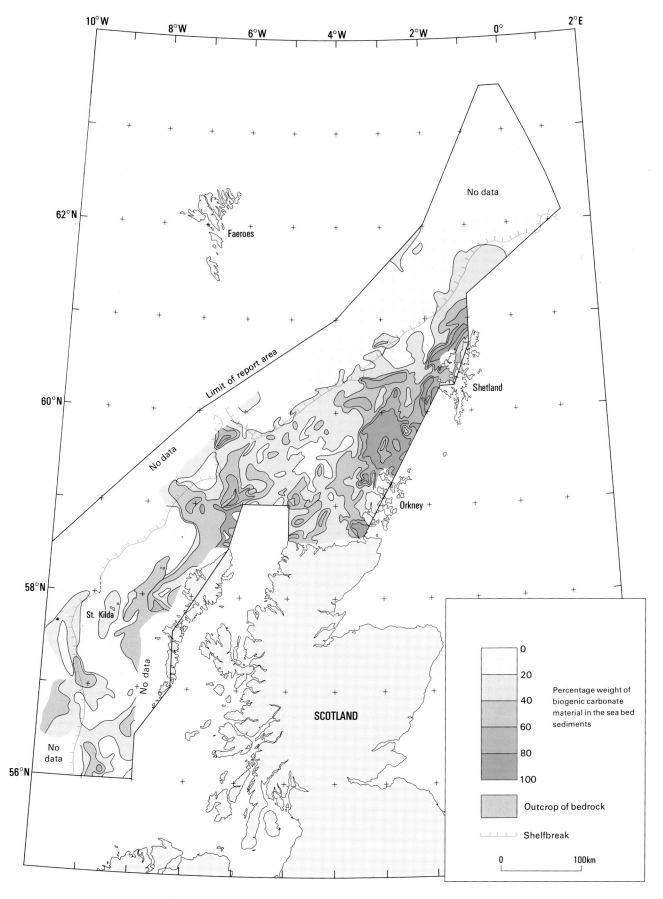

Figure 82   Carbonate content of sea-bed sediments.

123

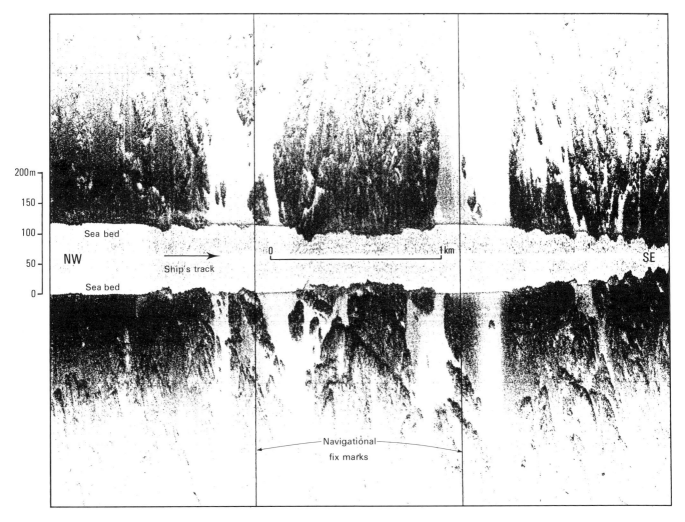

Figure 83 Sidescan sonar record showing basement rock at outcrop (dark), with sand and gravel deposits (paler) partially infilling an irregular rockhead. For location see Figure 81.

The carbonate component of the sand fraction on the shelf and upper parts of the slope consists mainly of biogenic debris broken down by bioerosion and hydraulic action. Typical concentrations in the sand fraction are within the range of 25 to 50 per cent, but in areas of high carbonate production, for example between Orkney and Shetland, it rises to almost 100 per cent (Farrow et al., 1984; BGS Orkney Sea Bed Sediments sheet). In general, areas of sandy sediment are being gradually enriched with carbonate, both from locally produced epifaunal and infaunal remains, and material derived from neighbouring elevated areas (Ferentinos, 1976; Farrow et al., 1984).

Foraminifera are a common component of the sand-grade carbonate, especially seaward of the shelfbreak where they are abundant; there is a progressive decline in macrofauna with increasing water depth. At the northern end of the Faeroe–Shetland Channel, foraminifera form the main constituent of the sand fraction in water depths greater than 1400 m (BGS Flett Sea Bed Sediments sheet). Siliceous sponge spicules also appear to be relatively common on the middle and lower slope (BGS Sula Sgeir and Foula Sea Bed Sediments sheets).

Muddy sediment

Muddy sediments occur rarely on the shelf (Figure 81). Exceptions are in sea lochs and other sheltered sites in the coastal zone, and bathymetric depressions on the inner shelf which range down to about 50 m below the level of the surrounding sea bed. By contrast, mud is widespread on the slope, where there is a progressive increase in the mud content of the sediments with increasing water depth.

The muddy sediments on the shelf in the report area generally occur within basins which have previously been partially infilled with soft, acoustically well-layered, late Pleistocene to early Holocene muds. At these locations, the superficial sediments are muddy sands and sandy muds, and are largely indistinguishable from the underlying deposits. It is likely that some deposition of fine-grained sediment has continued within these basins throughout the Holocene due to the reduction in current action compared with the surrounding, elevated sea bed.

A similar relationship between the superficial muddy sediments and the underlying deposits exists on the slope. On the southern Hebrides Slope, the sea-bed sediments in water depths greater than 900 m consist of silty clays which are indistinguishable from the underlying deposits. Micropalaeontological evidence indicates that Holocene sediments are up to 20 cm thick, lying conformably upon Pleistocene deposits (BGS St Kilda Sea Bed Sediments sheet).

The carbonate content of the muddy sediments is generally between 20 and 40 per cent, with concentrations of up to 60 per cent (Figure 82). These proportions result from the bioerosion and maceration of biogenic debris either produced locally or derived from surrounding areas (Farrow and Fyfe, 1988). A carbonate concretion dredged from the sea bed within St Magnus Bay has been on display at Lerwick

Figure 84 Cobble gravel at the top of the Hebrides Slope, at a water depth of 200 m. See Figure 81 for location.

Museum; this is similar to an aragonite-cemented concretion recovered from muddy sediment east of Shetland (Sabine, 1970). Carbonate concretions appear to be characteristic of mud-rich deposits around Scotland, although their formation is not fully understood (Farrow and Fyfe, 1988).

SEDIMENTARY BEDFORMS AND SEDIMENT TRANSPORT

Shelf areas

Sand streaks, sand ribbons and longitudinal sand patches are widespread on the shelf, where they range from several metres up to several hundred metres in width, and can be up to a few kilometres in length. The streaks and ribbons are of negligible thickness, and usually occur where there are relatively strong bottom currents or where supplies of mobile sand are limited, notably on the outer shelf. The sand patches can be up to 1 m thick, and have a much smaller length to width ratio; they appear to be relatively common on the middle and inner shelf, where sand is more abundant.

The long axes of linear bedforms are generally aligned along-shelf or parallel to the coastline; that is, parallel to the main tidal currents. Locally, the orientation is more variable, and would appear to be related to deflection of bottom-current flow in the vicinity of topographic features. For example, sand ribbons form a circular pattern around the islands of St Kilda (Perry, 1987).

Sand waves are relatively common on the middle and inner shelf (Figure 80), both as isolated features and in groups. In many cases, they are asymmetric in profile (Figure 86), and therefore provide an indication of the net direction of sediment transport. Sand waves are particulary well developed in regions of carbonate-rich sediments; between Orkney and Shetland, there are many sand-wave fields in which the amplitude of the waves ranges from about 3 to 8 m (Flinn, 1973; Allen, 1983).

Sand waves in the vicinity of Orkney and Cape Wrath occur in association with sandbanks which range in height from about 10 to 30 m above the surrounding sea bed (Figure 80; Allen, 1983). Three large sandbanks to the north of Orkney (Farrow et al., 1984) are up to 10 km long, 0.5 km wide and 30 m high. The thickness of Holocene sediments in these banks is uncertain, for at least one may contain a core of glacial deposits. Large sand waves with heights of up to 20 m, and wavelengths of 200 m, are developed on the slopes of these banks; their orientation may indicate a clockwise movement of sediment around the banks. Evidence of large-scale sediment movement in the vicinity of at least one of the banks, and also in the shape of the bank itself, has been obtained as a result of resurveying the same area after a gap of three years (Farrow et al., 1984).

The combined evidence of bedform orientation and bottom currents indicates that the main transport paths are probably aligned along the shelf or parallel to the land. There is no evidence for the transfer of sediment outwards from the inner shelf or for the transfer of sediment from the outer shelf to the slope. Provenance studies of lithic fragments within the sand fraction indicate that the distribution and concentration of basic igneous rock fragments is consistent with the material being derived from the Tertiary volcanic centres of north-west Scotland and Northern Ireland. This material is being transported northwards along the shelf, and eastwards towards the North Sea, a pattern of dispersal very similar to that of the water circulation.

Bedforms can however indicate locally complex transport patterns when studied in detail. Allen (1983) described a sand-wave field to the east of Foula where ripples are developed in the troughs of the subparallel, easterly facing bedforms. The crests of these ripples are aligned at right-angles to the crests of the larger sand waves (Figure 87). In the vicinity of Cape Wrath, variations in sand-wave asymmetry suggest that there is transport both to the east and to the west (Allen, 1983).

On the Hebrides Shelf, coarse-grained, carbonate-rich sediment is being transported in the nearshore in the vicinity of

Figure 85
Fine-grained
sediments with
pebbles and
cobbles on the
Hebrides Slope.
Water depth in
(a) is 600 m,
and 863 m in
(b). See Figure
81 for locations.
Photographs
courtesy of
Proudman
Oceanographic
Laboratory.

a)

b)

the Sound of Harris (Figure 81; Allen, 1983). Farther north, such sediments are being transported around the Butt of Lewis and into The Minch (Bishop and Jones, 1979). Net sediment transport by tidal currents west of Shetland is generally towards the north, although transport by storm surges tends to be towards the coastline (Beg, 1990).

Between Orkney and Shetland, carbonate-rich sediments are probably being transported towards the south-east and into the North Sea (Figure 80). South of Orkney, a bed-load parting zone occurs in the Pentland Firth; sediments are being transported from here both to the east and to the west

(Kenyon and Stride, 1970; Johnson et al., 1982). To the west of the Pentland Firth, the westerly facing sand waves merge into a zone of symmetrical sand waves where an apparent lack of net transport signified to Allen (1983) that there may be a bed-load convergence zone.

Slope areas

Long-range sonar data show that slope-parallel sand ribbons are a common feature on both the Hebrides and West Shetland slopes to water depths of 600 m and 500 m respec-

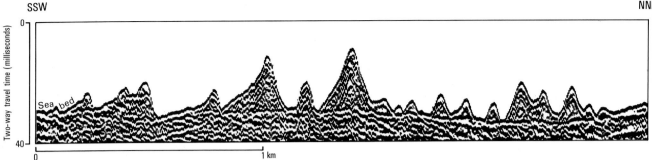

SSW   NNE

Sea bed

Figure 86   Sparker profile showing sand waves in the vicinity of Orkney. For location see Figure 81

tively (Kenyon, 1986). On the Hebrides Slope, the bedforms occur about 15 m apart, are up to 1500 m in length, and have very little vertical expression. Higher-resolution data from the slope north-west of St Kilda show that sand ribbons occur in water as deep as 780 m, where they are typically 2 to 3 m in width, less than 1 m in height, and are continuous for over 1 km. On some sections of the slope, the sand ribbons are sinuous and cross at very acute angles, giving the impression of along-slope braiding. The bedforms are thought to result from along-slope transport of sand-grade material by oceanic currents (Kenyon, 1986).

Visual observations confirm the along-slope movement of sediment; on the upper part of the Hebrides Slope, east–west-aligned sand waves with an amplitude of between 1 and 2 m, and a wavelength of 6 to 8 m, were observed during submersible dives (Eden et al., 1971). Smaller, asymmetric ripples developed on the crests of the sand waves indicate a northerly direction of transport. Photographs taken of the slope north-west of St Kilda show that in water depths of 600 m, the sea-bed sediments are rippled, with scour marks and sand shadows developed around cobbles (Figure 85a). Scour marks also occur around cobbles in water almost 900 m deep (Figure 85b).

OTHER BEDFORMS

Iceberg ploughmarks

Ploughmarks at the sea bed are relict features dating from the late Pleistocene and possibly the very early Holocene (Pantin, 1991), when drifting, grounded icebergs gouged into glacial deposits. Ploughmarks are very common on the outer shelf, the upper slope, and the Wyville–Thomson Ridge (Figure 80), in water depths ranging from 140 m to 500 m (Belderson et al., 1973; BGS Sea Bed Sediments sheets). Ploughmarks are typically 20 m in width and 2 m deep, although there are furrows up to 280 m wide and up to 10 m deep. They are commonly flanked by low ridges that consist of either exposed glacial deposits or coarse-grained, winnowed, lag deposits. In plan, the ploughmarks are usually sinuous and cross-cutting (Figure 88); the longest continuous furrows in the area extend for about 5.5 km (Belderson et al., 1973).

Since their formation, most of the ploughmarks have been degraded by hydraulic and sedimentary processes. The furrows are usually at least partly filled by sediment, usually sand. It is uncertain whether the present distribution relates to former shorelines and the extent of ice cover in the shelf areas, or whether ploughmarks once existed on the shallower

Figure 87
Photograph taken from the BGS unmanned submersible *Consub*, showing small, north–south-aligned sand waves developed in carbonate-rich sediments; smaller ripples are aligned east–west. The cables are part of the structure of the submersible. Water depth 38 m. See Figure 81 for location.

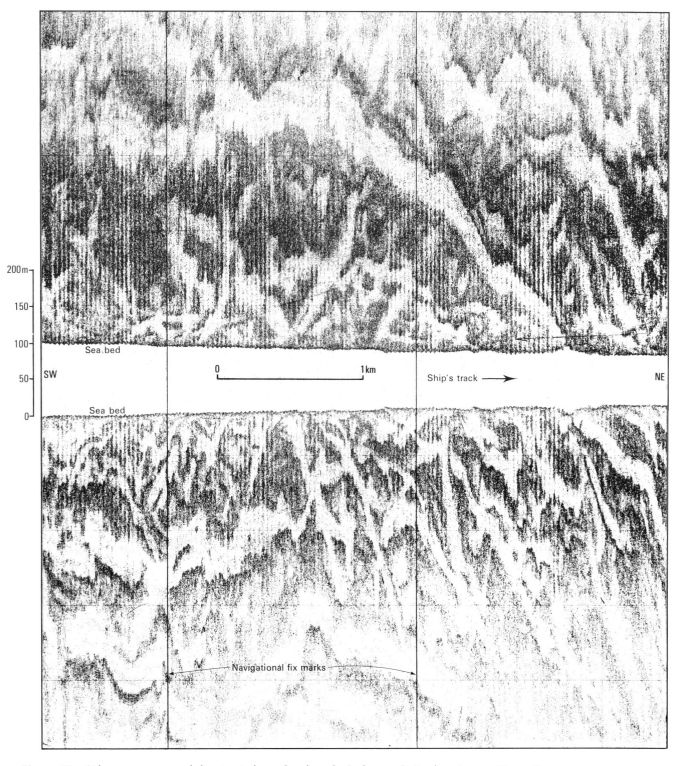

Figure 88 Sidescan sonar record showing iceberg ploughmarks (paler areas). For location see Figure 81.

areas of the shelf and have since been erased by a combination of strong current action and sediment infilling (Belderson et al., 1973). Buried ploughmarks occur beneath sediments on the eastern side of the Foula Channel, within infilled depressions west of the Hebrides, and on the Hebrides and West Shetland slopes (BGS Quaternary Geology and Sea Bed Sediments sheets; Stoker et al., 1992).

Pockmarks

Pockmarks are shallow depressions on the sea bed, and are relatively common in areas of muddy sediments on conti-

nental shelves; they occur widely in the northern North Sea and in the Norwegian Trench (Hovland and Judd, 1988), but appear to be very rare on the Hebrides and West Shetland shelves. The only convincing evidence for pockmarks is from a small area approximately 55 km north-east of Rona, where a few very small pockmarks occur in association with gas-charged sediments (BGS Rona Quaternary Geology sheet). The area of pockmarks differs from those in the North Sea in that the soft, silty sediment in which the pockmarks are formed appears to be covered by a thin layer of sand and gravel. This may imply that they are relict features.

Pockmarks were thought to occur elsewhere on the West Shetland Shelf, and also on the West Shetland Slope (Hovland and Judd, 1988). However, interpretation of BGS data in these areas suggests that most of the features originally identified as possible pockmarks more probably result from other causes, such as ploughmarking and slope instability. Seismic data do, however, indicate areas of pockmark-like features and possible acoustic blanking at the base of the Hebrides Slope.

14 Economic geology

The resources of greatest potential value within the report area are oil and gas, but only a single oilfield has been discovered to date, and this has yet to be fully appraised. Most hydrocarbon exploration has been undertaken north and west of Shetland, where possibly significant reserves remain undiscovered. The northern Rockall Trough and its margins are regions of considerable potential, but largely unexplored. Clathrates, or frozen gas hydrates, may also be present. Other resources within the report area include buried early Tertiary lignites, heavy minerals in placer deposits, and both carbonates and sand and gravel on the sea bed.

OIL AND GAS

Hydrocarbon exploration in the area to the north and west of Scotland began much later than in the North Sea. The first well in the area, 206/12-1 drilled by Esso on the flanks of the Rona Ridge (Figure 89), was not started until 1972. Since then, drilling activity has continued at a very low rate, with only minor peaks in 1974, 1977 and 1984–85 (Figure 90). Early exploration concentrated in and around the Rona Ridge, the West Shetland Basin and North Rona Basin. The Clair Oilfield (Figure 89), discovered by BP in 1977, is one of the largest fields in UK waters. Appraisal of the Clair Oilfield, and further drilling along strike to the north-east on the Rona Ridge, accounted for much of the drilling activity in the late 1970s. Exploration became more widespread in the early 1980s, and included targets at the south-eastern margin of the Faeroe–Shetland Basin, in the West Orkney Basin, and also north of 62°N (Figure 17). Significant discoveries have been announced (Department of Energy, 1991) for wells 214/30-1, 206/1-2 and 205/26a-3 (Figure 89).

In order to encourage exploration to the north-west of the UK, the Department of Energy's Ninth Round of Licensing in 1985 invited applications for pairs of blocks on the margin of the Rockall Trough near the West Lewis and West Flannan basins (Figure 17). The first well in this acreage was drilled in 1988. A further attempt to stimulate exploration interest was a special Frontier Round of licensing in 1990; this offer comprised tranches (groups) of blocks with favourable exploration conditions. Six such tranches were awarded in 1991, mainly in the Faeroe–Shetland Basin.

The relatively low level of exploration in the report area means that much of the deep geology, and therefore the hydrocarbon potential, remains unknown. Problems facing the industry in this area include the extensive lower Tertiary igneous rocks, which degrade seismic data. The igneous activity may also have had adverse affects on the source, migration and accumulation of hydrocarbons. Furthermore, the deep water and exposed conditions restrict the summer weather window for exploration, while lack of local oil-industry infrastructure militates against a significant increase in activity.

Results to date have yielded mainly gas or heavy oil, not the preferred lighter oils which are typical of the North Sea. However, it is estimated that between 20 and 270 million tonnes (150 to 2025 million barrels) of undiscovered, recoverable oil reserves are present in the general west Shetland area (Department of Energy, 1991). This figure does not include the northern Rockall Trough. Therefore, the hydrocarbon potential of the report area remains vast, and is likely to sustain exploration, albeit at a relatively low level, well into the next century.

Clair Oilfield

The Clair Oilfield was discovered in 1977 by BP well 206/8-1A, some 50 km west-north-west from the nearest point of the Shetland mainland (Figures 89 and 91). This well proved 696 m of Devonian to Lower Carboniferous (ORS) sandstone, siltstone and conglomerate that form the reservoir for the oilfield. The top of the ORS is 1576 m below sea level, and the main sandstone interval is 382 m thick with a net oil column of 240 m. Average porosity over the hydrocarbon-bearing interval is 12.8 per cent, and average permeability is 75 millidarcies (mD). Further exploration and appraisal drilling in block 206/8, and adjacent blocks 206/7, 9 and 12, helped to delimit the extent of the field, which has maximum dimensions of 35 × 9 km (Ridd, 1981), and a total area of approximately 200 km² (Blackbourn, 1987). The oil-in-place has been estimated at between 3.5 and 4.0×10^9 barrels, according to a BP press release in 1980; it is very thick, being in the range of 22° to 25° API. There is also a gas cap associated with the accumulation.

The structure of the field is made up of a complex series of faulted blocks, with associated folds, situated in a culmination of the Rona Ridge. The main ORS reservoir (see Chapter 5) consists largely of fluviatile facies, although intercalations of aeolian, fluviodeltaic, lacustrine, and marine sediments occur (Blackbourn, 1987; Meadows et al., 1987; Allen and Manje-Rajetsky, 1992). The ORS was probably deposited on an irregular, faulted, basement surface, and subsequent faulting and erosion have given rise to rapid lateral thickness variations in the reservoir. The source is most likely to be the Kimmeridgian to Ryazanian shales buried at greater depth in the Faeroe–Shetland Basin, although there may have been minor input from the West Shetland Basin. The cap rock for the field is provided by Upper Cretaceous mudstones.

Significant discoveries and other hydrocarbon shows

In addition to the Clair Oilfield, three significant discoveries, as defined by flow rates in well tests and not by commercial viability (Department of Energy, 1991), have been recorded from the report area (Figure 89). Drill-stem tests performed on well 214/30-1 yielded an average of 17.5 million standard cubic feet of gas per day (MMSCFD). Well 206/1-2 produced gas, but no flow rates have been published, and although well 205/26a-3 has also been designated a significant oil discovery, no details are available.

Gas shows have been recorded both from well 206/2-1A, which first drilled the sandstones of the Flett Basin, and from well 214/27-1 (Haszeldine et al., 1987). Gas shows were also reported in well 207/1-3 from an estimated 71 m-thick Lower Cretaceous sandstone resting on basement. Well 206/11-1 yielded an average of 1.65 MMSCFD, again from the Lower Cretaceous; the estimated porosity was good for the producing interval, although the permeability was poor.

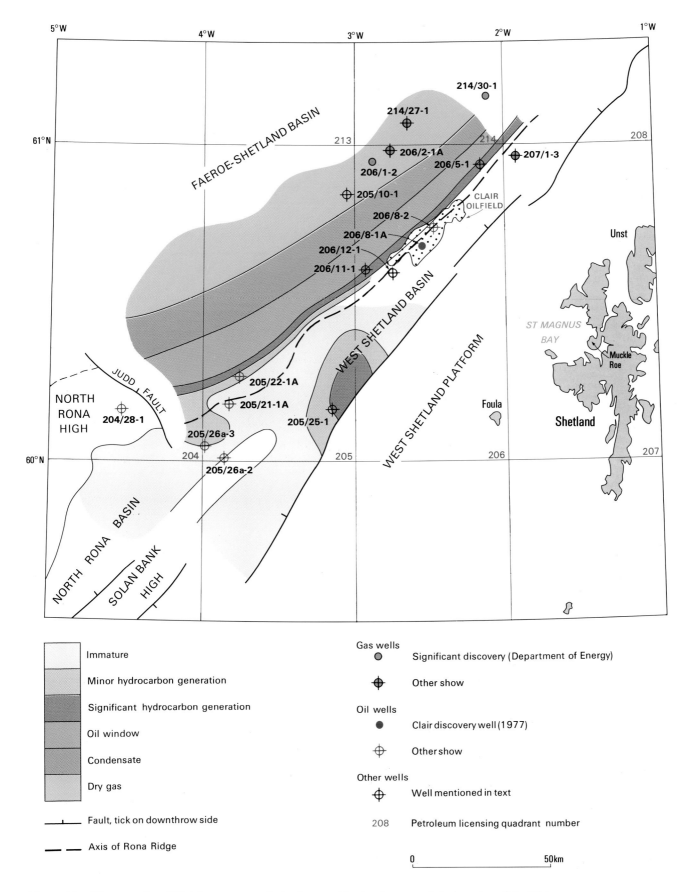

Figure 89 The maturity of Volgian source rocks in the west Shetland area, and the location of the Clair Oilfield and other wells.

Farther south, oil shows have been reported from wells 205/21-1A and 205/22-1A. Well 204/28-1 proved a 31 m-thick reservoir interval consisting of Upper Jurassic sandstone, siltstone and conglomerate, with average values for porosity and permeability of 30 per cent and 6 darcies respectively. However the oil is very thick, and only 200 barrels of oil per day of 12.9° API oil were produced from two zones within the sandstone and the underlying fractured basement. Further shows have been recorded in well 205/26a-2 from Hauterivian (Lower Cretaceous) breccia, but the formation is not an ideal reservoir due to low porosity and permeability.

Source rocks

Data concerning source rocks have been derived mainly from wells drilled west of Shetland (Bailey et al., 1987), where rocks of Volgian to Ryazanian (latest Jurassic to earliest Cretaceous) age constitute the principal source. These are equivalent to the prolific Kimmeridge Clay Formation, the source for many oilfields of the northern and central North Sea.

There are Volgian shales in the North Rona Basin and at the south-western end of the West Shetland Basin; these were deposited in anoxic basins, and have Total Organic Carbon (TOC) values up to 11.2 per cent, although south-east of the Rona Ridge, values of 6.0 to 6.9 per cent are more typical. However, these shales are generally immature, and have generated only very minor amounts of hydrocarbons (Bailey et al., 1987).

In the Faeroe–Shetland Basin (Figure 89), the Volgian is slightly less rich as a source, with TOC values of 3.9 to 7.3 per cent in well 206/5-1, and 1.5 per cent in well 205/22-1A. Nevertheless, these rocks have major source potential (Bailey et al., 1987), for the Volgian here is usually thicker and has been more deeply buried, and is therefore more mature. This source may also have been supplemented by Kimmeridgian shales. Within this basin, hydrocarbon generation probably started during the Late Cretaceous and continued throughout the Tertiary, with the source rocks producing progressively more gas than oil as depth of burial increased.

Other Jurassic shales to the west of Shetland are generally not significant as source rocks, for they usually lack either sufficient organic content of the right type, or are immature. Pre-Jurassic source rocks are unknown from the report area, and post-Ryazanian Cretaceous and Tertiary mudstones typically have TOC values in the range 0.5 to 1.1 per cent from reworked woody or inertinitic organic material. These represent poor source rocks with only limited potential for gas, even if mature. Some early Tertiary lignites are present in the North Rona Basin, as well as in the south-west of the West Shetland and Faeroe–Shetland basins; these are potentially a rich source for gas, but are immature.

Farther south, BGS boreholes 88/01 and 90/02, on the flanks of the West Lewis Basin (Figures 2 and 17), both proved dark grey to black, organic-rich, Bathonian (Middle Jurassic) mudstones which recorded TOC values in the range 3.2 to 6.3 per cent. In the same basin, borehole 90/05 drilled organic-rich Ryazanian (earliest Cretaceous) mudstone with extremely high TOC values, ranging from 10.4 to 14.5 per cent. Mudstones of similar age and lithology were also proved in borehole 90/09 in the West Flannan Basin. All these mudstones have excellent oil-source potential, and although immature at their drilled locations, have great significance for the prospectivity of the northern Rockall Trough (Hitchen and Stoker, in press). Should the same lithologies

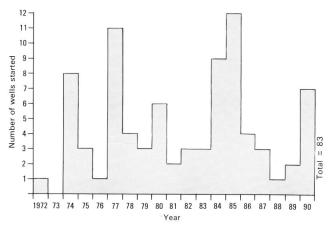

Figure 90 Drilling history in the report area. After Department of Energy (1991).

occur at depth, then there is the possibility of large amounts of hydrocarbons having been generated.

Reservoir rocks

Within the report area, hydrocarbons have been found within rocks ranging in age from Precambrian to Paleocene. Oil has been recovered from fracture porosity in basement metamorphic rocks at the Clair Oilfield, and also in well 204/28-1 (Figure 89), although rocks of this age and lithology are unlikely to become significant producers. Most potential reservoirs are sandstones in which hydrocarbons are contained in intergranular pores. Hence, reservoir characteristics are controlled both by primary depositional factors and secondary diagenetic effects (Meadows et al., 1987).

The ORS of the Clair Oilfield reservoir consists of stacked, partly conglomeratic, channel sands associated with finer-grained, overbank, floodplain deposits. The reservoir quality of the sands has been degraded by replacement clays and cements (Meadows et al., 1987).

Details of Permo-Triassic reservoir characteristics are largely unpublished, although thick sequences of this age are widespread. However, good primary porosity, with some secondary dissolution porosity, has been reported from red sandstone in BGS borehole 90/17 in the North Lewis Basin (Figures 2 and 17). Similar sandstone was drilled in the Barra Trough at BGS borehole 90/16.

Most of the Middle Jurassic and Lower Cretaceous sandstones are submarine-fan deposits located adjacent to contemporary structural highs such as the Rona Ridge and West Shetland Platform. These fans may coalesce to form elongate clastic wedges several hundred metres thick, as in wells 205/25-1 and 206/5-1 (Figure 89; Meadows et al., 1987; Haszeldine et al., 1987). Mid-fan sandstones offer the best reservoir quality, although diagenetic effects appear to have been most detrimental along the south-eastern margin of the Faeroe–Shetland Basin, adjacent to the most likely clastic source area.

Several wells have proved the Paleocene sands of the Flett Basin to be important reservoirs for gas. The sands were probably derived from the south-east, and were deposited from turbidity flows into a subsiding basin accumulating marine shales.

Clathrates

Clathrates are frozen accumulations of gas hydrates, usually methane and water, which form close beneath the sea bed.

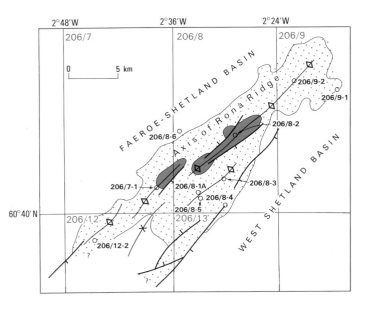

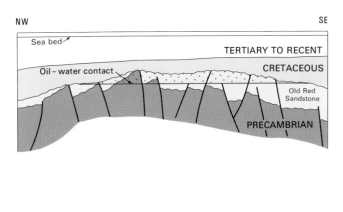

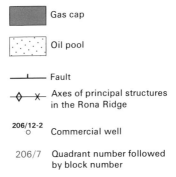

Gas cap

Oil pool

Fault

Axes of principal structures in the Rona Ridge

206/12-2 Commercial well

206/7 Quadrant number followed by block number

Figure 91 Structure of the Clair Oilfield, including a generalised cross-section. After Ridd (1981)

Their formation requires moderate to high pressures typical of water depths of over 400 m. Assuming a gas source is present, the vertical and lateral extent of any particular accumulation is dependent on the interaction between the controlling factors of temperature, pressure and geothermal gradient. The base of a clathrate may be recognised on seismic-reflection profiles as a reflector which approximately mimics the sea-bed topography. Accumulations may cover hundreds of square kilometres, and be several hundred metres thick. Clathrates may be an important resource in themselves, or may act as a cap rock for gaseous hydrocarbons trapped underneath. Water depths in the Faeroe–Shetland Channel and Rockall Trough are sufficient to produce the pressures required for clathrate formation, although none has yet been reported.

OTHER RESOURCES

Lignite and coal

Several wells south of 61°N have drilled lignites, most of which are thin and contained within upper Paleocene to lower Eocene sandstones, but Oligocene deposits also occur. The depth to these poor-quality coals varies considerably, from close to the sea bed in BGS borehole 77/07 (Figure 2), to 1823 m in well 205/10-1 (Figure 89) where there is a 2 m-thick band. Lignites have also been recorded from the Jurassic, and from the Lower Cretaceous in well 205/25-1, which contains eleven coal seams (Hitchen and Ritchie, 1987).

No coals have been drilled within the Devono-Carboniferous reservoir rocks of the Clair Oilfield. However, just to the south of the report area in the Donegal Basin, well 13/3-1 (Figure 29) has shown that Bolsovian and Duckmantian (Westphalian B and C) sediments contain up to 50 coal seams (Tate and Dobson, 1989a). Onshore, the nearest coal deposits that have been worked are at Ballycastle in Northern Island, and at Machrihanish on Kintyre; Carboniferous rocks may subcrop extensively under the Malin Shelf.

Placer deposits

There is very little information available regarding the extent of heavy-mineral placer deposits within the superficial sediments of the report area. The only area which has been examined in any detail is around Shetland, where concentrations of heavy minerals at the sea bed are generally low, constituting up to 1 per cent of the fine-sand fraction (Beg, 1990). The heavy minerals tend to be concentrated in the immediate vicinity of the islands, and are most likely to occur in sediments consisting predominantly of fine- to very fine-grained sands.

The only potentially economic deposits found in the vicinity of Shetland are restricted to inshore areas off Unst (Figure 89) on the eastern side, and north of Muckle Roe in St Magnus Bay to the west (Beg, 1990). At these locations, heavy minerals constitute more than 5 per cent of the fine-sand fraction, and consist mainly of garnet, haematite, magnetite and chromite; these are derived from nearby igneous and metamorphic rocks. Farther offshore, the only evidence for higher than normal concentrations of heavy minerals was found at a few localities in water depths of between 80 and 100 m; these are thought to be relict shoreline deposits.

In the vicinity of the Outer Hebrides, where the onshore geology includes basic and ultrabasic intrusions (Johnstone and Mykura, 1989), it is possible that potentially economic deposits may occur in the nearshore west of the Outer Hebrides. This supposition is supported by the distribution of heavy minerals in The Minch, where high concentrations occur in the nearshore along the east side of the Outer Hebrides (Bishop and Jones, 1979). High concentrations of heavy minerals are also likely to occur in the vicinity of Tertiary igneous centres, as off Rum (Figure 2; Fyfe et al., 1993).

Carbonate deposits

Within the report area, biogenic carbonate deposits of Holocene age are widespread on the continental shelf. Carbonate-rich sands and gravels are a potential source of raw material for making fertilisers and cement, and are worked as such in Iceland (Farrow et al., 1984). Beach deposits around

Figure 92 Carbonate resources in the report area, and potential extraction rates from selected areas. Taken from Allen (1983).

Table 1 Reserves.

Location	Total weight (× 10³ tonnes) Maximum	Minimum	Likely	Area(km²)
Barra Head	305.0	2.8	30.0	390
West Hebridean Platform	3739.0	35.0	366.0	4920
Butt of Lewis	50.1	0.5	4.8	66
Cape Wrath	311.0	9.5	102.7	138
Nun Bank	909.8	0.6	6.7	90
Solan Bank	155.0	1.4	15.4	216
North Orkney Platform	1824.0	8.7	885.0	1140
North Orkney sandbanks	222.0	17.5	358.0	39
Orkney Sounds	112.0	4.8	27.2	70
West Pentland Firth	620.0	11.6	123.0	234
West Shetland Platform	1552.0	13.8	148.0	2000
Foula	147.0	6.5	70.7	95

Table 2 Extraction estimates.

The equilibrium rate is the rate of extraction which equals the estimated net rate of accumulation of carbonate material. The 50-year rate is the extraction rate that is estimated to result in total depletion within 50 years.

Location	Reserves (× 10³ tonnes)	Equilibrium rate (tonnes/day)	50-year rate (tonnes/day)
Outer Hebrides area	401	183	22101
Cape Wrath	102	47	5674
Orkney area	2920	1333	161333

the west and north coasts of Scotland provide a source of lime for local farmers (Pantin, 1991).

Allen (1983) investigated the extent of the carbonate-rich deposits and their suitability for exploitation, and provided estimates of the size of the reserves as well as their sustainability (Figure 92). He concluded that although large reserves occur off Shetland, Cape Wrath and the Outer Hebrides, the most commercially attractive deposits are those in the vicinity of Orkney, where a total of 1000 million tonnes of carbonate may be present (Farrow et al., 1984). Chemical analysis of the carbonate material indicates that it generally has a low magnesium content of less than 4 per cent, which makes a suitable source of lime for cement, as well as for agriculture. With proper management, the offshore reserves could provide a long-term, and potentially renewable source of lime.

Sand and gravel

Terrigenous sands and gravels on the continental shelf are a potential source of aggregate, and are currently being exploited around the south of the UK (Ardus and Harrison, 1990; Pantin, 1991). Although gravelly sediments are widespread on the continental shelf within the report area (Figure 81), there is no information regarding their suitability as aggregate.

A large proportion of the gravelly sediments, especially on the inner shelf, contain high concentrations of biogenic carbonate which may render them unsuitable as a source of aggregate. Spreads of gravelly sediments on the middle and outer shelf to the west of Scotland would however appear to be largely terrigenous, and therefore more suitable, but perhaps inaccessible and too distant from the main markets.

References

Most of the references listed below are held in the Library of the British Geological Survey at Keyworth, Nottingham. Copies of the references can be purchased subject to the current copyright legislation.

Note references to BGS maps are not given here, but an index map showing their distribution is presented inside the back cover.

ABRAHAM, D A, and RITCHIE, J D. 1991.   The Darwin Complex, a Tertiary igneous centre in the Northern Rockall Trough.   *Scottish Journal of Geology*, Vol. 27, 113–126.

ABRAHAMSEN, N, SCHOENHARTING, G, and HEINESEN, M. 1984. Palaeomagnetism of the Vestmanna core and magnetic age and evolution of the Faeroe Islands.   93–108 in *The deep drilling project 1980–1981 in the Faeroe Islands*. BERTHELSEN, O, NOE-NYGAARD, A, and RASMUSSEN, J (editors). (Torshavn: Føroya Frodskaparfelag.)

AKHURST, M A. 1991.   Aspects of late Quaternary sedimentation in the Faeroe–Shetland Channel, northwest UK Continental Margin.   *British Geological Survey Technical Report*, WB/91/2.

ALLEN, J R L. 1979.   Old Red Sandstone facies in external basins, with particular reference to southern Britain.   65–80 *in* The Devonian System. *Palaeontological Association Special Paper*, No. 23.

ALLEN, N H. 1983.   Recent temperate carbonate deposits on the continental shelf north and west of Scotland: distribution, sedimentology and reserves. Unpublished PhD thesis, University of Strathclyde.

ALLEN, P A, and MANGE-RAJETSKY, M A. 1992.   Devonian–Carboniferous sedimentary evolution of the Clair area, offshore north-western UK: impact of changing provenance.   *Marine and Petroleum Geology*, Vol. 9, 29–52.

ANDERSEN, M S. 1988.   Late Cretaceous and early Tertiary extension and volcanism around the Faeroe Islands.   115–122 *in* Early Tertiary Volcanism and the opening of the NE Atlantic. MORTON, A C, and PARSON, L M (editors). *Special Publication of the Geological Society of London*, No. 39.

ANDERTON, R. 1985.   Sedimentation and tectonics in the Scottish Dalradian.   *Scottish Journal of Geology*, Vol. 21, 407–436.

— BRIDGES, P H, LEEDER, M R, and SELLWOOD, B N. 1979.   *A dynamic stratigraphy of the British Isles: a study in crustal evolution*. (London: George Allen & Unwin.)

— GIBBONS, W, and NICHOLSON, P G. 1992.   Precambrian. 5–12 *in* Atlas of palaeogeography and lithofacies. COPE, J C W, INGHAM, J K, and RAWSON, P F (editors). *Memoir of the Geological Society of London*, No. 13.

ANDREWS, I J. 1985.   The deep structure of the Moine Thrust, southwest of Shetland.   *Scottish Journal of Geology*, Vol. 21, 213–217.

— and six others. 1990.   *United Kingdom offshore regional report: the geology of the Moray Firth*. (London: HMSO for the British Geological Survey.)

ANDREWS, J E. 1987.   Jurassic clay mineral assemblages and their post-depositional alteration: upper Great Estuarine Group, Scotland.   *Geological Magazine*, Vol. 124, 261–271.

ARDUS, D A, and HARRISON, D J. 1990.   The assessment of aggregate resources from the UK Continental Shelf.   113–128 in *Ocean Resources*, Vol. 1, *Assessment and Utilisation*. ARDUS, D A, and CHAMP, M A (editors). (Dordrecht: Kluver.)

ASTIN, T R. 1983.   Discussion on implications for Caledonian plate tectonic models of chemical data from volcanic rocks of the British Old Red Sandstone.   *Journal of the Geological Society of London*, Vol. 140, 315–318.

— 1990.   The Devonian lacustrine sediments of Orkney, Scotland: implications for climate cyclicity, basin structure and maturation history.   *Journal of the Geological Society of London*, Vol. 147, 141–151.

BAILEY, N J L, WALKO, P, and SAUER, M J. 1987.   Geochemistry and source rock potential of the west of Shetlands. 711–721 in *Petroleum geology of North West Europe*. BROOKS, J, and GLENNIE, K W (editors). (London: Graham and Trotman.)

BARR, D, HOLDSWORTH, R E, and ROBERTS, A M. 1986. Caledonian ductile thrusting in a Precambrian metamorphic complex: The Moine of northwestern Scotland.   *Bulletin of the Geological Society of America*, Vol. 97, 754–764.

BEG, M A. 1990.   The distribution and dispersal of heavy minerals on the continental shelf around the Shetland Isles. Unpublished PhD thesis, University of Strathclyde.

BELDERSON, R H, KENYON, N H, and STRIDE, A H. 1970. Holocene sediments on the continental shelf west of the British Isles.   *Report of the Institute of Geological Sciences*, No. 70/14, 157–170.

— — and WILSON, J B. 1973.   Iceberg plough marks in the northeast Atlantic.   *Palaeogeography, Palaeoclimatology, Palaeoecology*, Vol. 13, 215–224.

BENTLEY, M R, MALTMAN, A J, and FITCHES, W R. 1988.   Colonsay and Islay: a suspect terrane within the Scottish Caledonides. *Geology*, Vol. 16, 26–28.

BENTLEY, P A D, and SCRUTTON, R A. 1987.   Seismic investigations into the basement structure of southern Rockall Trough.   667–675 in *Petroleum geology of North West Europe*. BROOKS, J, and GLENNIE, K W (editors). (London: Graham and Trotman.)

BERGGREN, W A, KENT, D V, and FLYNN, J J. 1985.   Jurassic to Paleogene: Part 2. Paleogene geochronology and chronostratigraphy.   141–195 *in* The chronology of the geological record. SNELLING, N J (editor). *Memoir of the Geological Society of London*, No. 10.

— and SCHNITKER, D. 1983.   Cenozoic marine environments in the North Atlantic and Norwegian–Greenland Sea.   495–584 in *Structure and development of the Greenland–Scotland Ridge: new methods and concepts*. BOTT, M H P, SAXOV, S, TALWANI, M, and THIEDE, J (editors). (New York and London: Plenum Press.)

BERTHELSEN, O, NOE-NYGAARD, A, and RASMUSSEN, J (editors). 1984. *The deep drilling project 1980–1981 in the Faeroe Islands*. (Torshavn: Forøya Frodskaparfelag.)

BIRKS, H J B, and PEGLAR, S M. 1979.   Interglacial pollen spectra from Sel Ayre, Shetland.   *New Phytologist*, Vol. 83, 559–575.

— and RANSOM, M E. 1969.   An interglacial peat at Fugla Ness, Shetland.   *New Phytologist*, Vol. 68, 777–796.

BISHOP, P, and JONES, E J W. 1979.   Patterns of glacial and post-glacial sedimentation in the Minches, North-West Scotland. 89–194 in *The North-West European shelf seas: the sea bed and the sea in motion — 1. Geology and sedimentology*. BANNER, F T, COLLINS, M B, and MASSIE, K S (editors). (Amsterdam: Elsevier.)

BLACKBOURN, G A. 1981.   Probable Old Red Sandstone conglomerates around Tongue and adjacent areas, north Sutherland.   *Scottish Journal of Geology*, Vol. 17, 103–118.

— 1987.   Sedimentary environments and stratigraphy of the Late Devonian-Early Carboniferous Clair Basin, west of Shetland. 75–91 in *European Dinantian environments*. MILLER, J, ADAMS, A E, and WRIGHT, V P (editors). (Chichester: John Wiley & Sons.)

BOLDREEL, L O, AND ANDERSEN, M S. In press.   Late Palaeocene to Miocene compression in the Faeroe–Rockall area.   *Proceedings of the 4th conference on Petroleum Geology in north-west Europe*, 1992.

BØEN, F, EGGEN, S, and VOLLSET, J. 1984. Structures and basins of the margin from 62° to 69°N and their development. 253–270 in *Petroleum geology of the North European Margin.* SPENCER, A M (editor). (London: Graham and Trotman.)

BOTT, M H P. 1984. Deep structure and origin of the Faeroe–Shetland Channel. 314–347 in *Petroleum geology of the North European Margin.* SPENCER, A M (editor). (London: Graham and Trotman.)

— ARMOUR, A R, HIMSWORTH, E M, MURPHY, T, and WYLIE, G. 1979. An explosion seismology investigation of the continental margin west of the Hebrides, Scotland, at 58°N. *Tectonophysics,* Vol. 59, 217–231.

— and BROWITT, C W A. 1975. Interpretation of geophysical observations between the Orkney and Shetland Islands. *Journal of the Geological Society of London,* Vol. 131, 353–371.

— SAXOV, S, TALWANI, M, and THIEDE, J (editors). 1983. *Structure and development of the Greenland–Scotland Ridge: new methods and concepts.* (New York and London: Plenum Press.)

— and SMITH, P J. 1984. Crustal structure of the Faeroe–Shetland Channel. *Geophysical Journal of the Royal Astronomical Society,* Vol. 76, 383–399.

— SUNDERLAND, J, SMITH, P J, CASTEN, U, and SAXOV, S. 1974. Evidence for continental crust beneath the Faeroe Islands. *Nature, London,* Vol. 248, 202–204.

— and WATTS, A B. 1970. Deep sedimentary basins proved in the Shetland–Hebridean Continental shelf and margin. *Nature, London,* Vol. 227, 265–268.

BOULTON, G S, PEACOCK, J D, and SUTHERLAND, D G. 1991. Quaternary. 503–543 in *Geology of Scotland* (3rd edition). CRAIG, G Y (editor). (Bath: Geological Society of London Publishing House.)

BOWEN, D Q. 1991. Time and space in glacial sediment systems of the British Isles. 3–11 in *Glacial Deposits of Great Britain and Ireland.* ELDERS, J, GIBBARD, P L, and ROSE, J (editors). (Rotterdam: A A Balkema.)

BREWER, J A, and SMYTHE, D K. 1984. MOIST and the continuity of crustal reflector geometry along the Caledonian–Appalachian orogen. *Journal of the Geological Society of London,* Vol. 141, 105–120.

— — 1986. Deep structure of the foreland to the Caledonian orogen, NW Scotland: results of the BIRPS WINCH profile. *Tectonics,* Vol. 5, 171–194.

BRIDGEWATER, D, WATSON, J, and WINDLEY, B F. 1973. The Archaean craton of the North Atlantic region. *Philosophical Transactions of the Royal Society of London,* Vol. 273A, 493–512.

BROOK, M. 1984. The age of the Conachair Granite. 40–41 *in* St Kilda: an illustrated account of the geology. HARDING, R R, MERRIMAN, R J, and NANCARROW, P H A (editors). *Report of the British Geological Survey,* Vol. 16, No. 7.

— BREWER, M S, and POWELL, D. 1976. Grenville age for the rocks in the Moine of northwestern Scotland. *Nature, London,* Vol. 260, 515–517.

BROOKS, J, and GLENNIE, K W (editors). 1987. *Petroleum geology of North West Europe.* (London: Graham and Trotman.)

BROWITT, C W A. 1972. Seismic refraction investigation of a deep sedimentary basin in the continental shelf west of Scotland. *Nature, London,* Vol. 236, 161–163.

BROWN, P E. 1991. Caledonian and earlier magmatism. 229–295 in *Geology of Scotland* (3rd edition). CRAIG, G Y (editor). (Bath: Geological Society of London Printing House.)

BUCKLEY, J S, and BAILEY, R J. 1975. Geophysical evidence on the nature of the Hebrides Terrace Seamount. *Scottish Journal of Geology,* Vol. 11, 37–45.

BUGGE, T, KNARUD, R, and MØRK, A. 1984. Bedrock geology on the mid-Norwegian continental shelf. 271–283 in *Petroleum geology of the North European Margin.* SPENCER, A M (editor). (London: Graham and Trotman.)

BUKOVICS, C, CARTIER, E G, SHAW, N D, and ZIEGLER, P A. 1984. Structure and development of the mid-Norway Continental Margin. 407–423 in *Petroleum geology of the North European Margin.* SPENCER, A M (editor). (London: Graham and Trotman.)

CAMERON, T D J, STOKER, M S, and LONG, D. 1987. The history of Quaternary sedimentation in the UK sector of the North Sea Basin. *Journal of the Geological Society of London,* Vol.144, 43–58.

CASHION, W W. 1975. The geology of the West Shetland Basin. 216.1–216.7 in *Proceedings of the Offshore Europe Conference 1975.* (Kingston-upon-Thames: Spearhead Publications.)

CASTON, V N D, DEARNLEY, R, HARRISON, R K, RUNDLE, C C, and STYLES, M T. 1981. Olivine-dolerite intrusions in the Fastnet Basin. *Journal of the Geological Society of London,* Vol. 138, 31–46.

CHALMERS, J, and WESTERN, P G. 1979. A Tertiary igneous centre north of the Shetland Isles. *Scottish Journal of Geology,* Vol. 15, 333–341.

CHAPELHOWE, R. 1965. On the glaciation in North Roe, Shetland. *Geographical Journal,* Vol. 131, 60–70.

CHEADLE, M J, McGEARY, S E, WARNER, M R, and MATTHEWS, D H. 1987. Extensional structures on the western UK continental shelf: a review of evidence from deep seismic profiling. 445–465 *in* Continental extensional tectonics. COWARD, M P, DEWEY, J F, and HANCOCK, P L (editors). *Special Publication of the Geological Society of London,* No. 28.

CHESHER, J A, SMYTHE, D K, and BISHOP, P. 1983. The geology of the Minches, Inner Sound and Sound of Raasay. *Report of the Institute of Geological Sciences,* No. 83/6.

CLIFF, R A, and REX, D C. 1989. Evidence for a 'Grenville' event in the Lewisian of the northern Outer Hebrides. *Journal of the Geological Society of London,* Vol. 146, 921–924.

COCKBURN, A M. 1935. The geology of St Kilda. *Transactions of the Royal Society of Edinburgh,* Vol. 58, 511–547.

COCKCROFT, D N. 1987. The Quaternary sediment of the Shetland Platform and adjacent continental shelf margin. Unpublished PhD thesis, University of Keele.

COLLINS, A G, and DONOVAN, N R. 1977. The age of two Old Red Sandstone sequences in southern Caithness. *Scottish Journal of Geology,* Vol. 13, 53–57.

COOK, D R. 1987. The Goban Spur — exploration in a deep-water frontier basin. 623–632 in *Petroleum geology of North West Europe.* BROOKS, J, and GLENNIE, K W (editors). (London: Graham and Trotman.)

COWARD, M P, and ENFIELD, M A. 1987. The structure of the West Orkney and adjacent basins. 687–696 in *Petroleum geology of North West Europe.* BROOKS, J, and GLENNIE, K W (editors). (London: Graham and Trotman.)

— — and FISCHER, M W. 1989. Devonian basins of northern Scotland: extension and inversion related to Late Caledonian–Variscan tectonics. 275–308 *in* Inversion tectonics. COOPER, M A, and WILLIAMS, G D (editors). *Special Publication of the Geological Society of London,* No. 44.

COWIE, J W, and JOHNSON, M R W. 1985. Late Precambrian and Cambrian geological time-scale. 47–64 *in* The chronology of the geological record. SNELLING, N J (editor). *Memoir of the Geological Society of London,* No. 10.

CROKER, P F, and SHANNON, P M. 1987. The evolution and hydrocarbon prospectivity of the Porcupine Basin, offshore Ireland. 633–642 in *Petroleum geology of North West Europe.* BROOKS, J, and GLENNIE, K W (editors). (London: Graham and Trotman.)

DAMUTH, J E, and OLSEN, H C. In press. Preliminary observations of Neogene–Quaternary depositional processes in the Faeroe–Shetland Channel revealed by high-resolution seismic facies analysis. *Proceedings of the 4th conference on Petroleum Geology in north-west Europe,* 1992.

DAVIES, H C, DOBSON, M R, and WHITTINGTON, R J. 1984. A revised seismic stratigraphy for Quaternary deposits on the inner continental shelf west of Scotland between 55°30'N and 57°30'N. *Boreas,* Vol. 13, 49–66.

DEEGAN, C E, and SCULL, B J (compilers). 1977. A proposed standard litho-stratigraphic nomenclature for the central and northern North Sea. *Report of the Institute of Geological Sciences*, No. 77/25; *Bulletin of the Norwegian Petroleum Directorate*, No. 1.

DEPARTMENT OF ENERGY. 1985. Environmental parameters on the United Kingdom Continental Shelf. *Offshore Technology Report*, OTH 84 201.

— 1991. *Development of the oil and gas resources of the United Kingdom.* (London: HMSO.)

DICKIN, A P, and BOWES, D R. 1991. Isotopic evidence for the extent of early Proterozoic basement in Scotland and northwest Ireland. *Geological Magazine*, Vol. 128, 385–388.

DIETRICH, V J, and JONES, E J W. 1980. Volcanic rocks from Rosemary Bank (Rockall Trough, NE Atlantic). *Marine Geology*, Vol. 35, 287–297.

DIXON, J E, FITTON, J G, and FROST, R T C. 1981. The tectonic significance of post-Carboniferous igneous activity in the North Sea Basin. 121–137 in *Petroleum geology of the continental shelf of North-West Europe.* ILLING, L V, and HOBSON, G D (editors). (London: Heyden and Son.)

DONOVAN, R N, ARCHER, R, TURNER, P, TARLING, D H. 1976. Devonian palaeogeography of the Orcadian Basin and the Great Glen Fault. *Nature, London*, Vol. 259, 550–551.

DUINDAM, P, and VAN HOORN, B. 1987. Structural evolution of the West Shetland continental margin. 765–773 in *Petroleum geology of North West Europe.* BROOKS, J, and GLENNIE, K W (editors). (London: Graham and Trotman.)

EARLE, M M, JANKOWSKI, E J, and VANN, I R. 1989. Structural and stratigraphic evolution of the Faeroe–Shetland Channel and Northern Rockall Trough. 461–469 in *Extensional tectonics and stratigraphy of the North Atlantic margins.* TANKARD, A J, and BALKWILL, H R (editors). *Memoir of the American Association of Petroleum Geologists*, No. 46.

EDEN, R A, ARDUS, D A, BINNS, P E, McQUILLIN, R, and WILSON, J B. 1971. Geological investigations with a manned submersible off the west coast of Scotland 1969–1970. *Report of the Institute of Geological Sciences*, No. 71/16.

— DEEGAN, C E, RHYS, G H, WRIGHT, J E, and DOBSON, M R. 1973. Geological investigations with a manned submersible in the Irish Sea and off western Scotland 1971. *Report of the Institute of Geological Sciences*, No. 73/2.

EHLERS, J, and WINGFIELD, R T R. 1991. The extension of the Late Weichselian/Late Devensian ice sheets in the North Sea Basin. *Journal of Quaternary Science*, Vol. 6, 313–326.

ELDHOLM, O. 1990. Paleogene North Atlantic magmatic-tectonic events: environmental implications. *Memoir of the Geological Society of Italy*, Vol. 44, 13–28.

— and MUTTER, J C. 1986. Basin structure on the Norwegian margin from analysis of digitally recorded sonobuoys. *Journal of Geophysical Research*, Vol. 91, 3763–3783.

ENFIELD, M A, and COWARD, M P. 1987. The structure of the West Orkney Basin, northern Scotland. *Journal of the Geological Society of London*, Vol. 144, 871–884.

ETHERIDGE, M A, SYMONDS, P A, and LISTER, G S. 1989. Application of the detachment model to reconstruction of conjugate passive margins. 23–40 in *Extensional tectonics and stratigraphy of the North Atlantic margin.* TANKARD, A J, and BALKWILL, H R (editors). *Memoir of the American Association of Petroleum Geologists*, No. 46.

EVANS, D, ABRAHAM, D A, and HITCHEN, K. 1989. The Geikie igneous centre, west of Lewis: its structure and influence on Tertiary geology. *Scottish Journal of Geology*, Vol. 25, 339–352.

— CHESHER, J A, DEEGAN, C E, and FANNIN, N G T. 1981. The offshore geology of Scotland in relation to the IGS shallow drilling programme, 1970–1978. *Report of the Institute of Geological Sciences*, No. 81/12.

FALLER, A M, and BRIDEN, J C. 1978. Palaeomagnetism of Lake District rocks. 17–24 in *The geology of the Lake District.*

MOSELEY, F (editor). *Yorkshire Geological Society Occasional Publication*, No. 3.

FANNIN, N G T. 1989. Offshore investigations 1966–87. *British Geological Survey Technical Report*, WB/89/2.

FARROW, G E, ALLEN, N H, and AKPAN, E T. 1984. Bioclastic carbonate sedimentation on a high-latitude, tide-dominated shelf: Northeast Orkney Islands, Scotland. *Journal of Sedimentology and Petrology*, Vol. 54, 373–393.

— and FYFE, J A. 1988. Bioerosion and carbonate mud production on high-latitude shelves. 281–297 in Non-tropical shelf carbonates—modern and ancient. NELSON, C S (editor). *Sedimentary Geology*, Vol. 60.

FERENTINOS, G K. 1976. Sedimentary distribution and transport processes on the outer continental shelf of the Hebridean Sea. *Marine Geology*, Vol. 20, 41–56.

FETTES, D J, HARRIS, A L, and HALL, L M. 1986. The Caledonian geology of the Scottish Highlands. 303–334 in *Synthesis of the Caledonian rocks of Britain.* FETTES, D J, and HARRIS, A L (editors). (Dordrecht: Reidel Publishing Company.)

— and MENDUM, J R. 1987. The evolution of the Lewisian complex in the Outer Hebrides. 27–44 in Evolution of the Lewisian and comparable Precambrian high grade terrains. PARK, R G, and TARNEY, J (editors). *Special Publication of the Geological Society of London*, No. 27.

— — SMITH, D I, and WATSON, J V. 1992. Geology of the Outer Hebrides. *Memoir of the British Geological Survey.*

FITCH, F J, HEARD, G L, and MILLER, J A. 1988. Basaltic magmatism of late Cretaceous and Palaeogene age recorded in wells NNE of the Shetlands. 253–262 in Early Tertiary volcanism and the opening of the NE Atlantic. MORTON, A C, and PARSON, L M (editors). *Special Publication of the Geological Society of London*, No. 39.

— HOOKER, P J, MILLER, J A, and BRERETON, N R. 1978. Glauconite dating of Palaeocene–Eocene rocks from east Kent and the time-scale of Palaeogene volcanism in the North Atlantic region. *Journal of the Geological Society of London*, Vol. 135, 499–512.

FLACK, C A, and WARNER, M. 1990. Three dimensional mapping of seismic reflections from the crust and upper mantle, north-west of Scotland. *Tectonophysics*, Vol. 173, 469–482.

FLETCHER, T P. 1977. Lithostratigraphy of the Chalk (Ulster White Limestone Formation) in Northern Ireland. *Report of the Institute of Geological Sciences*, No. 77/24.

FLETT, J S. 1920. The submarine contours around the Orkneys. *Transaction of the Edinburgh Geological Society*, Vol. 11, 42–49.

FLINN, D. 1964. Coastal and submarine features around the Shetland Isles. *Proceedings of the Geologists' Association*, Vol. 75, 321–340.

— 1969. On the development of coastal profiles in the north of Scotland, Orkney and Shetland. *Scottish Journal of Geology*, Vol. 5, 393–399.

— 1973. The topography of the seafloor around Orkney and Shetland. *Journal of the Geological Society of London*, Vol. 129, 39–58.

— 1977a. Transcurrent faults and associated cataclasis in Shetland. *Journal of the Geological Society of London*, Vol. 133, 231–248.

— 1977b. The erosion history of Shetland: a review. *Proceedings of the Geologists' Association*, Vol. 88, 129–146.

— 1978. The most recent glaciation of the Orkney–Shetland Channel and adjacent areas. *Scottish Journal of Geology*, Vol. 14, 109–123.

— 1983. Glacial meltwater channels in the northern isles of Shetland. *Scottish Journal of Geology*, Vol. 19, 311–320.

— 1985. The Caledonides of Shetland. 1159–1172 in *The Caledonide Orogen–Scandinavia and related areas.* GEE, D G, and STURT, B A (editors). (Chichester: John Wiley & Sons.)

— 1988.   The Moine rocks of Shetland.   74–85 in *Later Proterozoic stratigraphy of the Northern Atlantic regions.* WINCHESTER, J A (editor). (Glasgow: Blackie.)

— FRANK, P L, BROOK, M, and PRINGLE, I R.   1979.   Basement-cover relations in Shetland.   109–115 *in* The Caledonides of the British Isles — reviewed. HARRIS, A L, HOLLAND, C H, and LEAKE, B E (editors). *Special Publication of the Geological Society of London*, No. 8.

— MAY, F, ROBERTS, J L, and TREAGUS, J E.   1972.   A revision of the stratigraphic succession of the East Mainland of Shetland. *Scottish Journal of Geology*, Vol. 8, 335–343.

— MILLER, J A, EVANS, A L, and PRINGLE, I R.   1968.   On the age of the sediments and contemporaneous volcanic rocks of western Shetland.   *Scottish Journal of Geology*, Vol. 4, 10–19.

FOLK, R L.   1954.   The distinction between grain size and mineral composition in sedimentary rock nomenclature.   *Journal of Geology*, Vol. 62, 344–359.

FORSTER, S C, and WARRINGTON, G.   1985.   Geochronology of the Carboniferous, Permian and Triassic.   99–113 *in* The chronology of the geological record. SNELLING, N J (editor). *Memoir of the Geological Society of London*, No. 10.

FRANCIS, E H.   1991.   Carboniferous–Permian igneous rocks. 393–420 in *Geology of Scotland* (3rd edition). CRAIG, G Y (editor). (Bath: Geological Society of London Printing House.)

FROST, R T C, FITCH, F J, and MILLER, J A.   1981.   The age and nature of the crystalline basement of the North Sea Basin.   43–57 in *Petroleum geology of the continental shelf of North-West Europe.* ILLING, L V, and HOBSON, G D (editors). (London: Heyden and Son.)

FYFE, J A, LONG, D, and EVANS, D.   1993.   *United Kingdom offshore regional report: the geology of the Malin–Hebrides sea area.* (London: HMSO for the British Geological Survey.)

GABRIELSEN, R H, FOERSETH, R, HAMAR, G P, and RØNNEVIK, H. 1984.   Nomenclature of the main structural features on the Norwegian Continental Shelf north of the 62nd parallel.   41–60 in *Petroleum geology of the North European Margin.* SPENCER, A M (editor). (London: Graham and Trotman.)

GAILEY, R A.   1959.   Glasgow University expedition to North Rona.   *Scottish Geophysical Magazine*, Vol. 75, 48–50.

GATLIFF, R W, HITCHEN, K, RITCHIE, J D, and SMYTHE, D K.   1984. Internal structure of the Erlend Tertiary volcanic complex, north of Shetland, revealed by seismic reflection.   *Journal of the Geological Society of London*, Vol. 141, 555–562.

GEIKIE, J.   1894.   *The Great Ice Age* (3rd edition). (London: Stanford.)

GIBB, F G F, and KANARIS-SOTIRIOU, R.   1988.   The geochemistry and origin of the Faeroe–Shetland sill complex.   241–252 *in* Early Tertiary volcanism and the opening of the NE Atlantic. MORTON, A C, and PARSON, L M (editors). *Special Publication of the Geological Society of London*, No. 39.

— — and NEVES, R.   1986.   A new Tertiary sill complex of mid-ocean ridge basalt type NNE of the Shetland Isles: a preliminary report.   *Transactions of the Royal Society of Edinburgh: Earth Sciences*, Vol. 77, 223–230.

GIBBS, A D.   1984.   Structural evolution of extensional basin margins.   *Journal of the Geological Society of London*, Vol. 141, 609–620.

— 1987.   Linked tectonics of the northern North Sea basins. 163–171 *in* Sedimentary basins and basin-forming mechanisms. BEAUMONT, C, and TANKARD, A J (editors). *Memoir of the Canadian Society of Petroleum Geologist*, No. 12.

GRAHAM, D K, HARLAND, R, GREGORY, D M, LONG, D, and MORTON, A C.   1990.   The biostratigraphy and chronostratigraphy of BGS borehole 78/4, North Minch.   *Scottish Journal of Geology,*Vol. 26, 65–75.

GRAY, J M, and LOWE, J J.   1977.   The Scottish lateglacial environment: a synthesis.   163–181 in *Studies in the Scottish*

lateglacial environment. GRAY, J M, and LOWE, J J (editors). (Oxford: Pergamon Press.)

HALL, A M.   1991.   Pre-Quaternary landscape evolution in the Scottish Highlands.   *Transactions of the Royal Society of Edinburgh: Earth Sciences*, Vol. 82, 1–26.

— and WHITTINGTON, G.   1989.   Late Devensian glaciation of southern Caithness.   *Scottish Journal of Geology*, Vol. 25, 307–324.

HALLAM, A.   1975.   *Jurassic environments.* (Cambridge: Cambridge University Press.)

— 1981.   *Facies interpretation and the stratigraphic record.* (Oxford and San Francisco: W H Freeman and Company.)

— 1991.   Jurassic, Cretaceous and Tertiary sediments.   439–453 in *Geology of Scotland* (3rd edition). CRAIG, G Y (editor). (Bath: Geological Society of London Printing House.)

— HANCOCK, J M, La BRECQUE, J L, LAWRIE, W, and CHANNELL, J E T.   1985.   Jurassic to Paleogene: Part 1 Jurassic and Cretaceous geochronology, and Jurassic to Paleogene magnetostratigraphy. 118–140 *in* The chronology of the geological record. SNELLING, N J (editor). *Memoir of the Geological Society of London*, No. 10.

HALLIDAY, A N, McALPINE, A, and MITCHELL, J G.   1977.   The age of the Hoy Lavas, Orkney.   *Scottish Journal of Geology*, Vol. 13, 43–52.

HAMAR, G P, and HJELLE, K.   1984.   Tectonic framework of the Møre Basin and the northern North Sea.   349–358 in *Petroleum geology of the North European Margin.* SPENCER, A M (editor). (London: Graham and Trotman.)

HANCOCK, J M, and KAUFFMAN, E G.   1979.   The great transgressions of the Late Cretaceous.   *Journal of the Geological Society of London*, Vol. 136, 157–186.

HANISCH, J.   1984.   The Cretaceous opening of the northeast Atlantic.   *Tectonophysics*, Vol. 101, 1–23.

HAQ, B U, HARDENBOL, J, and VAIL, P R.   1987.   Chronology of fluctuating sea levels since the Triassic.   *Science,* Vol. 235, 1156–1167.

— — — 1988.   Mesozoic and Cenozoic chronostratigraphy and eustatic cycles.   71–108 *in* Sea level changes: an integrated approach. *Society of Economic Palaeontologists and Mineralogists Special Publication*, No. 42.

HARDING, R R, MERRIMAN, R J, and NANCARROW, P H A.   1984.   St Kilda: an illustrated account of the geology.   *Report of the British Geological Survey*, Vol. 16, No. 7.

HARKNESS, D D, and WILSON, H W.   1979.   Scottish Universities Research and Reactor Centre radiocarbon measurements III. *Radiocarbon*, Vol. 21, 203–256.

HARLAND, W B, and five others.   1982.   *A geologic time scale.* (Cambridge: Cambridge University Press.)

— and five others.   1990.   *A geologic time scale 1989.* (Cambridge: Cambridge UniversityPress.)

HARRIS, A L.   1983.   The growth and structure of Scotland.   1–22 in *Geology of Scotland* (2nd edition). CRAIG, G Y (editor). (Edinburgh: Scottish Academic Press.)

— BALDWIN, C T, BRADBURY, H J, JOHNSON, H D, and SMITH, R A. 1978.   Ensialic basin sedimentation: the Dalradian Supergroup. 115 138 *in* Crustal evolution in northwestern Britain and adjacent regions. BOWES, D R, and LEAKE, B E (editors). *Geological Journal Special Issue*, No. 10.

HARRIS, J P, and HUDSON, J D.   1980.   Lithostratigraphy of the Great Estuarine Group (Middle Jurassic), Inner Hebrides.   *Scottish Journal of Geology*, Vol. 16, 231–250.

HARRISON, R K (editor).   1975.   Expeditions to Rockall 1971–72. *Report of the Institute of Geological Sciences*, No. 75/1.

— 1982.   Mesozoic magmatism in the British Isles and adjacent areas.   333–341 in *Igneous rocks of the British Isles.* SUTHERLAND, D S (editor). (Chichester: John Wiley and Sons.)

HASZELDINE, R S, RITCHIE, J D, and HITCHEN, K.   1987.   Seismic and well evidence for the early development of the Faeroe–Shetland Basin.   *Scottish Journal of Geology*, Vol. 23, 283–300.

— and RUSSELL, M J. 1987. The Late Carboniferous northern North Atlantic Ocean: implications for hydrocarbon exploration from Britain to the Arctic. 1163–1175 in *Petroleum geology of North West Europe*. BROOKS, J, and GLENNIE, K W (editors). (London: Graham and Trotman.)

HAWKES, J R, MERRIMAN, R J, HARDING, R R, and DARBYSHIRE, D P F. 1975. Rockall Island: new geological, petrological, chemical and Rb-Sr age data. 11–51 in Expeditions to Rockall 1971–72. HARRISON, R K (editor). *Report of the Institute of Geological Sciences*, No. 75/1.

HESS, J C, and LIPPOLT, H J. 1986. $^{40}Ar/^{39}Ar$ ages of tonstein and tuff sanidines: new calibration points for the improvement of the Upper Carboniferous time scale. *Chemical Geology (Isotope Geoscience Section)*, Vol. 59, 143–154.

HIMSWORTH, E M. 1973. Marine geophysical studies between north-west Scotland and the Faeroe Plateau. Unpublished PhD thesis, University of Durham.

HITCHEN, K, and RITCHIE, J D. 1987. Geological review of the West Shetland area. 737–749 in *Petroleum geology of North West Europe*. BROOKS, J, and GLENNIE, K W (editors). (London: Graham and Trotman.)

— and RITCHIE, J D. In press. New K-Ar ages, and a provisional chronology, for the offshore part of the British Tertiary Igneous Province. *Scottish Journal of Geology*.

— and STOKER, M S. In press. Mesozoic rocks from the Hebrides Shelf and the implications for hydrocarbon prospectivity in the northern Rockall Trough. *Scottish Journal of Geology*.

HOPPE, G. 1965. Submarine peat in the Shetland Islands. *Geografiska Annaler*, Vol. 47A, 195–203.

— 1974. The glacial history of the Shetland Islands. *Institute of British Geographers Special Publication*, No. 7.

HOUSE, M R, and five others. 1977. A correlation of Devonian rocks of the British Isles. *Special Report of the Geological Society of London*, No. 7.

HOVLAND, M, and JUDD, A G. 1988. *Seabed pockmarks and seepages: impact on geology, biology and the marine environment* (London: Graham and Trotman.)

HUGHES, V J, WHITE, R S, and JONES, E J W. 1984. Seismic velocity structure of the northwest Scottish continental margin: some constraint imposed by amplitude studies. *Annales Geophysicae*, Vol. 2, 669–678.

HYDROGRAPHIC OFFICE. 1990. *Admiralty tide tables 1991, Vol. 1.* (Taunton: Hydrographer to the Navy.)

IRVING, E. 1964. *Palaeomagnetism and its application to geological and geophysical problems.* (New York: John Wiley and Sons.)

JACKSON, D I, MULHOLLAND, P, JONES, S M, and WARRINGTON, G. 1987. The geological framework of the East Irish Sea Basin. 191–203 in *Petroleum geology of North West Europe*. BROOKS, J, and GLENNIE, K W (editors). (London: Graham and Trotman.)

JANSEN, J H F. 1976. Late Pleistocene and Holocene history of the northern North Sea, based on acoustic reflection records. *Netherlands Journal for Sea Research*, Vol. 10, 1–43.

JARDINE, W G, and PEACOCK, J D. 1973. Scotland. 53–59 in A correlation of Quaternary deposits in the British Isles. MITCHELL, G F, PENNY, L F, SHOTTON, F W, and WEST, R G (editors). *Special Report of the Geological Society of London* , No. 4.

JEHU, T J, and CRAIG, R M. 1934. Geology of the Outer Hebrides. Part 4. North Harris and Lewis. *Transactions of the Royal Society of Edinburgh*, Vol. 57, 839–874.

JOHNS, C R, and ANDREWS, I J. 1985. The petroleum geology of the Unst Basin, North Sea. *Marine and Petroleum Geology*, Vol. 2, 361–372.

JOHNSON, H, RICHARDS, P C, LONG, D, and GRAHAM, C C. 1993. *United Kingdom offshore regional report: the geology of the northern North Sea.* (London: HMSO for British Geological Survey.)

JOHNSON, M A, KENYON, N H, BELDERSON, R H, and STRIDE, A H. 1982. Sand transport. 58–94 in *Offshore tidal sands*. STRIDE, A H (editor). (London: Chapman and Hall.)

JOHNSTONE, G S, and MYKURA, W. 1989. *British regional geology: the Northern Highlands of Scotland* (4th edition). (London: HMSO for British Geological Survey.)

— SMITH, D I, and HARRIS, A L. 1969. The Moinian assemblage of Scotland. 159–180 in North Atlantic — geology and continental drift. KAY, M (editor). *Memoir of the American Association of Petroleum Geologists*, Vol. 12.

JONES, E J W. 1978. Seismic evidence for a sedimentary trough of Mesozoic age on the Hebridean continental margin. *Nature, London*, Vol. 272, 789–792.

— 1981. Seismic refraction shooting on the continental margin west of the Outer Hebrides, north west Scotland. *Journal of Geophysical Research*, Vol. 86, 11553–11574.

— MITCHELL, J G, and PERRY, R G. 1986a. Early Tertiary igneous activity west of the Outer Hebrides, Scotland — evidence from magnetic anomalies and dredged basaltic rocks. *Marine Geology*, Vol. 73, 47–59.

— — SHIDO, F, and PHILLIPS, J D. 1972. Igneous rocks dredged from the Rockall Plateau. *Nature Physical Science, London*, Vol. 237, 118–120.

— PERRY, R G, and WILD, J L. 1986b. Geology of the Hebridean margin of the Rockall Trough. *Proceedings of the Royal Society of Edinburgh*, Vol. 88B, 27–51.

— and RAMSAY, A T S. 1982. Volcanic ash deposits of early Eocene age from the Rockall Trough. *Nature, London*, Vol. 299, 342–344.

— — PRESTON, N J, and SMITH, A C S. 1974. A Cretaceous guyot in the Rockall Trough. *Nature, London*, Vol. 251, 129–131.

— WHITE, R S, HUGHES, V J, MATTHEWS, D H, and CLAYTON, B R. 1984. Crustal structure of the continental shelf off northwest Britain from two-ship seismic experiments. *Geophysics*, Vol. 49, 1605–1621.

JOPPEN, M, and WHITE, R S. 1990. The structure and subsidence of Rockall Trough from two-ship seismic experiments. *Journal of Geophysical Research*, Vol. 95, 19821–19837.

KANARIS-SOTIRIOU, R, and GIBB, F G F. 1989. Plagiogranitic differentiates in MORB-type sills of the Faeroe–Shetland Basin. *Journal of the Geological Society of London*, Vol. 146, 607–610.

KELLING, G, PHILLIPS, W E A, HARRIS, A L, and HOWELLS, M F. 1985. The Caledonides of the British Isles: a review and appraisal. 1125–1146 in *The Caledonide Orogen–Scandinavia and related areas*. GEE, D G, and STURT, B A (editors). (Chichester: John Wiley and Sons.)

KENYON, N H. 1986. Evidence from bedforms for a strong poleward current along the upper continental slope of northwest Europe. *Marine Geology*, Vol. 72, 187–198.

— 1987. Mass-wasting features on the continental slope of northwest Europe. *Marine Geology*, Vol. 74, 57–77.

— and STRIDE, A H. 1970. The tide-swept continental shelf sediments between the Shetland Isles and France. *Sedimentology*, Vol. 14, 159–173.

KIDD, R B, and HILL, P R. 1986. Sedimentation on mid-ocean sediment drifts. 87–102 in North Atlantic palaeoceanography. SUMMERHAYES, C P, and SHACKLETON, N J (editors). *Special Publication of the Geological Society of London*, No. 21.

KIRTON, S R, and HITCHEN, K. 1987. Timing and style of crustal extension north of the Scottish mainland. 501–510 in Continental extensional tectonics. COWARD, M P, DEWEY, J F, and HANCOCK, P L (editors). *Special Publication of the Geological Society of London*, No. 28.

KNOX, R W O'B. 1977. Upper Jurassic pyroclastic rocks in Skye, west Scotland. *Nature, London*, Vol. 265, 323–324.

— and MORTON, A C. 1988. The record of early Tertiary North Atlantic volcanism in sediments of the North Sea Basin. 407–419 in Early Tertiary volcanism and the opening of the NE Atlantic. MORTON, A C, and PARSON, L M (editors). *Special Publication of the Geological Society of London*, No. 39.

KNUDSON, K L, and SEJRUP, H P. 1988. Amino acid geochronology of selected interglacial sites in the North Sea area. *Boreas*, Vol. 17, 347–354.

LAILEY, M, STEIN, A M, and RESTON, T J. 1989. The Outer Hebrides fault: a major Proterozoic structure in NW Britain. *Journal of the Geological Society of London*, Vol. 146, 253–259.

LAMBECK, K. 1991. Glacial rebound and sea-level change in the British Isles. *Terra Nova*, Vol. 3, 379–389.

LARSEN, V B. 1987. A synthesis of tectonically-related stratigraphy in the North Atlantic–Arctic region from Aalenian to Cenomanian time. *Norsk Geologisk Tidsskrift*, Vol. 67, 281–293.

LEE, A J, and RAMSTER, J W. 1981. *Atlas of the sea around the British Isles.* (Southampton: Ordnance Survey for HMSO and Ministry of Agriculture, Fisheries and Food.)

LEEDER, M R. 1988. Recent developments in Carboniferous geology: a critical review with implications for the British Isles and NW Europe. *Proceedings of the Geologists' Association*, Vol. 99, 73–100.

LINDSAY, N G, HASELOCK, P J, and HARRIS, A L. 1989. The extent of Grampian orogenic activity in the Scottish Highlands. *Journal of the Geological Society of London*, Vol. 146, 733–735.

LONG, D, and SKINNER, A C. 1985. Glacial meltwater channels in the northern isles of Shetland: comment. *Scottish Journal of Geology*, Vol. 21, 222–224.

LOVELL, J P B. 1991. Permian and Triassic. 421–438 in *Geology of Scotland* (3rd edition). CRAIG, G Y (editor). (Bath: Geological Society of London Publishing House.)

LUND, J. 1983. Biostratigraphy of interbasaltic coals from the Faeroe Islands. 417–423 in *Structure and development of the Greenland–Scotland Ridge: new methods and concepts.* BOTT, M H P, SAXOV, S, TALWANI, M, and THIEDE, J (editors). (New York and London: Plenum Press.)

MACDONALD, H, ALLAN, P M, and LOVELL, J P B. 1987. Geology of oil accumulation in Block 26/28, Porcupine Basin, offshore Ireland. 643–651 in *Petroleum geology of North West Europe.* BROOKS, J, and GLENNIE, K W (editors). (London: Graham and Trotman.)

MACINTYRE, R M, CLIFF, R A, and CHAPMAN, N A. 1981. Geochronological evidence for phased volcanic activity in Fife and Caithness necks, Scotland. *Transactions of the Royal Society of Edinburgh: Earth Sciences*, Vol. 72, 1–7.

MAKRIS, J, and five others. 1991. A new look at the Rockall margin, offshore Ireland. *Marine and Petroleum Geology*, Vol. 8, 410–416.

MANGERUD, J, FURNES, H, and JOHANSEN, J. 1986. A 9000 year old ash bed on the Faeroe Islands. *Quaternary Research*, Vol. 26, 262–265.

— LIE, S E, FURNES, H, KRISTIANSEN, I L, and LOMO, L. 1984. A Younger Dryas ash bed in western Norway, and its possible correlations with tephra in cores from the Norwegian Sea and the North Atlantic. *Quaternary Research*, Vol. 21, 85–104.

MARCANTONIO, F, DICKIN, A P, McNUTT, R H, and HEAMAN, L M. 1988. A 1,800 million year old Proterozoic gneiss terrane in Islay with implications for the crustal structure and evolution of Britain. *Nature, London*, Vol. 335, 62–64.

MARSHALL, J E A. 1988. Devonian miospores from Papa Stour, Shetland. *Transactions of the Royal Society of Edinburgh: Earth Sciences*, Vol. 79, 13–18.

— 1991. Palynology of the Stonehaven Group, Scotland: evidence for a Mid Silurian age and its geological implications. *Geological Magazine*, Vol. 128, 283–286.

MASSON, D G, and KIDD, R B. 1986. Tertiary seismic stratigraphy of the southern Rockall Trough. 1117–1126 in *Initial reports of the Deep Sea Drilling Project, Leg 94.* RUDDIMAN, W F, KIDD, R B, and fourteen others. (Washington DC: US Government Printing Office.)

McCAVE, I N, and TUCHOLKE, B E. 1986. Deep current-controlled sedimentation in the western North Atlantic. 451–468

in *The Western North Atlantic Region.* VOGT, P R, and TUCHOLKE, B E (editors). (Boulder, Colorado: Geological Society of America.)

McCLAY, K R, NORTON, M G, CONEY, P, and DAVIS, G H. 1986. Collapse of the Caledonian orogen and the Old Red Sandstone. *Nature, London*, Vol. 323, 147–149.

McGEARY, S E. 1989. Reflection seismic evidence for a Moho offset beneath the Walls Boundary strike-slip fault. *Journal of the Geological Society of London*, Vol. 146, 261–269.

— CHEADLE, M J, WARNER, M R, and BLUNDELL, D J. 1987. Crustal structure of the continental shelf around Britain derived from BIRPS deep seismic profiling. 33–41 in *Petroleum geology of North West Europe.* BROOKS, J, and GLENNIE, K W (editors). (London: Graham and Trotman.)

— and WARNER, M R. 1985. Seismic profiling the continental lithosphere. *Nature, London*, Vol. 317, 795–797.

McKENNA, M C. 1983. Cenozoic palaeogeography of North Atlantic land bridges. 351–399 in *Structure and development of the Greenland–Scotland Ridge: new methods and concepts.* BOTT, M H P, SAXOV, S, TALWANI, M, and THIEDE, J (editors). (New York and London: Plenum Press.)

McKENZIE, D P. 1978. Some remarks on the development of sedimentary basins. *Earth and Planetary Science Letters*, Vol. 40, 25–32.

McKERROW, W S, LAMBERT, R St J., and COCKS, L R M. 1985. The Ordovician, Silurian and Devonian periods. 73–80 *in* The chronology of the geological record. SNELLING, N J (editor). *Memoir of the Geological Society of London*, No. 10.

McQUILLIN, R, and WATSON, J V. 1973. Large-scale basement structures of the Outer Hebrides in the light of geophysical evidence. *Nature Physical Sciences, London*, Vol. 245, 1–3.

MEADOWS, N, MACCHI, L, CUBITT, J M, and JOHNSON, B. 1987. Sedimentology and reservoir potential in the west of Shetland, UK, exploration area. 723–736 in *Petroleum geology of North West Europe.* BROOKS, J, and GLENNIE, K W (editors). (London: Graham and Trotman.)

MILES, P R, and ROBERTS, D G. 1981. The magnetisation of Rosemary Bank Seamount, Rockall Trough, northeast Atlantic. *Earth and Planetary Science Letters*, Vol. 54, 442–448.

MILLER, J A, and FLINN, D. 1966. A survey of the age relations of Shetland rocks. *Geological Journal*, Vol. 5, 95–116.

— and PYE, K. 1987. Dating movement on geological faults. *Terra Cognita*, Vol. 7, 335.

MILLER, K G, and TUCHOLKE, B E. 1983. Development of Cenozoic abyssal circulation south of the Greenland–Scotland Ridge. 549–589 in *Structure and development of the Greenland–Scotland Ridge: new methods and concepts.* BOTT, M H P, SAXOV, S, TALWANI, M, and THIEDE, J (editors). (New York and London: Plenum Press.)

MITCHELL, G F, PENNY, L F, SHOTTON, F W, and WEST, R G. 1973. A correlation of Quaternary deposits in the British Isles. *Special Report of the Geological Society of London*, No. 4.

MITCHELL, J G, and EUWE, M G. 1988. A model of single-stage concomitant potassium-argon exchange in acidic lavas from the Erlend volcanic complex, north of Shetland Islands. *Chemical Geology (Isotope Geoscience Section)*, Vol. 72, 95–109.

MITCHELL, S M, and six others. In press. Paleogene sequence stratigraphic framework of the Faeroe Basin. *Proceedings of the 4th conference on Petroleum Geology in north-west Europe, 1992.*

MORGAN, G E. 1984. Palaeomagnetism. 38–39 *in* St Kilda: an illustrated account of the geology. HARDING, R R, MERRIMAN, R J, and NANCARROW, P H A (editors). *Report of the British Geological Survey*, Vol. 16, No. 7.

MORTON, A C and five others. 1988a. Early Tertiary volcanic rocks in well 163/6-1A, Rockall Trough. 293–308 *in* Early Tertiary volcanism and the opening of the NE Atlantic. MORTON, A C, and PARSON, L M (editors). *Special Publication of the Geological Society of London*, No. 39.

— Evans, D, Harland R, King, C, and Ritchie, J D. 1988b. Volcanic ash in a cored borehole west of the Shetland Islands: evidence for Selandian (late Palaeocene) volcanism in the Faeroes region. 263–269 in Early Tertiary volcanism and the opening of the NE Atlantic. Morton, A C, and Parson, L M (editors). *Special Publication of the Geological Society of London*, No. 39.

— and Parson, L M (editors). 1988. Early Tertiary volcanism and the opening of the NE Atlantic. *Special Publication of the Geological Society of London*, No. 39.

— and Taylor, P N. 1991. Geochemical and isotopic constraints on the nature and age of basement rocks from Rockall Bank, NE Atlantic. *Journal of the Geological Society of London*, Vol. 148, 631–634.

Morton, N. 1987. Jurassic subsidence history in the Hebrides, NW Scotland. *Marine and Petroleum Geology*, Vol. 4, 226–242.

— Smith, R M, Golden, M, and James, A V. 1987. Comparative stratigraphic study of Triassic–Jurassic sedimentation and basin evolution in the northern North Sea and north-west of the British Isles. 697–709 in *Petroleum geology of North West Europe*. Brooks, J, and Glennie, K W (editors). (London: Graham and Trotman.)

Mudge, D C, and Rashid, B. 1987. The geology of the Faeroe Basin area. 751–763 in *Petroleum geology of North West Europe*. Brooks, J, and Glennie, K W (editors). (London: Graham and Trotman.)

Mussett, A E, Dagley, P, and Skelhorn, R R. 1988. Time and duration of activity in the British Tertiary Igneous Province. 337–348 in Early Tertiary volcanism and the opening of the NE Atlantic. Morton, A C, and Parson, L M (editors). *Special Publication of the Geological Society of London*, No. 39.

Mykura, W. 1976. *British regional geology: Orkney and Shetland.* (Glasgow: HMSO for British Geological Survey.)

— 1991. Old Red Sandstone. 297–346 in *Geology of Scotland* (3rd edition). Craig, G Y (editor). (Bath: Geological Society of London Publishing House.)

— and Phemister, J. 1976. The geology of western Shetland. *Memoir of the Geological Survey of Great Britain.*

Naylor, D, and Shannon, P M. 1982. *Geology of offshore Ireland and West Britain.* (London: Graham and Trotman.)

Neish, J C K. 1990. Rockall Trough: crustal structure of a complex environment from composite seismic surveys. *Society of Economic Geologists, Abstracts*, Vol. 60, 301–303.

— 1992. Seismic structure of the Hatton–Rockall area: an integrated seismic/modelling study from composite data sets. *Petroleum Geology of North-west Europe, Abstracts*, 131.

Nelson, P H H, and Lamy, J-M. 1987. The Møre/West Shetlands area: a review. 775–784 in *Petroleum geology of North West Europe*. Brooks, J, and Glennie, K W (editors). (London: Graham and Trotman.)

Neves, R, and five others. 1973. Palynological correlation within the Lower Carboniferous of Scotland and northern England. *Transactions of the Royal Society of Edinburgh: Earth Sciences*, Vol. 69, 4–67.

Nisbet, H C, and Bowes, D R. 1961. The geology of north Rona. *Transactions of the Geological Society of Glasgow*, Vol. 24, 169–189.

Norton, M G, McClay, K R, and Way, N A. 1987. Tectonic evolution of Devonian basins in northern Scotland and southern Norway. *Norsk Geologisk Tidsskrift*, Vol. 67, 323–338.

Odin, G S. 1985. Remarks on the numerical scale of Ordovician to Devonian times. 41–46 in The chronology of the geological record. Snelling, N J (editor). *Memoir of the Geological Society of London*, No. 10.

Omran, M A. 1990. Geophysical studies in the Hebrides Terrace Seamount area. Unpublished PhD thesis, University of Wales.

O'Reilly, K J. 1983. Composition and age of the conglomerate outliers around the Kyle of Sutherland, Scotland. *Proceedings of the Geologists' Association*, Vol. 94, 53–64.

Owens, B, and Marshall, J (compilers). 1978. Micropalaeontological biostratigraphy of samples from around the coast of Scotland. *Report of the Institute of Geological Sciences*, No. 78/20.

Palmer, T J, McKerrow, W S, and Cowie, J W. 1980. Sedimentological evidence for a stratigraphical break in the Durness Group. *Nature, London*, Vol. 287, 721–722.

Pankhurst, R J. 1982. Geochronological tables for British igneous rocks. 575–581 in *Igneous rocks of the British Isles.* Sutherland, D S (editor). (Chichester: John Wiley and Sons.)

Pantin, H M. 1991. The sea-bed sediments around the United Kingdom: their bathymetric and physical environment, grain size, mineral composition and associated bedforms. *British Geological Survey Research Report*, SB/90/1.

Park, R G. 1980. The Lewisian of NW Britain. 8–13 in United Kingdom: introduction to general geology and guides to excursions 002, 055, 093 and 151. Owen, T R (editor). *26th International Geological Congress, Paris.*

— 1991. The Lewisian Complex. 25–64 in *Geology of Scotland* (3rd edition). Craig, G Y (editor). (Bath: Geological Society of London Printing House.)

— and Tarney, J. 1987. The Lewisian complex: a typical Precambrian high-grade terrain. 13–25 in Evolution of the Lewisian and comparable Precambrian high-grade terrains. Park, R G, and Tarney, J (editors). *Special Publication of the Geological Society of London*, No. 27.

Parnell, J. 1988. Significance of lacustrine cherts for the environment of source-rock deposition in the Orcadian Basin, Scotland. 205–217 in Lacustrine petroleum source rocks. Fleet, A J, Kelts, K, and Talbot, M R (editors). *Special Publication of the Geological Society of London*, No. 40.

Peacock, J D. 1984. Quaternary geology of the Outer Hebrides. *Report of the British Geological Survey*, Vol. 16, No. 2.

— 1991. Glacial deposits of the Hebridean region. 109–119 in *Glacial deposits in Great Britain and Ireland*. Ehlers, J, Gibbard, P L, and Rose, J (editors). (Rotterdam: A A Balkema.)

— and Harkness, D D. 1990. Radiocarbon ages and the full-glacial to Holocene transition in seas adjacent to Scotland and southern Scandinavia: a review. *Transactions of the Royal Society of Edinburgh: Earth Sciences*, Vol. 81, 385–396.

— and five others. 1992. Late Devensian and Flandrian palaeoenvironmental changes on the Scottish continental shelf west of the Outer Hebrides. *Journal of Quaternary Science*, Vol. 7, 145–161.

Pearce, T H, Gorman, B E, and Birkett, T C. 1975. The TiO_2–K_2O–P_2O_5 diagram: a method of discriminating between oceanic and non-oceanic basalts. *Earth and Planetary Science Letters*, Vol. 24, 419–426.

Peddy, C P. 1984. Displacement of the Moho by the Outer Isles Thrust shown by seismic modelling. *Nature, London*, Vol. 312, 628–630.

Pegrum, R M. 1984. Structural development of the south-western margin of the Russian–Fennoscandian platform. 359–370 in *Petroleum geology of the North European Margin*. Spencer, A M (editor). (London: Graham and Trotman.)

Penn, I E, and seven others. 1983. The Larne No. 2 borehole: discovery of a new Permian volcanic centre. *Scottish Journal of Geology*, Vol. 19, 333–346.

Perry, R G. 1987. A geological and geophysical investigation of the Hebridean continental margin. Unpublished PhD thesis, University of London.

Piasecki, M A J, and van Breemen, O. 1983. Field and isotopic evidence for a c.750 Ma tectonothermal event in Moine rocks in the Central Highland region of the Scottish Caledonides. *Transactions of the Royal Society of Edinburgh: Earth Sciences*, Vol. 73, 119–134.

Pitcher, W S, Elwell, R W D, Tozer, C F, and Cambray, F W. 1964. The Leannan Fault. *Quarterly Journal of the Geological Society of London*, Vol. 120, 241–273.

PRICE, I, and RATTEY, R P. 1984. Cretaceous tectonics off mid-Norway: implications for the Rockall and Faeroe–Shetland troughs. *Journal of the Geological Society of London*, Vol. 141, 985–992.

PRINGLE, I R. 1970. The structural geology of the North Roe area, Shetland. *Geological Journal*, Vol. 7, 147–170.

PRINGLE, J. 1944. The Carboniferous rocks of Glas Eilean, Sound of Islay, Argyllshire: with an appendix on the petrography by E B Bouley. *Transactions of the Geological Society of Glasgow*, Vol. 20, 249–259.

RICHARDS, P C, BROWN, S, DEAN, J M, and ANDERTON, R. 1988. A new palaeogeographic reconstruction for the Middle Jurassic of the northern North Sea. *Journal of the Geological Society of London*, Vol. 145, 883–886.

— RITCHIE, J D, and THOMSON, A R. 1987. Evolution of deep-water climbing dunes in the Rockall Trough — implications for overflow currents across the Wyville–Thomson Ridge in the (?)Late Miocene. *Marine Geology*, Vol. 76, 177–183.

RIDD, M F. 1981. Petroleum geology west of the Shetlands. 414–425 in *Petroleum geology of the continental shelf of North-West Europe*. ILLING, L V, and HOBSON, G D (editors). (London: Heyden and Son.)

— 1983. Aspects of the Tertiary geology of the Faeroe–Shetland Channel. 91–108 in *Structure and development of the Greenland–Scotland Ridge: new methods and concepts*. BOTT, M H P, SAXOV, S, TALWANI, M, and THIEDE, J (editors). (New York and London: Plenum Press.)

RISE, L, ROKOENGEN, K, SKINNER, A C, and LONG, D. 1984. *Nordlige Nordsjø. Kvartaergeologisk kart mellom 60° 30' og 62° N, og øst for 1° Ø* (Northern North Sea. Quaternary geology map between 60°30' and 62°N, and east of 1°E). 1:500,000. (Trondheim: Institutt for Kontinentalsokkelundersøkelser (IKU), Norway.)

RITCHIE, J D, and DARBYSHIRE, D P F. 1984. Rb-Sr dates on Precambrian rocks from marine exploration wells in and around the West Shetland Basin. *Scottish Journal of Geology*, Vol. 20, 31–36.

— HITCHEN, K, and MITCHELL, J G. 1987. The offshore continuation of the Moine Thrust north of Shetland as deduced from basement isotopic ages. *Scottish Journal of Geology*, Vol. 23, 163–173.

— SWALLOW, J L, MITCHELL, J G, and MORTON, A C. 1988. Jurassic ages from intrusives and extrusives within the Forties igneous province. *Scottish Journal of Geology*, Vol. 24, 81–88.

RITCHIE, W. 1966. The post-glacial rise in sea level and coastal changes in the Uists. *Transactions of the Institute of British Geographers*, Vol. 39, 79–86.

ROBERTS, A M, STRACHAN, R A, HARRIS, A L, BARR, D, and HOLDSWORTH, R E. 1987. The Sgurr Beag Nappe: a reassessment of the stratigraphy and structure of the Northern Highland Moine. *Bulletin of the Geological Society of America*, Vol. 98, 497–506.

— YIELDING, G, and BADLEY, M E. 1990. A kinematic model for the orthogonal opening of the late Jurassic North Sea rift system, Denmark–Mid Norway. 180–199 in *Tectonic evolution of the North Sea rifts*. BLUNDELL, D J, and GIBBS, A D (editors). (Oxford: Clarendon Press.)

ROBERTS, D G. 1969. New Tertiary volcanic centre on the Rockall Bank, eastern North Atlantic Ocean. *Nature, London*, Vol. 223, 819–820.

— 1972. Slumping on the eastern margin of the Rockall Bank, North Atlantic Ocean. *Marine Geology*, Vol. 13, 225–237.

— 1975a. Marine geology of the Rockall Plateau and Trough. *Philosophical Transactions of the Royal Society of London*, Vol. 278A, 447–509.

— 1975b. The solid geology of the Rockall Plateau. 1–10 in Expeditions to Rockall 1971–72. HARRISON, R K (editor). *Report of the Institute of Geological Sciences*, No. 75/1.

— 1989. Basin inversion in and around the British Isles. 131–150 in Inversion tectonics. COOPER, M A, and WILLIAMS, G D (editors). *Special Publication of the Geological Society of London*, No. 44.

— and five others. 1970. New sedimentary basin on Rockall Plateau. *Nature, London*, Vol. 225, 170–172.

— BOTT, M H P, and URUSKI, C. 1983. Structure and origin of the Wyville–Thomson Ridge. 133–158 in *Structure and development of the Greenland–Scotland Ridge: new methods and concepts*. BOTT, M H P, SAXOV, S, TALWANI, M, and THIEDE, J (editors). (New York and London: Plenum Press.)

— FLEMING, N C, HARRISON, R K, and BINNS, P E. 1974. Helen's Reef: a Cretaceous microgabbroic intrusion in the Rockall intrusive centre. *Marine Geology*, Vol. 16, M21–M30.

— GINZBERG, A, NUNN, K, and McQUILLIN, R. 1988. The structure of the Rockall Trough from seismic refraction and wide-angle reflection measurements. *Nature, London*, Vol. 332, 632–635.

— HUNTER, P M, and LAUGHTON, A S. 1977. *Continental margin around the British Isles*. 1:2 400 000. (Taunton: Hydrographer of the Navy for Institute of Oceanographic Sciences.)

— — — 1979. Bathymetry of the northeast Atlantic: continental margin around the British Isles. *Deep-Sea Research*, Vol. 26A, 417–428.

— and JONES, M T. 1978. A bathymetric, magnetic and gravity survey of the Rockall Bank, *HMS Hecla* 1969. *Admiralty Marine Science Publication*, No. 19. (Taunton: Hydrographic Department, Ministry of Defence.)

— MASSON, D G, and MILES, P R. 1981. Age and structure of the southern Rockall Trough — new evidence. *Earth and Planetary Science Letters*, Vol. 52, 115–128.

— MORTON, A C, and BACKMAN, J. 1984. Late Paleocene–Eocene volcanic events in the northern North Atlantic Ocean. 913–923 in *Initial report of the Deep Sea Drilling Project*, Vol. 81. ROBERTS, D G, SCHNITKER, D, and eleven others. (Washington: US Government Printing Office.)

RODDOM, D S, MILLER, J A, and FLINN, D. 1989. Permo-Carboniferous mylonite formation in the Walls Boundary fault system, Shetland. *Proceedings of the Yorkshire Geological Society*, Vol. 47, 339–343.

ROGERS, D A, MARSHALL, J E A, and ASTIN, T R. 1989. Devonian and later movements on the Great Glen fault system, Scotland. *Journal of the Geological Society of London*, Vol. 146, 369–372.

ROGERS, G, DEMPSTER, T J, BLUCK, B J, and TANNER, P W G. 1989. A high precision U-Pb age for the Ben Vuirich granite: implications for the evolution of the Scottish Dalradian Supergroup. *Journal of the Geological Society of London*, Vol. 146, 789–798.

RUDDIMAN, W F, and BOWLES, F A. 1976. Early interglacial bottom-current sedimentation on the eastern Reykjanes Ridge. *Marine Geology*, Vol. 21, 191–210.

— KIDD, R B, and fourteen others. 1986. *Initial reports of the Deep Sea Drilling Project*, Vol. 94. (Washington DC: US Government Printing Office.)

RUMPH, B, REAVES, C M, ORANGE, V G, and ROBINSON, D L. In press. Structuring and transfer zones in the Faeroe Basin in a regional tectonic context. *Proceedings of the 4th conference on Petroleum Geology in north-west Europe*, 1992.

RUSSELL, M J, and SMYTHE, D K. 1978. Evidence for an early Permian oceanic rift in the northern North Atlantic. 173–179 in *Petrology and geochemistry of continental rifts*. NEUMANN, E R, and RAMBERG, I B (editors). (Dordrecht: Reidel Publishing Company.)

SABINE, P A. 1960. The geology of Rockall, North Atlantic. *Bulletin of the Geological Survey*, Vol. 16, 156–178.

— 1970. A bowl-like object of aragonite limestone from Shetland waters. *Proceedings of the Geologists' Association*, Vol. 81, 539–548.

SANDERSON, R W, DARBYSHIRE, D P F, ROBERTS, D G, and EDEN, R A. 1975. The petrology and isotopic age dating of in situ rock samples from the *D E Vickers Voyager* and *Pisces III* cruise to Rockall Bank, 1973. *Journal of the Geological Society of London*, Vol. 131, 334.

SCOFFIN, T P. 1988. The environments of production and deposition of calcareous sediments on the shelf west of Scotland. *Sedimentary Geology*, Vol. 60, 107–124.

SCRUTTON, R A. 1971. Gravity and magnetic interpretation of Rosemary Bank, North-East Atlantic. *Geophysical Journal of the Royal Astronomical Society*, Vol. 24, 51–58.

— 1972. The crustal structure of Rockall Plateau microcontinent. *Geophysical Journal of the Royal Astronomical Society*, Vol. 27, 259–275.

— 1986. The geology, crustal structure and evolution of the Rockall Trough and the Faeroe–Shetland Channel. *Proceedings of the Royal Society of Edinburgh*, Vol. 88B, 7–26.

— and STOW, D A V. 1984. Seismic evidence for early Tertiary bottom-current controlled deposition in the Charlie Gibbs Fracture Zone. *Marine Geology*, Vol. 56, 325–334.

SELBY, I. 1989. The Quaternary geology of the Hebridean continental margin. Unpublished PhD thesis, University of Nottingham.

SERANNE, M. 1992. Devonian extensional tectonics versus Carboniferous inversion in the northern Orcadian basin. *Journal of the Geological Society of London*, Vol. 149, 27–37.

SHACKLETON, N J, and sixteen others. 1984. Oxygen isotope calibration of the onset of ice-rafting and history of glaciation in the North Atlantic region. *Nature, London*, Vol. 307, 620–623.

SHANNON, P M. 1991. The development of Irish offshore sedimentary basins. *Journal of the Geological Society of London*, Vol. 148, 181–189.

SISSONS, J B. 1977. The Loch Lomond Readvance in the northern mainland of Scotland. 45–59 in *Studies in the Scottish lateglacial environment*. GRAY, J M, and LOWE, J J (editors). (Oxford: Pergamon Press.)

SMITH, A G, and BRIDEN, J C. 1977. *Mesozoic and Cenozoic palaeocontinental maps*. (Cambridge: Cambridge University Press.)

— HURLEY, A M, and BRIDEN, J C. 1981. *Phanerozoic palaeocontinental world maps*. (Cambridge: Cambridge University Press.)

SMITH, D B. 1976. A review of the Lower Permian in and around the British Isles. 14–22 in *The continental Permian in Central, West, and South Europe*. FALKE, H (editor). (Dordrecht: D Reidel.)

— BRUNSTOM, R G W, MANNING, P I, SIMPSON, S, and SHOTTON, F N. 1974. A correlation of Permian rocks in the British Isles. *Special Report of the Geological Society of London*, No. 5.

SMITH, P J. 1974. A seismic refraction study of crustal structure between the Faeroe Isles and Scotland. Unpublished PhD thesis, University of Durham.

— and BOTT, M H P. 1975. Structure of the crust beneath the Caledonian foreland and Caledonian belt of the north Scottish shelf region. *Geophysical Journal of the Royal Astronomical Society*, Vol. 40, 187–205.

SMYTHE, D K. 1983. Faeroe–Shetland escarpment and continental margin north of the Faeroes. 109–119 in *Structure and development of the Greenland–Scotland Ridge: new methods and concepts*. BOTT, M H P, SAXOV, S, TALWANI, M and THIEDE, J (editors). (London and New York: Plenum Press.)

— 1989. Rockall Trough — Cretaceous or Late Palaeozoic? *Scottish Journal of Geology*, Vol. 25, 5–43.

— and six others. 1982. Deep structure of the Scottish Caledonides revealed by the MOIST reflection profile. *Nature, London*, Vol. 299, 338–340.

— CHALMERS, J A, SKUCE, A G, DOBINSON, A, and MOULD, A S. 1983. Early opening history of the North Atlantic — 1. Structure and origin of the Faeroe–Shetland Escarpment. *Geophysical Journal of the Royal Astronomical Society*, Vol. 72, 373–398.

SNELLING, N J. 1985. An interim time-scale. 261–265 *in* The chronology of the geological record. SNELLING, N J (editor). *Memoir of the Geological Society of London*, No. 10.

SNYDER, D B. 1990. The Moine Thrust in the BIRPS data set. *Journal of the Geological Society of London*, Vol. 147, 81–86.

— and FLACK, C A. 1990. A Caledonian age for reflectors within the mantle lithosphere north and west of Scotland. *Tectonics*, Vol. 9, 903–922.

STEEL, R J. 1974. Cornstone (fossil caliche) — its origin, stratigraphic and sedimentological importance in the New Red Sandstone in western Scotland. *Journal of Geology*, Vol. 82, 351–369.

— and WILSON, A C. 1975. Sedimentation and tectonism (?Permo-Triassic) on the margin of the North Minch Basin, Lewis. *Journal of the Geological Society of London*, Vol. 131, 183–202.

STEERS, J A. 1973. *The coastline of Scotland*. (Cambridge: Cambridge University Press.)

STEIN, A M. 1988. Basement controls upon basin development in the Caledonian foreland, NW Scotland. *Basin Research*, Vol. 1, 107–119.

— and BLUNDELL, D J. 1990. Geological inheritance and crustal dynamics of the northwest Scottish continental shelf. *Tectonophysics*, Vol. 173, 455–467.

STEWART, F S. 1991. A reconstruction of the eastern margin of the late Weichselian ice sheet in northern Britain. Unpublished PhD thesis, University of Edinburgh.

— and STOKER, M S. 1990. Problems associated with seismic facies analysis of diamicton-dominated, shelf glacigenic sequences. *Geo-Marine Letters*, Vol. 10, 151–156.

STEWART, M. 1932. Notes on the geology of north Rona. *Geological Magazine*, Vol. 69, 179–185.

— 1933. Notes on the geology of Sula Sgeir and the Flannan Islands. *Geological Magazine*, Vol. 70, 110–116.

STOKER, M S. 1982. Old Red Sandstone sedimentation and deformation in the Great Glen fault zone, NW of Loch Linnhe. *Scottish Journal of Geology*, Vol. 18, 147–156.

— 1988. Pleistocene ice-proximal glaciomarine sediments in boreholes from the Hebrides Shelf and Wyville–Thomson Ridge, NW UK Continental Shelf. *Scottish Journal of Geology*, Vol. 24, 249–262.

— 1990. Glacially-influenced sedimentation on the Hebridean slope, northwestern United Kingdom continental margin. 349–362 *in* Glacimarine environments: processes and sediments. DOWDSWELL, J A, and SCOURSE, J D (editors). *Special Publication of the Geological Society of London*, No. 53.

— HARLAND, R, and GRAHAM, D K. 1991. Glacially influenced basin plain sedimentation in the southern Faeroe–Shetland Channel, northwest United Kingdom continental margin. *Marine Geology*, Vol. 100, 185–199.

— — MORTON, A C, and GRAHAM, D K. 1989. Late Quaternary stratigraphy of the northern Rockall Trough and Faeroe–Shetland Channel, northeast Atlantic Ocean. *Journal of Quaternary Science*, Vol. 4, 211–222.

— and HOLMES, R. 1991. Submarine end-moraines as indicators of Pleistocene ice-limits off northwest Britain. *Journal of the Geological Society of London*, Vol. 148, 431–434.

— and five others. 1988. Early Tertiary basalts and tuffaceous sandstones from the Hebrides Shelf and Wyville–Thomson Ridge, NE Atlantic. 271–282 *in* Early Tertiary volcanism and the opening of the NE Atlantic. MORTON, A C, and PARSON, L M (editors). *Special Publication of the Geological Society of London*, No. 39.

— and eleven others. 1992. A multidisciplinary study of mid-Tertiary to Quaternary sediments recovered in BGS borehole 88/7,7A, Hebrides Slope, northern Rockall Trough region. *British Geological Survey Technical Report*, WB/92/5.

STORETVEDT, K M, and STEEL, R J. 1977. Palaeomagnetic evidence for the age of the Stornoway Formation. *Scottish Journal of Geology*, Vol. 13, 263–269.

STOW, D A V, and HOLBROOK, J A. 1984. Hatton Drift contourites, northwest Atlantic, Deep Sea Drilling Project Leg 81. 695–699 in *Initial report of the Deep Sea Drilling Project*, Vol. 81.

ROBERTS, D G, SCHNITKER, D, and eleven others. (Washington DC: US Government Printing Office.)

STRACHAN, P, and EVANS, D. 1992. A local deep-water failure on the northwest slope of the UK. *Scottish Journal of Geology*, Vol. 27, 107–111.

STRIDE, A H, CURRAY, J R, MOORE, D G, and BELDERSON, R H. 1969. Marine geology of the Atlantic continental margin of Europe. *Philosophical Transactions of the Royal Society of London*, Vol. 264A, 31–75.

SUTHERLAND, D G. 1984a. The Quaternary deposits and landforms of Scotland and the neighbouring shelves: a review. *Quaternary Science Reviews*, Vol. 3, 157–254.

— 1984b. The submerged landforms of the St Kilda archipelago, western Scotland. *Marine Geology*, Vol. 58, 435–442.

— 1987. Submerged rock platforms on the continental shelf west of Sula Sgeir. *Scottish Journal of Geology*, Vol. 23, 251–260.

— 1991. The glaciation of the Shetland and Orkney Islands. 121–127 in *Glacial deposits in Great Britain and Ireland*. EHLERS, J, GIBBARD, P L, and ROSE, J (editors). (Rotterdam: A A Balkema.)

— BALLANTYNE, C K, and WALKER, M J C. 1984. Late Quaternary glaciation and environmental change on St Kilda, Scotland, and their palaeoclimatic significance. *Boreas*, Vol. 13, 261–272.

— and WALKER, M J C. 1984. A late Devensian ice-free area and possible interglacial site on the Isle of Lewis, Scotland. *Nature, London*, Vol. 309, 701–703.

TALWANI, M, and ELDHOLM, O. 1972. Continental margin off Norway: a geophysical study. *Bulletin of the Geological Society of America*, Vol. 83, 3575–3606.

TARLING, D H. 1970. Palaeomagnetic results from the Faeroe Islands. 193–208 in *Palaeogeophysics*. RUNCORN, S K (editor). (London: Academic Press.)

— 1985. Palaeomagnetic studies of the Orcadian Basin. *Scottish Journal of Geology*, Vol. 21, 261–273.

— and GALE, N H. 1968. Isotopic dating and palaeomagnetic polarity in the Faeroe Islands. *Nature, London*, Vol. 218, 1043–1044.

TATE, M P, and DOBSON, M R. 1989a. Pre-Mesozoic geology of the western and north-western Irish continental shelf. *Journal of the Geological Society of London*, Vol. 146, 229–240.

— — 1989b. Late Permian to early Mesozoic rifting and sedimentation offshore NW Ireland. *Marine and Petroleum Geology*, Vol. 6, 49–59.

THIEDE, J, and ELDHOLM, O. 1983. Speculations about the palaeodepth of the Greenland–Scotland Ridge during Late Mesozoic and Cenozoic times. 445–456 in *Structure and development of the Greenland–Scotland Ridge: new methods and concepts*. BOTT, M P H, SAXOV, S, TALWANI, M, and THIEDE, J (editors). (New York and London: Plenum Press.)

THIRLWALL, M F. 1979. The petrochemistry of the British Old Red Sandstone volcanic province. Unpublished PhD thesis, University of Edinburgh.

— 1981. Implications for Caledonian plate tectonic models of chemical data from volcanic rocks of the British Old Red Sandstone. *Journal of the Geological Society of London*, Vol. 138, 123–138.

— 1983. Discussion on implications for Caledonian plate tectonic models of chemical data from volcanic rocks of the British Old Red Sandstone: reply. *Journal of the Geological Society of London*, Vol. 140, 315–318.

TING, S. 1937. The coastal configuration of western Scotland. *Geografiska Annaler*, Vol. 19, 62–83.

TORSVIK, T H, SMETHURST, M A, BRIDEN, J C, and STURT, B A. 1990. A review of Palaeozoic palaeomagnetic data from Europe and their palaeogeographical implications. 25–41 in Palaeozoic palaeogeography and biogeography. MCKERRA, W S, and SCOTESE, C R (editors). *Memoir of the Geological Society of London*, No. 12.

TRUEBLOOD, S, and MORTON, N. 1991. Comparative sequence stratigraphy and structural styles of the Slyne Trough and Hebrides Basin. *Journal of the Geological Society of London*, Vol. 148, 197–201.

UPTON, B G J, FITTON, J G, and MACINTYRE, R M. 1987. The Glas Eilean lavas: evidence of a Lower Permian volcano-tectonic basin between Islay and Jura, Inner Hebrides. *Transactions of the Royal Society of Edinburgh, Earth Sciences*, Vol. 77, 289–293.

VANNEY, J R, and STANLEY, D J. 1983. Shelfbreak physiography: an overview. 1–24 in The shelfbreak: critical interface on continental margins. STANLEY, D J, and MOORE, G T (editors). *Society of Economic Paleontologists and Mineralogists Special Publication*, No. 33.

VAN WEERING, Tj C E, and DE RIJK, S. 1991. Sedimentation and climate-induced sediments on Feni Ridge, northeast Atlantic Ocean. *Marine Geology*, Vol. 101, 49–69.

VON WEYMARN, J A. 1979. A new concept of glaciation in Lewis and Harris, Outer Hebrides. *Proceedings of the Royal Society of Edinburgh*, Vol. 77B, 97–105.

— and EDWARDS, K J. 1973. Interstadial site on the island of Lewis, Scotland. *Nature, London*, Vol. 246, 473–474.

WAAGSTEIN, R. 1988. Structure, composition and age of the Faeroes basalt plateau. 225–238 in Early Tertiary volcanism and the opening of the NE Atlantic. MORTON, A C, and PARSON, L M (editors). *Special Publication of the Geological Society of London*, No. 39.

— and HALD, N. 1984. Structure and petrography of a 660 m lava sequence from the Vestmanna-1 drillhole, lower and middle basalt series, Faeroe Islands. 39–65 in *The deep drilling project 1980–1981 in the Faeroe Islands*. BERTHELSEN, O, NOE-NYGAARD, A, and RASMUSSEN, J (editors). (Torshavn: Føroya Frodskaparfelag.)

— MORTON, A C, PRAEGEL, N-O, and TAYLOR, P N. 1989. Highly alkaline lapilli tuffs from Rosemary Bank: evidence for continental lithosphere beneath the northern part of the Rockall Trough. *Terra Abstracts*, Vol. 1, 31–32.

WARNER, M R, and MCGEARY, S. 1987. Seismic reflection coefficients from mantle fault zones. *Geophysical Journal of the Royal Astronomical Society*, Vol. 89, 223–230.

WARRINGTON, G, and eight others. 1980. A correlation of Triassic rocks in the British Isles. *Special Report of the Geological Society of London*, No. 13.

WATSON, J V. 1983. Lewisian. 23–47 in *Geology of Scotland* (2nd edition). CRAIG, G Y (editor). (Edinburgh: Scottish Academic Press.)

— 1984. The ending of the Caledonian orogeny in Scotland. *Journal of the Geological Society of London*, Vol. 141, 193–214.

WATTS, A B. 1971. Geophysical investigations on the continental shelf and slope north of Scotland. *Scottish Journal of Geology*, Vol. 7, 189–218.

WERNICKE, B. 1985. Uniform sense of normal simple shear of the continental lithosphere. *Canadian Journal of Earth Sciences*, Vol. 22, 108–125.

WHITE, R S. 1988. A hot-spot model for early Tertiary volcanism in the North Atlantic. 3–13 in Early Tertiary volcanism and the opening of the North East Atlantic. MORTON, A C, and PARSON, L M (editors). *Special Publication of the Geological Society of London*, No. 39.

WILSON, G V, EDWARDS, W, KNOX, J, JONES, R C B, and STEPHENS, J V. 1935. The geology of the Orkneys. *Memoir of the Geological Survey of Great Britain*.

WILSON, J B. 1979. Biogenic carbonate sediments on the Scottish continental shelf and on Rockall Bank. *Marine Geology*, Vol. 33. M85–M93.

— 1982. Shelly faunas. 126–171 in *Offshore tidal sands*. STRIDE, A H (editor). (London: Chapman and Hall.)

— 1988. A model for temporal changes in the faunal composition of shell gravels during a trangression on the continental shelf around the British Isles. *Sedimentary Geology*, Vol. 60, 95–105.

WINCHESTER, J A. 1988. Later Proterozoic environments and tectonic evolution in the northern Atlantic lands. 253–270 in *Later Proterozoic stratigraphy of the northern Atlantic regions.* WINCHESTER, J A (editor). (Glasgow: Blackie.)

WOOD, M V, HALL, J, and VAN HOORN, B. 1987. Post-Mesozoic differential subsidence in the north-east Rockall Trough related to volcanicity and sedimentation. 677–685 in *Petroleum geology of North West Europe*. BROOKS, J, and GLENNIE, K W (editors). (London: Graham and Trotman.)

— — and DOODY, J J. 1988. Distribution of early Tertiary lavas in the NE Rockall Trough. 283–292 *in* Early Tertiary volcanism

and the opening of the NE Atlantic. MORTON, A C, and PARSON, L M (editors). *Special Publication of the Geological Society of London*, No. 39.

WOODROW, D L, FLETCHER, F W, and AHRNSBRAK, W E. 1973. Palaeogeography and palaeoclimate of the deposition sites of the Devonian Catskill and Old Red facies. *Bulletin of the Geological Society of America*, Vol. 84, 3051–3064.

ZIEGLER, P A. 1982. *Geological atlas of Western and Central Europe*. (Amsterdam: Elsevier for Shell International Petroleum, Maatschappij, BV.)

— 1988. Evolution of the Arctic–North Atlantic and the western Tethys. *Memoir of the American Association of Petroleum Geologists*, No. 43.

INDEX

146

BRITISH GEOLOGICAL SURVEY

Keyworth, Nottingham NG12 5GG
(0602) 363100

Murchison House, West Mains Road, Edinburgh EH9 3LA
031-667 1000

London Information Office, Natural History Museum
Earth Galleries, Exhibition Road, London SW7 2DE
071 589 4090

The full range of Survey publications is available through the
Sales Desks at Keyworth and at Murchison House,
Edinburgh, and in the BGS London Information Office in
the Natural History Museum Earth Galleries. The adjacent
bookshop stocks the more popular books for sale over the
counter. Most BGS books and reports are listed in HMSO's
Sectional List 45, and can be bought from HMSO and
through HMSO agents and retailers. Maps are listed in the
BGS Map Catalogue, and can be bought BGS approved
stockists and agents as well as direct from BGS.

*The British Geological Survey carries out the geological survey of
Great Britain and Northern Ireland (the latter as an agency
service for the government of Northern Ireland), and of the
surrounding continental shelf, as well as its basic research
projects. It also undertakes programmes of British technical aid
in geology in developing countries as arranged by the Overseas
Development Administration.*

*The British Geological Survey is a component body of the
Natural Environment Research Council.*

HMSO publications are available from:

HMSO Publications Centre
(Mail, fax and telephone orders only)
PO Box 276, London SW8 5DT
Telephone orders 071-873 9090
General enquiries 071-873 0011
Queueing system in operation for both numbers
Fax orders 071-873 8200

HMSO Bookshops
49 High Holborn, London WC1V 6HB
(Counter service only)
071-873 001   Fax 071-873 8200
258 Broad Street, Birmingham B1 2HE
021-643 3740   Fax 021-643 6510
33 Wine Street, Bristol BS1 2BQ
0272-264306   Fax 0272-294515
9 Princess Street, Manchester M60 8AS
061-834 7201   Fax 061-883 0634
16 Arthur Street, Belfast BT1 4GD
0232-238451   Fax 0232-235401
71 Lothian Road, Edinburgh EH3 9AZ
031-228 4181   Fax 031-229 2734

HMSO's Accredited Agents
(see Yellow Pages)

And through good booksellers

1:250 000 MAP SERIES

All maps have been given names (see index map above), but can also be referred to by the latitude and longitude of their south-western corner. Thus the St Kilda sheet may also be referred to as 57°N 10°W. The list below shows the types of maps available for each sheet in the report area using the following key:

BA   Bouguer Gravity Anomaly
A   Aeromagnetic Anomaly
S   Solid Geology
Q   Quaternary Geology
SBS   Sea Bed Sediments
SBS & Q   Sea Bed Sediments and Quaternary

TIREE (56°N 08°W)
BA, A, S, Q, SBS

PEACH (56°N 10°W)
BA, A, S, SBS & Q

LITTLE MINCH (57°N 08°W)
BA, A, S, SBS & Q

ST KILDA (57°N 10°W)
BA, A, S, Q, SBS

CAITHNESS (58°N 04°W)
BA, A, S, SBS & Q

SUTHERLAND (58°N 06°W)
BA, A, S, SBS & Q

LEWIS (58°N 08°W)
BA, A, S, Q, SBS

GEIKIE (58°N 10°W)
BA, A, S, Q, SBS

ORKNEY (59°N 04°W)
BA, A, S, SBS & Q

RONA (59°N 06°W)
BA, A, S, Q, SBS

SULA SGEIR (59°N 08°W)
BA, A, S, Q, SBS

SHETLAND (60°N 02°W)
BA, A, S, SBS & Q

FOULA (60° 04°W)
BA, A, S, Q, SBS

JUDD (60°N 06°W)
BA, A, S, Q, SBS

CORMORANT (61°N 00°)
BA, A, S, Q, SBS

MILLER (61°N 02°W)
BA, A, S, Q, SBS

FLETT (61°N 04°W)
BA, A, S, Q, SBS

LAND GEOLOGY MAPS

The index map shows sheet numbers of published maps at 1:250 000, 1:63 360 and 1:50 000 scale.

OTHER BGS MAPS

Other smaller-scale maps produced by BGS that cover all or part of the region include:

Sea bed sediments around the United Kingdom (North Sheet). Scale 1:1 000 000

Quaternary Geology of the British Isles and the adjacent Continental Shelf (North sheet). Scale 1:1 000 000

Geology of the United Kingdom, Ireland and the adjacent Continental Shelf (North sheet). Scale 1:1 000 000

Aeromagnetic map of Great Britain, north sheet. Scale 1:625 000

Geological map of the United Kingdom, North. Scale 1:625 000

The diagrams in this report were produced by the Cartographic Production Group, BGS, Keyworth under the supervision of R J Parnaby. Cartography was co-ordinated by J D Hodgson, S Rippon and R J Demaine and reprography by S Wilkinson.

Book Production was supervised by M B Simmons. The typesetting was carried out by J B A Evans, page make-up was by D Rayner.